*Some advance tributes to
The Domesday Dictionary:*

"It is not remotely like any other recent book I know of. The format of a philosophical dictionary is used in order to present in an ordered way a vision of our peculiar mid-20th-century world: a moral phenomenon quite as much as a material one. The central gesture of the age is nowhere directly stated, but it is never out of sight. How could it be in a book of this kind, which is both serious and honest. As impressive as anything in the book is the actual writing; measured and brilliant handling of tragic irony which in itself would make the book a delight and perhaps even a weapon in the Great Lost Cause which the definition of the human imagination, and of human anything, appears to have become."
—W. S. MERWIN

"*The Domesday Dictionary* is an imaginative work. It integrates paradox with infuriatingly true characterizations in a surprising and original manner." —THEODOR REIK

T HE PURPOSE OF *The Domesday Dictionary* is to catalogue the artifacts and conceits of our civilization. It attempts to show us our holdings and debits—both intellectual and moral. It reverberates with the antecedents and potentials of the present human condition, as it inventories man's current resources for controlling his fate.

The book is cast in the form of a lexicon whose entries are words and names—scientific, political, psychoanalytic—with key meanings for

[CONTINUED ON BACK FLAP]

[CONTINUED FROM FRONT FLAP]

today. Each of the definitions is a compression of fact, inference, and highly controlled moral energy—as if a Fowler had collaborated with a modern Jeremiah.

The manner in which the old and the new, the objective and the subjective, the real and the unreal, are juxtaposed, effects a continual shifting of perspectives. This is a mosaic portrait conceived with a classic oneness: science and literature are put to the service of each other. The authors and editor, a poet, a psychoanalyst, and an educator, have strong backgrounds in the physical and social sciences; their writing combines meticulous research with poetic vision.

The unusual importance of *The Domesday Dictionary,* and its power to move and inform the reader, have been recognized even before publication—*vide* the tributes on the jacket.

---

### A NOTE ABOUT THE TITLE

The Norman Conquest in 1066 profoundly altered the political and economic realities of life in England. Almost immediately, while the changes were still new, and their import by many unperceived, William the Conqueror commanded his surveyors to make an inventory of all the land in the country and reckon its potential value. The record of the survey, completed in 1086 (and including many fragmentary notes of customs, records of military service due, of markets, of political, ecclesiastical, and social history), was the famous Doomsday or Domesday Book.

---

**JACKET DESIGN BY JEANYEE WONG**

PHOTOGRAPH BY TONY RUTA

## ABOUT THE AUTHORS

DONALD M. KAPLAN *(left)* is a practicing psychoanalyst in New York City. He attended City College (B.A.), Columbia University (M.A.), New York University (Ph.D.), and received his psychoanalytic training at the NPAP Institute, where he was a recipient of the Robert M. Lindner Scholarship. He is a member of the American Psychological Association, the American Orthopsychiatric Association, and other national and local societies, and is currently on the editorial board of the *Psychoanalytic Review*.

ARMAND SCHWERNER *(middle)* was born in Antwerp, Belgium, and came to the United States as a child. He is the author of a volume of poems, *The Lightfall*. He was graduated from Columbia University and attended the Columbia Graduate Schools of English and Anthropology. He has played the clarinet professionally (he studied with Lennie Tristano), was co-owner of a bookshop, associate editor of Hawk's Well Press, and has taught for a number of years. He lives in New York City with his wife, Doloris, a painter, and their son, Adam.

LOUISE J. KAPLAN *(right)* is the wife of Donald Kaplan and the mother of Ann and David. The formulation, organization, and research for *The Domesday Dictionary* have occupied her for nearly two years. Mrs. Kaplan is a Ph.D. candidate in the Educational Psychology Department at New York University (where she received her Master's degree in 1959), and is currently at work on her thesis, "The Development of Moral Judgment in the Child."

# THE
# DOMESDAY
# DICTIONARY

**Donald M. Kaplan**     **Armand Schwerner**

EDITED BY LOUISE J. KAPLAN

1963

SIMON AND SCHUSTER     •     NEW YORK

FIRST PRINTING

*The quotation from Sir James Jeans is reprinted by permission of Cambridge University Press from* Through Space and Time *by Sir James Jeans, published 1943 by Cambridge University Press, London and New York.*

*The quotations from "Song of the Peasants," "A Warning by the Emperor Yao," and "The Snow" are reprinted by permission of Robert Payne from* The White Pony, *edited by Robert Payne, published 1947 by John Day Company, Inc., New York.*

*The quotation from Johan Huizinga is reprinted by permission of Routledge and Kegan Paul, Ltd., London, from* Homo ludens, *by Johan Huizinga.*

LIBRARY OF CONGRESS CATALOG CARD NUMBER: 63-9282
MANUFACTURED IN THE UNITED STATES OF AMERICA
BY H. WOLFF BOOK MFG. CO., NEW YORK, N.Y.

*The numerals pertaining to the effects of nuclear weapons are not to be taken as precise quantities but rather as extrapolations from existing data, and even the extrapolations vary from expert to expert and season to season. However, the order of magnitude of the numbers and the magnitude of the effects given in this book may be safely taken as correct.*

*For Doloris,*
*Adam, Ann and David*

*If he does really think that there is no dis-tinction between virtue and vice, why, sir, when he leaves our houses let us count our spoons.*

—SAMUEL JOHNSON

A

## ABC (Atomic-Biological-Chemical) Warfare

All toilet-training must wait for a certain amount of maturity in the child's central nervous system.
> —Ilg and Ames, *Child Behavior*

The nerve agents represent the most recent development in offensive chemical warfare. . . . A single droplet splash or even an invisible spray of these agents on the skin would be enough to cause death. . . . If liquid nerve agent gets on the skin or clothing, remove it at once. Liquid agent on the skin should be blotted with one of the cloths from the Protective Ointment Kit, M5A1, or with a handkerchief or a piece of outer clothing. The blotting should be done with a minimum of rubbing, as vigorous rubbing increases the absorption of nerve agents. Next, flush the contaminated area with water for at least 30 seconds, or swab it with a fresh cloth, soaked with water. (If water is not available, blot off the agent and follow the rest of the instructions.) Next, apply Protective Ointment M-5 freely to the contaminated skin, rub it in for 30 seconds, and wipe off the excess ointment. Then, make a second application of ointment and allow it to remain on the skin as a visible film. *Do not use Protective Ointment M-5 in or near the eyes.* Quickly remove or cut away contaminated clothing and discard. Continue your combat duties. . . . Exposure to high concentrations of nerve agents may bring on a lack of coordination, mental confusion, and collapse so fast that a casualty may not be able to perform self-aid measure.
> —*ABC Warfare Defense,* Navy Training Course 1960,
> Navpers 10099

A powerful state, or group of states, moved to insure the success of a military strike, has at its disposal a number of interesting and useful methods. In many cases the most effective attack would consist of exploiting some of the following in *combined effects:* radiation, blast and searing heat (AW); bacteria, rickettsiae, viruses, fungi, protozoa and toxins (BW); chemical nerve agents, blister agents, blood agents, choking agents, vomiting agents and tear agents (CW). Any conceivable combination must waste a certain percentage of the total energy input by the duplication of effects; tacticians must know what to use, whom to use it on, when and where to use it on him. A rule of thumb invoked in the strategic planning of attacks states that no enemy soldier be eliminated more than three times, no civilian enemy more than twice. (For the metaphysics of differentiating between combatants and non-combatants, *see* Just War.)

To win, or at least to prevail (*q.v.*), requires an obstinate and ferreting concern with technological progress. It is the great fortune of technology that it can improve on itself, a trait peculiar to non-value systems.

The rewarding application of a *combined effect* waits upon a nice development of its constituents. The progressive improvement of Chemical Warfare Blister Agents serves to illustrate the successful operations of technology in CW. When common use of gas masks by the Allies in 1917 undercut the going success of German lung irritants, German technologists developed a new agent, mustard gas, directed at poisoning the entire body. In winter, the new agent, evaporating slowly over the cold slits and trenches, remained active for weeks, irritating the eyes, producing reddening, blistering and ulceration of the skin, and often inducing acute difficulty in breathing.

Mustard had some built-in disadvantages; mustard occasionally lingered so long, hovering over deserted fields, that occupying corps got reddened, blistered, ulcerated and choked. The United States of America developed the arsenic compound lewisite, a newer agent, acting more quickly on personnel and lasting a shorter time, capable of poisoning the bloodstream rapidly. The newer agent has a more pronounced effect on the eyes; its arsenic content, in addition, produces further harassing effects.

On occasion, War-Gaming (*q.v.*) might furnish indications for a *new-newer* combination, a salutary mixture in the absence of plans to occupy territory right away: mustard for the time span, arsenic for the eyes. A later variant, nitrogen mustard, is rather long-lived and cannot corrode metals, unlike lewisite, which can corrode metals; but nitrogen mustard is worse for the eyes than arsenic, and much worse for the eyes than the older mustard.

Atomic warfare (AW) produces severe damages on material and equipment (*see* Firestorm; Blast Effects; Thermal Effects), but may afflict personnel to a significant degree as well, with anemia, anomie, apathy, hospitalism, intestinal death, central nervous system death, leukemia, bone tumor (*qq.v.*) and some other maladies.

Biological warfare (BW) also offers a good number of usable techniques, against both personnel and plants. Various fungi, for instance, may hurt either plants or people: blastomycosis, a fungus disease, chronically infects the skin, lungs, bones, spleen, liver or kidneys in people; other fungi produce useful pathologies in plants—potato blight, cotton root rot, wheat rust, and corn smut.

The U. S. Army Chemical Corps at Fort Detrick in Frederick, Maryland, is preparing for defensive military activity by rearing infected insects appropriate in the dissemination of yellow fever (mosquitoes), tularemia (ticks), plague (fleas), cholera, anthrax and dysentery (houseflies).

The primary usefulness of BW and CW lies in their selective inattention to buildings and equipment. The range of possible AW, BW and CW combinations, permutations and methods of delivery constitutes a formidable responsibility for war planners, who control the transportation of cancer, ticks, fleas, flies, gas, blight, rust, rot and smut.

## Action

When the form and effect of a pursuit could not have been predicted from the variables of its context, the pursuit is said to have been an *action*. In this, actions differ from *behavior*. Behavior is consistent with the variables of its context and is more or less predictable;

it can be studied and controlled; it can be reproduced in machines; it supplies constancy to the environment. Actions connote deeds; they produce innovation, and, in concert, revolution. That actions vanish under observation—they are total victims of the reflexive phenomenon—is one reason why innovation becomes habit, and revolutions are lost.

**Adenauer, Konrad** (1876–      )
Adolf Hitler's successor, after a five-year lapse of national autonomy, as chief of state of Germany. Chancellor uninterruptedly from 1949 for more than a decade, a major factor in the survival of West Berlin and the defense of the Free World (*q.v.*). "God," said Chancellor Adenauer in an interview with Pope John XXIII on January 22, 1960, had "entrusted a special task to the German people—that of being a dike for the West against the powerful influence from the East."

**Africa**   *See* Colonialism; Upper Volta.

**Aggression**
By word or deed, an act directed against a person, thing or situation with the aim of altering, destroying or appropriating it.

The origin of this class of behavior is a subject of controversy. One prominent view maintains that aggression is not part of the fundamental "nature" of people but is simply a reaction to frustration; that is, only when we do not get what we want do we become aggressive. In this view, it does not exist until it is created by circumstances. Another view, equally prominent, maintains that aggression is a fundamental urge arising in the very vitality of an individual regardless of external provocation; that is, whether or not we get what we want, we are still driven by aggression. In this view, circumstance does not supply the aggression but only the kinds of opportunity for expressing it.

From a practical standpoint, however, neither view leads to the possibility that people or circumstances can be perfected beyond the point where aggression

no longer needs to be dealt with as a fact of life. Since
people can always wish for more than they can have
and often have to wait for what they want, some
amount of frustration is always suffered. Nor can any
situation supply continual and unrestricted opportunities for the direct release of aggression—there are
always rules.

But it is beyond controversy that the most primitive
forms of aggression, e.g., killing, plundering, occur
when individuals act aggressively as a group. Though
separate individuals do, of course, commit acts of
primitive aggression—murderers, for example—these
acts, compared to primitive acts of groups, are exceptional. (*See* Group.)

## Air

Air, Anaximenes teaches, is the primal element.

Air, he teaches, is necessary to life, and the universe
is surrounded by Air: out of Air all things come. The
process of growth includes condensation and rarefac-
tion. Cloud, water and stone result from the former;
fire and aether from the latter.

Others teach that Air corresponds to the Humour
Blood, and incorporates Heat and Moisture. The Air
which surrounds Earth and Water is thick; it holds up
the birds by its thickness. There clouds are born, and
rains, thunder and lightning. The sun warms and dries
the things of the Earth like a damp wash; the rising
vapors accumulate and hide the sun; finally they re-
solve themselves into rain; and the sun, which then
reappears, creates the rainbow. The order of colors in
the rainbow corresponds to the order of the elements
which they signify: red is the color of Fire and is the
highest; blue, the color of Water, is in the center;
green is the color of Earth, and lies at the bottom of
rainbows. No rainbow will appear for a period of 40
years before the Last Judgment, as a sign of the dryness to precede the final conflagration.

The collision of winds produces shining flashes of
fire, which occasionally fall and which are often put
out by the water held in suspension in clouds: thence
comes a noise comparable to that of a red-hot iron

plunged into water. We see the flash before hearing the burst because sight is more subtle than hearing.

The upper layers of the atmosphere are colder than those underneath: the lower Air is thicker; it is more shaken by winds, and all things which remain still are colder than those in movement. In winter the sun moves away from Earth and then the upper Air is so cold that snow occurs: the snow, which never falls on the high seas.

Threats fall through the Air. Münster teaches that Stones, Frogs, Mice and Rats are manifestly observed by the inhabitants of sad regions to descend and fall with some feculent showers and consume all that is green. Valleriola relates that Locusts come down in infinite swarms all of a sudden, and devour all the grass and fruits, to everybody's consternation; he concludes it could not be from natural causes and must come from heaven. Whether they are lifted up into the middle region by the sunbeams and thence fall with showers, or there engendered, is disputed. Richard Burton reports that Cornelius Gemma is of the opinion that they are there conceived by celestial influences; others suppose they are immediately from God, or prodigies raised by art and illusions of spirits, which are Princes of the Air.

## Air Burst

A nuclear explosion detonated at an altitude high enough to prevent its fireball (*q.v.*) from intersecting the ground. The major portion of explosive energy thus released is widely distributed over the target without interference by Earth's surface. An air burst produces greater thermal effects, more world-wide widespread firestorms and blast effects, and more atmospheric fallout than a surface burst (*qq.v.*); but an air burst will produce less local fallout and there will be less radiation damage to living organisms. (*See* Enola Gay; Great Artiste.)

## Air Raid, Early Mathematics of

In 1938, with reference to the Spanish Civil War, the following probability formula for a person's being killed by an aerial bomb was worked out by a British professor of mathematics. The professor was embittered at the novel inhumanity of air raids on civilian populations. His mathematics are satiric:

$$P = \int n/A \; pdxdy,$$

where $n$ is the expected number of bombs falling over a person's neighborhood (say, 1 square mile) and $p$ is the probability that one bomb falling at one point $x, y$ in this area will kill him. The values of $n$ and $p$ vary for each type of bomb, so that summations are required. Since the person will be in different places during the war, a summation for this factor is necessary. Finally, $P$ must be summed for the whole nation. The integration in the above equation is taken over the whole neighborhood of area $A$.

## Air Raid, Higher Mathematics of

In 1958, with reference to a hypothetical attack (q.v.) the following formulas for population casualties were worked out by two mathematicians at the Institute for Defense Analysis, Washington, D.C., and were presented to the Special Subcommittee on Radiation of the United States Congress in June, 1959.

For a strategy $D(\rho)$ to be optimal it must satisfy:

$$D(\rho) = 0 \qquad\qquad (0 \leqq \rho < \rho_0)$$
$$d\bar{R}/dD = (\rho_0/\rho)(\bar{R}^*/D^*) \qquad (\rho_0 \leqq \rho \leqq \infty)$$

where $\qquad \bar{R}^*/D^* = \max_D [\bar{R}(D)/D].$

An optimal attack strategy would maximize the total casualties incurred by a predetermined weapon yield. A further property of an optimal strategy is that regions of low population density are not attacked and regions of high density are always attacked.

The final formula would be:

$$\bar{R}(\mu,\sigma,\xi,\eta) = \Phi\left[(\mu - \xi)/\sqrt{\sigma^2 + \eta^2}\right] = \Phi(\chi),$$

which is a function of:

$$\chi = (\mu - \xi)/\sqrt{\sigma^2 + \eta^2}.$$

This equation, combined with:

$$\sigma^2 = \ln(1 + 35.4/D), \qquad \mu = 4.5 - \tfrac{1}{2}\sigma^2 + \ln D,$$

would summarize the expected casualties.

## Alamogordo

An installation of the U.S. Air Force in the New Mexico desert to which component parts of the first atomic bomb were brought by automobile caravan from the Los Alamos laboratory 200 miles away. The bomb assembly began on July 12, 1945. Since no explosion occurs until a critical mass is attained, it was necessary to design a full-sized bomb to test the accuracy of theoretical studies. *Trinity* was the code name of this test. The assembly was carried on in an old ranch house on the air base. Tension pervaded the process. Lightning had touched off a charge of TNT placed on the bomb tower for a preliminary practice test. Therefore some changes had to be made to preclude the premature explosion of the atomic bomb. The weather too had already grown threatening, and caused a delay of the test from 4:00 A.M. to 5:30 A.M. on the morning of July 16, 1945. The process of constructing the bomb involved the fitting together of parts machined to perfection. Near the end of the task one component refused to slide into place. This problem too came to a successful resolution. When the pillar of cloud formed by the explosion cleared, the tower had disappeared and a 400-yard-wide crater fissured the earth; the observers, Julius Robert Oppenheimer (*q.v.*), General Leslie Groves, General Farrell, and many others, could echo Albert Einstein: "The fairest thing we can experience is the mysterious. It is the fundamental emotion which stands at the cradle of true science." General Farrell wrote, "Atomic fission would no longer be hidden in the cloisters of the theoretical physicists' dreams. It was almost full grown at birth. It was a great new force to be used for good or evil. There was a feeling in that shelter that those concerned with its nativity should dedicate their lives to the mission that it would always be used for good and never for evil." General Groves remarked, "One or two of those things and Japan will be finished." Julius Robert Oppenheimer was a member of the study group which, in the spring of 1945, selected the site of the second atomic bomb explosion. (*See* Manhattan District; Tinian Island; Enola Gay.)

## Alliance for Progress

A financial arrangement with Latin American states, instituted by the United States in the spring of 1961, operating as a surrogate for revolutionary fervor. In the first year of the Alliance, the United States paid out $1,000,000,000 to Latin America in return for promises of peaceful change in the areas of political equality, economic advance and social justice. The Alliance, said President Kennedy in March, 1962, counts among its most impressive accomplishments "the dramatic shift in thinking and attitudes which has occurred in our hemisphere in these seven months."

To a significant degree, the success of such a program depends upon the capacity of a national idea for generating enthusiasm in other states. It also depends upon a history of altruistic assistance at a time when choice was still possible and more or less gratuitous actions conceivable. But revolutionary impetus in the United States had for some time been approaching the last of the ebb; what remains is hardening; and the search for what is valid in the past becomes less a fertilizer for the future than the earnest of a present exhausted by the unpaid promissory notes of old ideals derived from Washington, Jefferson and Bolívar. The eighteenth century finds itself renewed in the White House decor for the first time in modern history; but the old universal fraternity for the world, a dream of democratic union, plays itself out within a flow of new relatives, not all of whom have acknowledged the same gods.

The United States, along with its most able opponent, waits for something very like the end of a brief Caucasian civilization. As it waits, in the salutary company of Minuteman and Polaris, it mourns the incapacity of such states as Bolivia, Peru, Argentina, Colombia, Ecuador, Brazil and Guatemala to arrive at a unanimous recognition of the values inherent in the North American concept of representative government. By a peculiar historical reversal, these states, though incompletely urbanized, industrialized and psychoanalyzed, have displayed in their internal behavior the most deep-lying aspects of fraternity: sibling rivalry, fratricide, and unremitting internecine appetites.

Recent Latin American history has impressed observers. In March, 1962, the appeal of a demagogic Peronist movement attracted powerful popular support in Argentina; fortunately the armed forces were on their toes to suppress the suppression of the democracy they had previously resurrected. In Guatemala, students fought police in protest against the recent Congressional elections in that state. Brazil has experienced violent upheavals at the top levels of government. Colombia, prey for 14 years to the mercies of backlands war that had already cost thousands of lives, was subject to a series of important suggestions for various degrees of revolutionary solutions to its troubles. In July a Peruvian military junta declared void the announced results of a national election, imprisoned the constitutional President and dissolved parliament. Peru in 1958 stood ready to receive an excess destroyer from the United States; this disturbed Ecuador, which wanted one too, though its upkeep promised to be a strain on the national treasury. The hemisphere defense strategy was at stake, however, and Ecuador got its destroyer.

As to the paymaster, the unparalleled American experiment is an effort to demonstrate that revolution can be purchased without the cost of revolt. It exemplifies again the pragmatic anti-tragic American genius for the abrogation of a moral apothegm once thought to express the nature of things: that in the critical turnings of history there are some things it takes more than money to buy. This maxim, a primal heresy in a mercantile society, could not long have gone unchallenged. (*See* Action.)

## Alpha

One of the three principal types of nuclear emission of radioactivity (*q.v.*), the other two being beta and gamma (*qq.v.*).

The science of the twentieth century permits a dualistic view of atomic-ray phenomena. A ray can be regarded as a beam of discontinuous particles, or as the axis of a continuous wave of energy. In the case of the alpha ray, the particle characteristics predominate so strongly that the emission is usually referred to as alpha particles. An alpha particle is several thousand times the mass of the beta particle. Also, compared to beta and gamma emissions, which attain very high velocities near that of light, the alpha particle travels at moderate speed.

The alpha particle has another significant characteristic. It carries a strong electrical charge. This comes about from its structure: the alpha particle is thought of as two neutrons (neutral) and two protons (positive) bound up in an exceedingly firm unit, a unit identical with the nucleus of the helium atom. A partial atom devoid of the external electrons (negative) that would give it electrical relief, the alpha particle extorts electrons from its environment.

Its large mass, moderate speed, and most important its strong propensity for electron seizure cause the alpha ray to have a peculiar effect on living tissue. Fettered by its weight, sluggishness and quick electron satiation, this ray does not penetrate deeply. Its energy is spent in a layer of five cells. On the other hand, an alpha track through these cells is thick and immensely destructive. (*See* Ionizing Radiation.) On the surface of the skin, such a track is often inconsequential; skin surface abounds in dead cells as it is. However, the surface of internal organs is composed of living cells. Here an alpha track is quite significant. Radioactive fallout from nuclear bursts and the waste from other atomic-energy activity abound in alpha radiation. These products get into the atmosphere and are inhaled, or get into food and are eaten. Inside the body, alpha particles go about their business.

## Anabiosis

Suspended animation during which an astronaut's need for food, water and atmosphere would be eliminated. (*See* Aquarium.) The boredom and emotional stress of long space flights would also be eliminated. Biological aging would cease, and crews would endure for several life spans. Experiments have shown that instantaneous freezing of animals leads to a cessation of metabolic processes but not necessarily to irreversible death. It has been known that certain Alaskan and Siberian insects undergo natural anabiosis for months during Arctic winters; they revive to complete health following months of a lifeless, solid state. However, the freezing must be instantaneous, which is difficult with large, warm-blooded creatures like humans. If current experiments in this direction succeed, astronauts would be frozen solid at launching and would be restored to animation by automatic warming devices as they approached their destination, years or even centuries later.

## Anemia

A generic term for various forms of disease in which the red blood corpuscles are insufficient, or the amount of hemoglobin decreases. In both cases, the effect is the same: a reduction in the oxygen-bearing power of the blood.

The red blood corpuscles carry oxygen to the tissues and are essential in the transfer of carbon dioxide from the tissues to the lungs. The red bone marrow, in healthy organisms, functions as supplier to the blood of red corpuscles to take the place of those destroyed in the liver, spleen and other tissues. When the bone marrow is badly damaged (see Ionizing Radiation), it may fail to produce new cells. Aplastic anemia, the red-cell deficiency, runs its course without remission.

## Anomie  (from Greek $a$ = without; hence, not; and *nomikos* = customary)

*Non*adjustment, as opposed to *mal*adjustment. The latter implies a determined but repeatedly ineffectual effort at getting on in one's environment. The former (*anomie*) also involves not getting on in one's environment but without the determination or the effort to do so. Hence, *anomic* individuals are the eccentrics, the hermits, those bizarre but "harmless" characters who go about their business entirely "out of things," indifferent to groups, to culture, to events current in the community. They are found, in cities, living peculiar and isolated lives on the borders of, rather than in, neighborhoods. They usually give the impression of being maintained by strange sources of income. Actually, most anomics are supported and looked after by resigned and patient relatives.

Anomie is thought to result when an individual has been brought up strictly and narrowly to survive in a highly particular social structure, which somehow changes. Thus, the aged, whose lives do span social change, are especially prone to anomie; likewise numerous members of those populations exposed to sudden social revolution or extreme environmental alteration as by natural or man-made disasters.

## Antimatter

One of the plausibilities of a physics which has succeeded in discovering both more and less than it can account for. (*See* Particle.)

Thus, the observations and mathematics of the currently numerous subatomic particles require the view that matter resides at two energy levels: a plus level and a minus level. Matter at the plus level composes that universe whose existence has always been apparent. Matter at the minus level also exists, but its existence, in respect to matter at the plus level, is only potential. On statistically concrete occasions a particle of matter at the minus level is struck by a vagrant ray of some kind, say, a cosmic ray (*q.v.*), and the particle thereby acquires sufficient energy to materialize at the plus level. At this instant, a counterpart at the plus level may drop out of existence into the vacated energy hole, or a collision may occur between the materialized particle and a counterpart and both simply disappear in a wink of energy.

The likelihood of a cancellation of the cosmos in one swoop is small, according to the mathematics that separates the two levels of matter.

## Anxiety

A painful sense of impending dread available only to a creature whose mentality has evolved sufficiently to entertain three prerequisite notions: *freedom of choice, the future,* and *the unknown.* It differs from *fear,* wherein the danger is actual and external. In anxiety, the danger is internal (= psychological) and only imminent.

Anxiety originates very early in life in the course of the child's transformation from a wild to a domesticated animal. This transformation includes the lesson that certain impulses, e.g., aggression (*q.v.*), create dangerous situations, e.g., loss of love, which means to the infant loss of protection and a threat to survival. Henceforth, when the lesson is learned, anxiety intervenes whenever a dangerous impulse threatens to arise. Anxiety becomes a signal to avoid a dangerous interpersonal situation. This continues to be its function throughout life, a signal alerting the individual to consider his impulses in respect to other people. Abundant anxiety leads to self-consciousness and restriction. But a lack of anxiety leads to varying degrees of interpersonal inconsideration, from homicide to plain indifference. As a feeling, anxiety never loses its association with that terrifying sense of helplessness and possible annihilation to which the infant is always exposed. (*See* Tranquilizer.)

## Apathy
An extreme absence of sensation and interest brought about by a continual inability to obtain relief from suffering. The dull stupor observed in young war orphans and also in long-term concentration-camp prisoners. A perilous condition since the victim cannot respond adequately to danger and hence cannot avoid injury. To be distinguished from indifference, which is a more or less conscious removal of attention from specific situations.

The earliest model of apathy is the infant whose pain goes unattended.

## Appeasement
An old demonstration of animal cunning.

Of the beaver one reads that when it is pursued, knowing this to be on account of the virtue of its testicles for medicinal uses, not being able to flee any farther it stops and in order to be at peace with its pursuers bites off its testicles with its sharp teeth and leaves them to its enemies.

—Leonardo da Vinci

## Aquarium

The microenvironment for the far-ranging man in space. An aquarium is a closed system characterized by a steady equilibrium between atmosphere, food and waste. Abundant air tanks, pantry and toilet are out of the question for long trips into space; vehicular design allows for little more than fuel, instruments and passengers.

A controlled atmosphere has to remove unwanted additions to the cabin environment; it must regenerate the atmospheric materials and conditions essential to the life of the passengers. Carbon dioxide, exhaled in breathing, may induce asphyxiation if it replaces a certain percentage of the oxygen in the microatmosphere. Another problem arises from the fact that the human being eliminates more water than he drinks; the metabolism of food produces water which is given off in urine, perspiration and breath. If uncontrolled, this water would not only saturate the microatmosphere, creating an insufferable humidity; it would also materialize as liquid through which the passengers would soon find themselves sloshing about. In addition, ammonia gas from urine, various gaseous constituents in feces, methane in perspiration, deadly carbon monoxide from overheated equipment must all be disposed of *within* the spacecraft and in such a way that proper percentages of oxygen are maintained constantly.

Chemical, mechanical and biological processes are being advanced for the construction of a successful aquarium. In chemical regulations of the microatmosphere, toxic gases and a certain amount of water are absorbed by crystals of lye or blocks of carbon. The principle is similar to that on which gas masks function; sooner or later, however, chemicals become saturated and their usability comes to an end. Mechanical methods, such as refrigeration, can freeze out water vapor and carbon dioxide from the microatmosphere.

Distilling apparatus can then convert part of this water into drinkable water. However, a surfeit of water is accumulating. Carbon dioxide has to be stored. Organic wastes are building up, which remain practically untouched by chemical and mechanical processes. Especially on long sallies, like the trip to Mars, which will take over a year, these organic wastes must be reconverted into food and atmosphere. For this, biological processes hold the most promise.

Photosynthesis is the biological process whereby green plants, using the radiant energy of light, transform carbon dioxide and water into oxygen and carbohydrate. Algae are small, rootless green plants found as ocean seaweed or the scum on the surface of quiet ponds. Five pounds of a strain of alga called Chlorella pyrenoidosa can absorb the exhaled carbon dioxide of one man and provide him with a continuing supply of oxygen. Certain other strains are even more efficient. Algae are also rich in proteins, carbohydrates, minerals and vitamins. For short visits to the moon, or orbital flights around Earth, concentrated foods in squeezable (and edible) tubes are sufficient. For long trips, algae may solve the food problem. Thus as algae, in tanks under fluorescent lights, photosynthesize in the microatmosphere, they also grow and can be spooned off at mealtime. Although they do not taste very good, they can be flavored to approximate the taste of meat, fish, chocolate, jams. Mashed with edible fuel tanks, algae could contribute to a nutritious biscuit.

If astronautic urine and feces could be converted into food and drinkable water, a great number of aquarial problems would be solved. Here again algae hold promise. Some constituents of urine such as ammonia are metabolized by algae; feces blended with algae undergo purification into glucose, a very nutritive food essential to life. This solid fare is supplemented with necessary water from sweat, urine and the moisture of feces. The School of Aviation Medicine owns a space simulator in which such sources of water are subjected to chemical treatment, filtering, superheating, freezing and subsequent filtration to produce thirst-quenching water, also usable for morning ablutions.

Finally, the death of human inhabitants of the aquarium needs to be faced. A large corpse undergoing decay would surely strain the microenvironment's subtle equilibrium. If the psychological problems surrounding cannibalism could be ironed out, a cadaver would be a source of comparatively festive steaks, chops, sweetmeats, soups. However, at the present time the psychological problems seem insurmountable. For the time being, it is expected that the deceased will be laid to rest in empty fuel tanks; these coffins will be placed in eternal orbit when a suitable opportunity arises. (*See also* Anabiosis.)

## A-Ring
The circle of complete destruction from a multimegaton bomb.

## Asteroid Bomb
On the first night of the nineteenth century, the astronomer Piazzi discovered Ceres, a small planet revolving between the orbits of Mars and Jupiter, the first of a great host of small bodies known also as minor planets or asteroids. They range from 100 feet to 480 miles or more in diameter.

In their search for effective deterrents, missile and space vehicle scientists see in the asteroid one of the most promising agents in the struggle against the dangers of nuclear warfare. The United States rocket program expects by 1968 to have constructed the Nova, a rocket of 9,000,000 pounds booster thrust—enough to propel an asteroid out of orbit and crash it into a predetermined spot on Earth. A small planet, if dropped, for instance, on the state of Kentucky, could knock out the eastern half of the United States; if dropped into the Atlantic Ocean, the tidal wave caused by the fall would destroy the Atlantic seaboard of the United States as well as a large part of Western Europe.

Although the asteroid bomb is no Doomsday Machine (*q.v.*), it has its advantages. Minor planets are not manufactured items and the major expense would

consist of finishing the Nova. Mercury and Mars, the
smallest planets, with diameters of 3,100 and 4,200
miles respectively, do not come within the present
scope of the program.

## Asteroidism

The seizure of minor planets, or asteroids, as founda-
tions and sources of structural materials for manned
space stations (*q.v.*).

**Atom**   (from Greek *atomos*, *a* = not, *tomos* = divided, hence that which cannot be split)
A construction idealizing the material world at the
most elementary and imperishable level, the atom has
existed in Western science for at least 2,500 years. The
product, only and always, of ideas about facts, the
atom mitigates the controversy between the spiritual
and the physical, the conception and the observed, the
ideal and the real. Thus the atom is a theory.

Empedocles taught (450 B.C.) that all matter originated in varying combinations of four elements,
earth, water, air, and fire, and atoms were the smallest
quantites of these elements. The atoms of Democritus
(*c.* 400 B.C.) were many in size and shape but identical
in substance; "strong in solid singleness," these atoms
conform to the Pythagorean doctrine of integral
monads—number as the ultimate reality. (*See* Quantum.) Aristotle speaks (*c.* 330 B.C.) of four elemental
opposites: the hot and the cold, the wet and the dry,
combinations of which form the elements earth, water,
air, and fire (*qq.v.*).

Atoms move in the void and catching each other up jostle
together, and some recoil in any direction that may chance,
and others become entangled with one another in various
degrees according to the symmetry of their shapes and sizes
and positions and order, and they remain together and thus
the coming into being of composite things is effected.
—Simplicius

The atom of John Dalton is among the most famous
of all atoms of history. Appearing in 1808, this British
atom was practical and dogmatic:

All bodies of sensible magnitude are constituted of a vast number of extremely small particles, or atoms of matter. . . . Chemical analysis and synthesis go no farther than to the separation of particles one from another, and to their reunion. . . . No new creation or destruction of matter is within reach. . . . We might as well attempt to introduce a new planet into the solar system, or to annihilate one already in existence as to create or destroy a particle of, for example, hydrogen.

Dalton distinguished 20 different atoms basic to 20 different elements (matter of "sensible magnitude") and represented these different atoms with a variety of dots, crosses and stars drawn within little circles. He furnished a mathematics of atomic combination and assigned some relative weights to the different atoms.

For decades hence the Dalton atoms increased in variety, and were counted, weighed and sorted, and their interactions with themselves and with different environments, like heat and pressure, were studied and described.

The Dalton atom ceased to exist in 1897, when one Sir Joseph Thomson asserted that the atom contained a large number of smaller bodies, which he called corpuscles: "In the normal atom, the assemblage of corpuscles forms a system which is electrically neutral." But under special conditions, as when an X ray is turned on matter, some of these corpuscles come loose and unbalance the atom. (*See* Ionization.) Thus, in addition to its long-standing external relationships, the atom acquired internal relationships to itself. Its unity had become a multiple. Thomson's corpuscles were soon given the name "electrons."

The Rutherford-Bohr atom of the New Zealander Ernest Rutherford and the Dane Niels Bohr arrived around 1913. It was the culmination of numerous and complex internal relationships. Though short-lived in the scientific mentality—actually it perished during the 1920s, dismissed even by its sires—this atom has yet to be shaken from the popular imagination where it resides as the simplistic image of a miniature solar system, with its planetary electrons in circular orbit about a nucleus.

The symbolic ramifications of the atom exist in analogy with the données that furnish particular historical periods with their leading images. The twentieth-century reductionism which makes the atom a visually reproducible little sun has added no greater accuracy to the concept, while it has overseen the loss of those fruitful symbolic resonances in which more illiterate and less miseducated societies delighted. The little sun of the mass media, stranger to the mathematical atom of the physicist, can be drawn on the blackboard.

## Atom, Twentieth-Century

No preceding atom has had to sustain as much of the physics and mathematics of its age as this one. The twentieth-century atom fidgets so nervously with contemporary measurement and conjecture that it has been likened to the final stages of Ptolemaic astronomy, when planetary motions acquired baffling intricacy in order to keep Earth in the center of the universe. This is a decadent atom that satisfies nobody, least of all its creators. Its inner dynamics are incongruous with the principles established for the rest of nature; it is governed by special laws having application nowhere else in the universe—"God may be obscure, but He's not plain mean," Einstein insisted as he struggled in vain to reconcile this atom with the rest of the universe. The corpuscular composition of this atom is so numerous and seething as to verge on the comic. The dualistic character of this atom is so frank—it is wave, yet particle; empty yet full; forward yet backward— that it is feared this atom is a psychological fiasco, an unabashed extension of the mind-body duality of its creators. Also, its technology is fantastic, being joyless, somber, suicidal.

Whereas previous atoms have been typified by their minuteness, the twentieth-century atom, also minute, is at the same time vast. The distances, for example, between its nucleus and its external electron configurations exceed, in terms of relative size of the bodies involved, the distances between the sun and its planets. The spaciousness of the atom is relatively greater than the spaciousness of the solar system. Within the atom the spaces between the particles are perfect vacuums; they are filled with particles in negative energy states capable of manifestation upon the absorption of energy from a stray particle entering the vastness of the atom. (*See* Antimatter.) Thus the atomic void is the stage upon which energy transformations are played out continuously. A chance gamma particle bypasses the electron clouds and penetrates the deep void of an atom, where the particle now comes to a halt, surrendering its energy to the appearance of two different particles, precise conversions of energy which leap across the gigantic voids, disappearing in collisions with quivering, spinning electrons to unleash a new particle, or two, or three, or perhaps escaping outside the atom as brief spectacles before ducking off into a new transformation. This atom trembles, sputters, radiates, expands, collapses, splits, absorbs, discharges, disappears, reappears.

## Atomic Accident, Bikini

On March 1, 1954, the first fission-fusion-fission bomb (*q.v.*), was set off by the United States on a coral island in a lagoon at Bikini Atoll in the Pacific Ocean.

For weeks before the detonation, the Atomic Energy Commission had disseminated information about the boundaries of a 30,000-square-mile danger zone in the Pacific. Airplanes surveyed the expanse for days before the test to warn away ships. Special weather studies were made over an area greater than that of the United States. It did not seem probable that the test would occur on the "ready" date, March 1. Because of the large amount of fission products expected, the shot could take place only under the most favorable wind conditions—due north. Eniwetok lay to the west, Rongelap, Rongerik and Utirik Islands to the east, Kwajalein to the south.

The wind on March 1 was blowing to the northeast. It might be months before the ideal winds occurred, so the O.K. was given.

The island that had served as a platform for the bomb disintegrated into pulverized coral from the force of the explosion. The wind veered to the east. Marshall Islanders, American participants in the test, and Japanese fishermen (*see* Lucky Dragon) found themselves in the path of the fallout, visible because particles of coral had been gathered up by the rising cloud.

236 Marshall Islanders, residents of Rongelap and Utirik, were evacuated by destroyer as quickly as possible. None of the 64 inhabitants of Rongelap had been present in that part of the atoll exposed to 2,300 r, a fatal dose of radiation; nevertheless, the wind-shift effects did produce injuries particularly to themselves and to their island. (*See* Rongelap.)

## Atomic Accident, Gnome

Like Chariot (*q.v.*), Gnome was part of Plowshare, a project to use nuclear energy for peace. In December, 1961, 1,200 feet under a stretch of desert southeast of Carlsbad, New Mexico, the Atomic Energy Commission exploded a nuclear charge in a formation of salt rock. Scientists hoped to carry out a heat-extraction experiment, to investigate the possibilities of tapping for productive uses the superheated steam and neutrons resulting from the explosion. In order to insure conditions of maximum safety, the project director chose a sparsely populated region for the experiment: the danger of any radiation escaping from so far below the ground was "so low as to approach the impossible," said the AEC, but the Commission maintained scientific caution. Many more precautions had also been taken: the tunnel was packed with bags of salt and blocks of concrete to arrest the spread of radioactivity. The U.S. Weather Bureau had analyzed wind patterns for an entire week and the shot had been delayed for four hours to take advantage of felicitous wind direction. Shortly before the explosion, the yield had been reduced from 10 kilotons to 5. Immediately after the explosion, a white vapor, denoting accidental escape of radioactivity, rose from an elevator shaft sunk into the earth. The wind was blowing north-northwest, and almost all of the radioactivity disappeared into the atmosphere and missed the nearest town, so it was all right.

# Atomic Accident, Small

The last entry in the logbook at the Nuclear Reactor Testing Station west of Idaho Falls said, "Replacing plugs, thimbles, etc., to all rods."

On December 23, 1960, the reactor—SL-1—was "shut down," and some necessary repairs were made. The process of deactivating SL-1 involved the manipulation of rods by three young technicians: John Byrnes, 27, a journeyman reactor operator; Richard Legg, 26, a specialist, operator, and shift supervisor; Richard McKinley, 22, transferred to SL-1 two months before. 40 sandwich rods, encased in the core of SL-1, held a total of 30 pounds of uranium—enough to produce several atomic bombs. SL-1 had been producing 30,000 kilowatts of heat, an experimental operation designed to test the efficiency of such production for distant Arctic bases.

In addition to the 40 hot rods, 9 control rods were built into SL-1, only one of which, No. 9, could initiate a chain reaction. The other 8 could only increase or decrease the tempo of the reaction. This safety feature permitted only $\frac{1}{9}$ of the control mechanisms to put the reactor into operation.

In addition, the men had been stringently cautioned to operate within the context of another safety measure: under no condition should any of the 9 rods be moved more than 4 inches.

The safety factor built into SL-1, however, allowed for a movement of 19 inches, more than enough to meet any foreseeable contingency.

When SL-1 was shut down, the 9 rods, each 7 feet long, were disconnected from the overhead drive apparatus. On the night of January 3, Byrnes, Legg and McKinley were pulling up each control rod by hand to engage the drive again. At 9:01, SL-1 started by mistake.

A blast shot up through openings in the top of the reactor vessel. Metal shielding tore outward with great force. An automatic alarm immediately rang at Atomic Energy Commission Security Headquarters. At 9:10 automobiles brought an assistant fire chief, a security officer and a health physicist.

Nothing in the atmosphere, no cries, no disturbance

at the site. Only the meters they brought in disclosed the presence of radioactivity. Byrnes, Legg and McKinley were not found in any of the surrounding buildings. Radio contact confirmed that they had not left the area. The only place was the 48-foot silo, housing SL-1. Two men, the first rescue team, started up the silo stairs. They retreated when their radioactivity meters read *Full Scale,* 25 roentgens per hour. Meters with higher readings were needed.

A second crew started up. Their meters read 200 roentgens per hour; they retreated before they reached the top.

A third crew, a fireman and a health physicist, dashed up the stairs. They looked in: the lights were on, no sign of fire, no one around. Their meters read 500 roentgens per hour, *Full Scale,* indication of a fatal dose. The fireman and the health physicist retreated.

The radioactivity level menaced the rescuers; but if Byrnes, Legg or McKinley was alive he must be got out. At 10:35 four combustion engineering men went into the silo. They saw two technicians inside, one moving. The rescuers retreated.

A fifth crew split up. Group 1 seized the survivor and brought him down the stairs on a stretcher to a waiting truck. Group 2 got to the second technician; he was dead. They retreated.

Three minutes had elapsed.

At a junction of a highway and the road leading from SL-1, an AEC doctor met the survivor and pronounced him dead at 11:04 P.M.

In the meantime the sixth rescue group had found the third technologist. His body had apparently been hurled upward by the explosion and pinned to a beam in the ceiling above the reactor. The radiation was very strong there. Six days later the body was dislodged, caught in a net handled by a crane and remote-control television cameras. Six teams worked; each man was allowed one minute for his part in the liberation of the body.

The bodies were decontaminated; one gave off 400 roentgens per hour. The technologists' clothes were soaked in radioactive material; so were their skin and hair. Two of the men, according to the post-mortem, had died instantly; the third had received a fatal head wound. Had Byrnes, Legg or McKinley survived the explosion, only days or at most weeks of agony would have been his portion before death. There are no specifics for such overexposure.

The AEC reported on January 23, "Radiation levels are such as to permit the conduct of normal burial services." However, a little lead shielding coated the inside of the coffins.

What happened is hard to say. The AEC later stated that a "nuclear excursion," resulting from motion of rod No. 9, had killed Byrnes, Legg and McKinley.

## Atomic Age
The period of history beginning December 2, 1942 (3:25 P.M., Chicago time), when the first self-sustaining chain reaction releasing nuclear energy was achieved by the scientist Enrico Fermi and his colleagues in a converted squash court under the grandstands of an athletic field at the University of Chicago. The Atomic Age was toasted in by the small assemblage present that Wednesday afternoon with Italian red wine doled out in paper cups and was announced by a coded telephone message to an absent associate: "The Italian navigator has landed in the New World." (*See* Great God K.)

## Atomic Bomb    *See* Fission Bomb.

## Atom-Smasher
Also accelerator. The family name of a breed of increasingly spectacular machines for probing the incommodious interior of the atom. The most famous has been the cyclotron. Others include the betatron, synchrotron, synchro-cyclotron, cosmotron and bevatron.

These machines are elaborations of the vest-pocket atom-smasher of Lord Ernest Rutherford, whose original apparatus was a virtual shoebox with a hole at one end. Just outside the hole was an observation device in the form of a small fluorescent screen with a microscope trained on it. When nitrogen gas is boxed up with a speck of radium, traces of oxygen gas eventually appear amidst the nitrogen. Microscopic scintillations of nascent energy appear on the screen. Measurements of these observations lead to the conclusion that some of the fast-moving particles emitted from the radium had managed to penetrate some of the nitrogen atoms sufficiently to disrupt their atomic structures and to alter them to oxygen structures. Energy is released from this transformation. By studying this process, a good deal can be learned about the nitrogen atom, or almost any atom introduced with the radium.

This was atom smashing at the end of World War I. The point of it was to ascertain the structure of atoms. The usefulness of Rutherford's particular apparatus was soon exhausted. For one thing, radium emissions —alpha rays—create only a limited kind of interesting phenomenon; for another, different velocities produce different phenomena, but the velocity of radium emissions is unvarying. However, the idea behind Rutherford's procedure has not been exhausted: particles are still fired against a target of matter in sight of an observing device near the target. The device captures telltale tracks of energy of different shapes and sizes. This is the technical model for the most ambitious laboratory equipment ever constructed.

By the nineteen-thirties, Rutherford's radium device had spawned a race of giants. Particles are accelerated to high velocities artificially by means of high electrical voltage. The Massachusetts Institute of Technology had no building large enough to house its first accelerator, so huge was the electrical generator. A nearby airship hangar was borrowed. Ten million volts were attained with this early generator which released a rope of lightning against the steel hangar roof as it accelerated a beam of particles against a target at fairly high speeds. Thereupon the University of California located a 60-ton electromagnet abandoned in China in 1918 by the defunct Federal Telegraph Company and brought it across the Pacific for the university's first accelerator, the 85-ton cyclotron. Columbia University constructed a 75-ton cyclotron, and the University of California went on to build a 225-ton device and to plan and begin construction of a 4,900-ton device. The growing variety of energy tracks at the target sites of these accelerators added steady detail to the conception of the atom. By 1939, the Soviet Union constructed the first atom-smasher on the European continent.

World War II interrupted this pounding of the atom. Money and attention were diverted to a different phase of atomic technology.

In 1947, the University of California built a 32-million-electron-volt accelerator. (*See* Electron Volt.) The university also acquired an electromagnet weighing 200 tons, then another weighing 4,000 tons. Beams of particles were being driven up to ranges of hundreds of millions of electron volts on electrical paths extending over miles. Huge cooling systems were added to carry away the heat generated in the magnets.

During the nineteen-fifties atom-smashers cropped up in a pack of universities, in private industry, at Brookhaven, in England, France, Israel, Russia, Switzerland—all over. The electron volts were driven up into the billion range, as miles of electrical course were added and generators were expanded. In the present decade there is talk of a financial collaboration between the United States and the Soviet Union on an atom-smasher that would accelerate particles 13 miles toward a target with a velocity of a trillion electron volts. Money seems to be the only limit on the knowledge gained from these machines.

But at a high altitude in a clear atmosphere, like the top of the Andes Mountains, a small photographic plate cogently placed between the poles of a comparatively small electromagnet will record a natural cosmic ray (*q.v.*), smashing an atom into a debris of 20 parts. This leaves all accelerators far behind.

**August 13, 1937**
The first death registered at the concentration camp Buchenwald.

**August 15, 1937**
The second and third deaths registered at the concentration camp Buchenwald.

**August 6, 1945**
The first atomic bomb exploded over a civilian population.

**August 9, 1945**
The last atomic bomb exploded over a civilian population. (*See* Fission-Fusion-Fission Bomb.)

**Autokinetic Effect**
In complete darkness, such as in a closed room, a point of small light that is kept perfectly still seems to move slowly and haphazardly in all directions. This effect occurs in everyone without exception. It also works on a cloudy night with a stationary point of light in the distance, which then takes on the appearance of movement. And it is commonly experienced when looking at a single star in the sky. In short, the autokinetic effect occurs whenever an illuminated object lacks a frame of reference.

How much movement is attributed to the object varies from individual to individual. However, if two persons are in a darkened room exposed to a stationary point of light which is repeatedly flashed on for several seconds at a time, and if one of them does not know about the autokinetic effect, namely, that the light is really stationary, and the other does know, the one who knows can invariably influence the other's perception of the apparent distance of movement by simply deciding beforehand to do so. Thus, the informed person can decide to influence the naïve one to see the light move, say, 8 inches. He can accomplish this by having himself and the naïve person take turns in estimating the movement of the flashing light. If the informed person persists without variation in announcing that he sees the light move around 8 inches, the naïve one will soon begin to adjust his estimates to this distance. (*See* Brainwash.)

**Averager**
A person who maintains one of two opposing positions as regards radiation hazard. (For his opponent, *see* Hot-Spotter.)

In establishing standards of protection against deleterious radiation, Averagers are those who focus attention on a general population—usually in groups of one million—rather than on individuals or atypical variations within the population. This approach is consistent with genetic science.

An example of how it works out in respect to radiation hazard is the situation associated with certain areas in Nevada and Utah close to atomic-bomb testing grounds. The National Committee on Radiation Protection and Measurement, a committee of Averagers, established a little less than ½ roentgen unit per person per year as a standard of acceptable radiation dosage. Substantial areas in Nevada and Utah were receiving 10 roentgen units as early as 1955 and about forty additional communities were receiving average doses of between 1 and 8 units. Gordon Dunning, a leading Averager of the Atomic Energy Commission, discussed his approach to this matter at a Congressional hearing:

In terms of the general populace around the Nevada test site, I had a little problem finding a million people for a general population, but if one mentally makes larger and larger circles until he encompasses a million people, then the average exposure to the one million is one tenth of a roentgen unit for six years of testing, which is at the rate of half a roentgen unit per 30 years, which is one twentieth of the maximum exposures recommended by the committees.

# B

## Baby Teeth

Also, first teeth; deciduous teeth. Developed and then shed during childhood, baby teeth are tangible evidence to the child of growth, for which there is the customary reward of a prize, usually monetary; upon retiring at night, the child puts the baby tooth he has shed during the day under his pillow, and he wakes up the following morning to the discovery that during the night he has been visited by a proud and benevolent fairy who made off with the tooth and left in its stead a coin.

Of late, shed baby teeth have acquired a more specific utility having to do with a specific feature of growth in the second half of the twentieth century. Being similar to bone in possessing a stable calcium structure, baby teeth reveal, upon analysis, the presence of strontium 90 (*q.v.*). Since it has been found that a practically perfect relationship exists between the uptake of strontium 90 by the skeleton and the uptake by the teeth, the amount of this leukemogenic isotope present in the entire skeleton can now be computed from the amount present in baby teeth. The feasibility of this computation is quite an advance. Skeletons of a population are not readily available for analyses. The amount of strontium 90 in the human skeleton cannot be confidently estimated from the quantity of that element in soil and plants.

How realistic is this excellent idea of using baby teeth for strontium 90 studies? Baby teeth collecting began in January, 1959, under the sponsorship of a St. Louis, Missouri, citizens' committee with the cooperation of local health officials, schools, media, churches. In two and a half years 61,000 teeth were collected, with accompanying data on the backgrounds of the youthful donors. The present rate of collection promises to double this amount, and there is no reason to believe that collecting will not spread far beyond St. Louis. To the donor the customary prize is now a button: "I gave my tooth to science."

## Bacteria

A large, widely distributed group of typically one-celled microorganisms (class Schizomycetes), chiefly parasitic or saprophytic. They exhibit three chief typical shapes: spherical (coccus), rod-shaped (bacillus), spiral and threadlike (spirillum). Many bacteria are disease-producing; many are active in processes such as fermentation, the conversion of dead organic matter into soluble food for plants, and the fixing of atmospheric nitrogen.

The potential usefulness of the bacteria in the modern period suggests to biologists reaches of the imagination nearly overwhelming in their promise. Progress, in some cases significant progress, has been registered in the application of the bacteria to the dissemination of disease to the conducting tissues of plants—interference with water movements, invasion of soft tissues of leaves and roots, the inhibiting of growth or the causing of lesions, rusts or galls on specific parts of plants. The use of bacteria on living organisms other than plants in some geopolitical situations produces a large range of interesting effects. The bacteria, in this instance, may be transferred from one place to another by animal vectors (rats), sabotage, free balloons, aerial bombs, airplane spray, and shells. The nature and quality of these modes of transfer are the concern of various scientists employed by a number of public institutions.

Clearly, the possibilties for useful exploitation of the bacteria present challenges of the highest order for professional workers in the field. Recent research indicates that indeed bacteria may compete with nuclear energy in still other realms of modern existence. Bacteria occupying a seven-inch-long test tube of seawater have powered a radio transmitting over a range of 15 miles. This "biochemical fuel cell" works on the same principle as that observed in the action of bacteria on chemicals in the sea to generate electrical currents. The bacteria may also be able to supply the power needs of entire communities at costs less than power produced by steam, hydroelectric techniques and nuclear reactors. One overriding advantage of the bacteria as compared with other sources of power lies in their resistance to radiation and antibiotics. Some bacteria adapt quickly to new circumstances. In a short time, they may develop resistance to antibiotics that once killed them. Today there are bacteria that need streptomycin in order to live. Others thrive on cyanide. Some bacteria have made their home in an atomic reactor. There they endured more than 1,000,000 roentgens, a quantity about 2,000 times that required to kill a human being. They populated the reactor so effectively in several days that they impeded the proper functioning of the apparatus. The Board Committee on Civil Defense of the American Chemical Society prepared a "Summary Report" on October 19, 1959, presenting the position that the threat from biological agents must be considered as on a par with the nuclear threat. Although the shelters of the Atomic Energy Commission and the American Chemical Society provide for protection against germs as well as fallout, widespread use of biological warfare implies such uncontrollable pathology that maybe nobody will use it. If the reproduction of bacteria were not checked by adverse conditions, the descendants of a single bacterium would exceed the total bulk of the earth in several days. In this rich exfoliation, the bacterium might be joined by the cockroach, which absorbs more than 100,000 roentgens with indifference.

## Bambi

An acronym for Ballistic Missile Boost Intercept, an American project for the development of a bombing satellite capable of destroying enemy ballistic-missile launch installations. (*See also* Orbiting H-Bomb.)

## Banking, Thermonuclear

The continuance of banking activity after nuclear

bombardment will be essential to the survival and cohesion of the affected country as a whole as well as supplying an imperative need born from possible divisiveness among the various parts of the nation, a situation known as "secession," which constitutes a real danger insofar as the seceding areas would thus put themselves into a nonresponsible sociopolitical position as well as into an economic *avant-garde* free from the duties which the necessities of the modern state require for the perpetuation of its national integrity, necessities including the sometimes difficult and occasionally painful and renunciatory aspects of shouldering a proportionate amount of the burdens of the body politic, in which connection it is not irrelevant to remember that the ancient Greeks called those who fled from such responsibilities "idiots." The United States Loss Sharing Plan (*see* Loss Sharing) would enable persons escaping from damaged areas and those living in undamaged areas to have their checks "honored on banks in other parts of the country, even if they had no proof of deposits or if the banks had been destroyed. Loss to cheaters would be absorbed by the nation as a whole."

## Barophobia

A fear of gravity. The barophobic lives in dread that he will be weakened by gravity or that gravity will increase, making it difficult or impossible for him to get around. There is the fantasy of being crushed against the floor or ground. Since gravity, like air pressure, is omnipresent and uniform and therefore not likely to be experienced consciously as other environmental phenomena are, it is exceedingly rare as a phobic object, and not enough barophobics have turned up for a decent study of this clinical manifestation. However, as space travel objectifies the experience of gravity, barophobia may increase sufficiently to fill this gap in our current knowledge.

## Beach Energy

A unit of fission energy; one Beach, two Beach; after the motion picture *On the Beach,* concerned with apocalyptic nuclear adventurism. The mathematician Freeman J. Dyson has assigned to the Beach an approximate magnitude of $3 \times 10^6$ megatons, or 3,000,-000,000,000 tons. Planetary fallout resulting from the atmospheric explosion of one Beach of fission energy would suffice to kill half of Earth's population by radiation. Quantitative hypotheses have not yet been made for lower orders of magnitude within the Beach gestalt, such as a Boardwalk or a Bathhouse. (*See, however,* Kahn Energy *and* Stockpile Energy.)

## Beta

One of three principal types of nuclear emission of radioactivity (*q.v.*), the other two being alpha and gamma (*qq.v.*).

Beta rays are streams of electrons (*q.v.*) traveling at prodigious velocity, near that of light. These rays are distinguished from other, usually less energetic, electron streams produced in radio and electron tubes. Electrons comprising these latter streams, called cathode rays, come off the outer regions of the atom. Beta rays, on the other hand, originate in the radioactive decay of the inner nuclei of atoms and are liberated with about three times the velocity of most artificially induced electron streams.

Unlike the penetrating gamma ray, which can cause total body irradiation death, the beta ray, like the alpha ray, is not especially penetrating and needs to be introduced into the body by inhalation and ingestion in order to achieve maximum biological affectiveness. Strontium 90 (*q.v.*), a high beta emitter, has become one of the common vehicles for transporting beta radiation inside the body. Once inside, beta radiation corrodes local tissue sites and can lead to a variety of malignancies like leukemia, bone tumor (*qq.v.*) and bone cancer.

Beta irradiation of the epidermis can also occur, but only comparatively close to nuclear bursts. Such irradiation is conveyed to the skin by radioactive dusts windblown from ground zero (*q.v.*). This results in "beta burns"—superficial inflammation, irritations, sores, loss of body hair, discoloration and, ultimately, scarring and disfiguration. However, in evaluating the effects of nuclear-bomb injuries, most experts (*q.v.*) put "beta burns" into the category "harmless."

**BEV**   *See* Electron Volt.

**Biological Half-Life**   *See* Effective Half-Life.

**Biome**
The name given to a major terrestrial community. The most stable, self-perpetuating life form in a biome —the climax life form—exists in harmony with the configuration, the drainage, the average temperature and rainfall peculiar to that land area. Intervening minor climaxes, consisting of other life forms, take place in developmental stages leading up to the most stable organisms appropriate to the area. The various stages are often dominated by different animals in a large cycle of change proper to the biome.

Man occasionally maintains stable communities unrepresentative of the climax. Continuous overgrazing by livestock may produce a desert community where the native conditions would permit, say, a grassland biome. Such a desert is known as a disturbance climax, or disclimax.

Earth has approximately 10 or 11 principal biomes, a good many less than it has countries.

**Blast Effects**
Blast injury to living targets depends on the pressure pulse from the explosion, the movement of material surrounding the explosion, and what happens when the pressure and movement interact with the target and its environment.

Blast effects may be grouped in three main categories: (a) primary blast effects, caused by variations in pressure following upon explosions, due to the initial pressure pulse and also to pressure reflection from structures and objects; (b) secondary effects, including impact of penetrating and nonpenetrating objects become missiles by the carrying force of blast winds; (c) tertiary effects, damage received by displacement of the biological target, or blast flight.

In the primary category, the greatest damage tends

to occur in the air-containing organs of the body: the lungs, the eardrums and the sinuses. The most dangerous effect results in lung damage, characterized by the presence of air bubbles in general circulation; such effects usually result in death within minutes. An additional hazard in the primary category involves suffocation from lung hemorrhage, with heart failure from lack of oxygen; if victims of hemorrhage do not rest, bleeding recurs. Beyond these effects, bruising of the heart, the liver, the spleen and other abdominal organs, including subsequent hemorrhage and possible rupture of the viscera, may take place.

Most estimates of primary-effect thresholds for damage to man are based on laboratory experimentation. Overpressure required to injure fatally 50 per cent of mice, guinea pigs, rabbits, monkeys and goats in various laboratory inquiries give an extrapolated figure of 390–470 pounds per square inch (p.s.i.) for 50 per cent fatalities in man. The best data available for estimating human tolerance to long-duration overpressures come from experiments in which animals were exposed in cages bolted to a metal plate closing the end of a shock tube in which they had been placed; this valuable series of experiments gives a figure of 40–50 p.s.i. for 50 per cent fatalities. A classic study, made in 1906, applied slowly increasing pressures to the eardrums of human cadavers and obtained a range of 5.5–44.1 p.s.i. for rupture. A 10-megaton blast injures eardrums out to 9 miles and lungs out to a distance of 5.5 miles.

Injuries in the second category are caused by missiles penetrating body cavities and damaging the eyes, the brain, the heart, the liver, the spleen and other organs. External, nonpenetrating missiles striking the chest can inflict damage to the lungs similar to that achieved by primary effects, and may be lethal. In addition, nonpenetrating missiles may injure the skull, rupture the liver and crush the spleen, with resultant hemorrhage.

In an experimental study of the effects of penetrating missiles, data was gathered by firing irregular glass fragments against the abdominal walls of dogs, in order to define the conditions for expectancies of missile arrival into the abdominal cavity. An extrapolated impact velocity for human abdominal damage from glass fragments was fixed at 115 feet per second for a 10-gram glass fragment. This minimal velocity can be found 11 miles from ground zero for a 10-megaton burst.

In the third category, two general kinds of damage are significant: differential displacement, or loss of a hand, foot, leg, arm, finger, toe, thigh or other part of the body; and total displacement of the entire organism. These hazards present no unusual characteristics, but the great range and long duration of blast winds in nuclear explosions underline their importance.

Experiments involving the dropping of human cadavers feet first, with knees locked, onto a hard surface from heights of 1, 2, 3, 4, and 6 feet conclude that the threshold for fracture of the heel, foot and ankle bones lies within a range of 11–16 feet per second. Another experiment, subjecting heads of human cadavers to impact, produced fractures at minimal impact velocities of 13.5 feet per second: for purposes of computation man is treated as a missile. Calculations at 6 p.s.i. for a yield of 10 megatons indicate that a 160-pound man would reach a maximal velocity of 97 feet per second (66 miles per hour); at that point the distance traveled would have been 330 feet. In or near cities obstacles would probably cut down his flight.

The burst could pick up a man more than 10 miles from ground zero (q.v.) and smash him into a wall.

Some difficulties obtain in the area of protective techniques. A wall might protect against displacement; however, pressure reflection hazard would then be greater. On the other hand, avoidance of walls to minimize overpressures increases the possibilities for displacement.

In general, the potential hazards are greatest from displacement, less threatening from missile damage, and less threatening yet from primary blast effects.

The statistics for these three categories assume surface bursts (q.v.). Air bursts (q.v.) do more damage.

Damage to buildings or other structures is significant. It results either from the force of the shock front, over pressure from the accompanying drag forces, or from the subsequent vacuum. A 20-megaton air-burst would collapse almost all brick dwellings within a radius of 10 miles. Within 15 miles, the damage, though attenuated, would suffice to tear doors from their hinges, smash them, and send broken window glass spearing through the house. (*See* Thermal Effects; Radiation Effects. *See also* Translation.)

## Blunting Mission

A retaliatory action designed to implement security through offense. The Blunting Mission seeks its targets on enemy ground: airfields, missile sites, nuclear stockpiles, grounded aircraft. A Blunting Mission differs from generally recognized offensive actions primarily by the nature of targets and the factor of speed. Thus a Blunting Mission constitutes a fast offensive strike which is not quite offensive.

## BMEWS

Ballistic Missiles Early Warning System. Immense ground-based radar installations scan the skies for ICBMs as they approach an altitude of approximately 600 miles above sea level. The BMEWS gives at least 12 minutes of warning time.

## Bold Orion

A project, under U.S. Air Force supervision, attempting to increase the stability of deterrence by investigating the use of bombers as missile-launching platforms.

## Bone Tumor

Malignant tumors may arise in bones, and are known as sarcomas. There are two types. The first arises within the ends of the long bones and expands the bone in which it arises to the eventual destruction of its interior. Ultimately what is left consists of a large swelling surrounding the tumor itself. The covering layer is so thin that a finger's pressure in examination may crack it like an eggshell. This malignancy has a minimal tendency to spread and can on occasion be arrested by the removal of the affected limb.

The second type grows from the outer surface. Amputation is the common indication; however, the

disease often returns in the stump or as secondary
deposits in the lung. The percentage of cures in this
category is lower than that in most other malignancies.

Bone cancers, or carcinomas, originate in other organs: the breast, the prostate gland, the thyroid gland
(*see* Iodine 131), the kidney. The lymph or blood carries the cancer to bones in the arms, thighs or spine.
At a late point in this pathology, ordinary muscular
movements of the affected areas may cause spontaneous
fractures, with almost no known remission. (*See* Radiation Effects.)

## Boredom
An unpleasurable state of mind combining an intense
need for activity with a lack of purpose. In boredom,
excitation is experienced but its aim has been forgotten. The environment may be shunned in an effort
to relieve the excitation through fantasy. More likely,
however, the environment is sought in the hope that
relief will come through some chance encounter with
a purpose similar to the one forgotten. Bored persons
pass from situation to situation like someone who has
misplaced a valuable possession and inquires incessantly for its whereabouts. But the discovery of purpose has the disadvantage of responsibility. Hence, the
environment is enlisted not for gratification—unknown
aims cannot be gratified—but for continued diversion
and distraction.

## Boy
In atomic-weapon parlance, a device that explodes suc-
cessfully. Since 1945 there have been over 200 boys.
American boys have been announced on the following
occasions: Trinity, Hiroshima, Nagasaki, Crossroads,
Sandstone, Ranger, Greenhouse, Buster-Jangle, Tum-
bler-Snapper, Ivy, Upshot-Knothole, Castle, Teapot,
Wigwam, Redwing, Plumb-bob, Hardtack, Dominic.

## Brainwash
Journalese of current origin (*c.* 1951). Those methods
employed by the Chinese Communists during the
Korean War to convert captured United Nations
troops to the Communistic point of view. A systematic

control of the physical and social environment, these methods included repetitive instruction, repetitive interrogation, repetitive demands for self-criticism of personal beliefs, and were carried out in an unpredictable atmosphere of reward and punishment. Physical torture as a feature of these methods was for weakening rather than injuring the prisoner. Considerable conversion and collaboration were elicited, but the program was ultimately a failure, since its effects wore off upon repatriation of the war prisoners.

Also applied to the methods for extracting public confessions. And by extension, to any attempt to coerce a person into line with a particular religious or political ideology. To apply this term, as is commonly done, to the Nazi concentration camp system is to abuse the term as well as to miss the point of this particular penal system. Prisoners under the Nazi regime were deemed to be hopeless failures of one sort or another rather than candidates for political rehabilitation.

**Bravo**   *See* Fission-Fusion-Fission Bomb.

## Breeding

The replenishing of any stock through some kind of reproductive behavior of the stock itself.

The term finds a current application in that type of nuclear reactor (*q.v.*) which replenishes its supply of fuel as a consequence of consuming the fuel. When a fissionable variety of uranium atom fissions, it releases on the average more than one neutron; if one neutron goes on to produce energetic fission in a neighboring atom and the other goes on to convert a nonfissionable variety of uranium atom into a fissionable variety, the process, while producing energy, would constantly supply more fuel and neutrons. A nuclear reactor which brings this off is called a breeder. The United States has developed at least one such breeder.

If more than two usable neutrons could be exploited from each fission, the reactor would actually breed more fissionable material than it used up. The search for this technological fertility has been named Operation Bootstrap.

### Broken-Backed War

The war which follows when the first huge exchange of thermonuclear weapons has failed to settle the situation decisively. The primary mode of continuity in such a situation involves Improvisation, a modality presenting certain difficulties in imposing the national will on the enemy. The Improvisation which the survivors of thermonuclear attack may find it within their capacities to carry out will have to be largely occupied with restoring the bare means of life. The Broken-backed conception of war offers problems to war planners. They have in time past found it impossibly difficult to predicate a war plan on the assumption of national disaster at the outset. History demonstrates the magnificence of Improvisation following upon certain disasters. In each of those cases the means of making war, including such vital intangibles as established governmental authority operating through accustomed channels of communication, remained intact. A few battleships sunk, a few armies defeated and lost, large territories yielded, some tens of thousands of lives lost may not be relevant to the burden that can be placed on thermonuclear Improvisation.

### Bulgur

Nuclear Spam. *See* Survival Biscuit.

### Button

> Pray you undo this Button,
> —*King Lear*, V, iii, 309

A small knob or stud attached to any object for use or ornament. The contemporary importance of the Button far outshines the pale light of its past history. Increase in Buttons is potentially in inverse proportion to increase in population. A famous Button expert (*q.v.*) observed in 1960 that the probability of nuclear accident in 1961 would be much lower than it might be later. For one thing, the Buttons ordinarily would be kept unconnected; for another, there would not be a lot.

# C

**Californium Bullet**
A bullet made of californium, a fissionable element of high efficiency useful in very small amounts for the production of pistol or rifle bullets. Presently prohibitive in cost. A reduction in manufacturing expense could provide soldiers, hunters, police and thieves with a side arm capable of exploding its charge with a force estimated at approximately 10 tons of TNT.

**Capability**   *See* Credibility.

**Carbon 14**   *See* Fission-Fusion-Fission Bomb; Neutron; Clean.

**Central Nervous System**
The brain and the spinal cord constitute the central nervous system. In invertebrates, the central nervous system is a solid cord of tissue; clusters of nerve-cell bodies at the front end are dominant, but they do not manifest the complexity of the analogous organ in the higher creatures, the brain.

In the evolutionary development of simple organisms, some cells became more irritable than others. They gave rise to receptor cells, particularly sensitive to stimuli, and to conducting cells. The resulting network formed the first nervous system. In the worm, the ganglia, or clusters of nerve cells, first appear, one or two ganglia in each body segment. They act as simple centers of coordination. One category of nerve cells, or neurones, conducts impulses into the ganglia; another relays impulses from the ganglia to muscles or glands. At this general level of development, chains of ganglia came into being and initiated a rudimentary central nervous system. Even in the higher creatures the spinal cord retains a segmental pattern.

The ganglia of the head segments in invertebrates followed an evolutionary process of fusion; the resulting large centers of nerve cells comprised the ancestors of the brain. The oldest parts of the brain in the higher creatures manifest atavistic traces of segmentation.

From both sides of the spinal cord and the brain, the nerves extend throughout the entire body and constitute the peripheral nervous system. Each spinal nerve contains a mixture of fibers coming into the central nervous system and fibers leaving the system, constituting an organization of reflex activity analogous to but infinitely more complex than the intermediary functions of primitive ganglia in such lower creatures as the worm.

The brain is the center to which the primary sense organs are connected. In the higher creatures the brain is closely associated with organs of taste and smell. The surface receptors in worms and insects enable such organisms to experience odor, light and vibrations on the particular area affected by exterior phenomena, but the higher creatures are characterized by receptors evolving from such primitive types: distance receptors, which introduce another dimension of perception.

The sight of the traffic of fish and snails in an aquarium, the tentacular weavings of certain marine organisms, the distant sound of bells, are not experienced as occurring immediately on the surface of the receptor; higher creatures place the source of sight or sound farther away than on the surface of the eye or on the membrane of the ear. The disturbances are projected outward to their apparent source.

In the higher creatures, the brain has acquired functions beyond the stage of increased sensory activity. It has become the location for the trove of past realities in man and a center for the nervous activities of sophisticated mentation. The nervous system of, say, the sea anemone, is diffuse and leaves to each part of the organism a large independence of action. The tentacles of the sea anemone, located near the mouth and used in getting food, will continue to respond to the presence of meat after the tentacles have been cut away from the animal; its creeping foot will continue to creep after excision. The tentacle itself contains the nerve necessary for its response. In contrast, the central nervous system of the higher creatures is largely an interdependent network which enables some of them to develop and transmit such idiosyncratic inventions as religion, science, art and chauvinism (*see* Central Nervous System Death; Minutemen).

## Central Nervous System Death

Doses of ionizing radiation above 5,000 rad generally cause central nervous system death. The nerve tissues are rapidly destroyed at this level. The nerve cells lose their ability to discriminate between sodium and potassium.

In the one accidental human case on record, incapacitation was complete by 5 minutes after exposure. Acute nausea, vomiting and diarrhea occur within minutes; symptoms similar to shock, irrational behavior, and general collapse develop within minutes after exposure. Partial symptomatic recovery may take place within hours; at the end of this period, convulsions, irrationality and coma precede death by minutes or hours. Victims of CNS Death lose no hair and suffer no secondary infections; the course of the disease is too short.

Relatively few cases of central nervous system death will be available for observation after a nuclear detonation. The intensities of radioactivity required to induce this pathology will usually occur in areas subject to primary blast and thermal effects (*qq.v.*), which may mask the damage to the central nervous system.

## Cesium 137

A comparatively long-lived radioisotope (*q.v.*) which chemically resembles the biologically vital element potassium. Unlike strontium 90 (*q.v.*), which tends to be discriminated against in favor of its chemical cousin, calcium, cesium 137 is actually preferred to potassium by the body. Cesium 137 distributes itself widely throughout the body, which favors its being eliminated in a relatively short time; on the other hand, this wide distribution, and the highly penetrating gamma radiation of its decay, favors cesium 137's reaching the genes (*q.v.*) and generating hereditary hazards.

Because of the penetrating properties of gamma radiation, cesium 137 is dangerous not only internally but also externally, on the soil and other objects in the environment. The radiation of cesium 137 passes through tissue and emerges from the surface of the body. Thus the level of this particular radioisotope in the body is rather easy to determine with a radiation counter applied close to the outside of the body.

## Chariot

Like Gnome near Carlsbad, New Mexico, and Vintage near Rifle, Colorado, a subproject in Plowshare. Plowshare is the Atomic Energy Commission's program for peaceful uses of nuclear explosives. Project Chariot involves the use of five atomic bombs exploded underground at the Ogotoruk Creek in Alaska, one of 200,-000 tons and four of 20,000 tons, each for the purpose of earth-moving. What would take many men many months of labor can thus be accomplished with a few blows—the moving of 20 million cubic yards of dirt.

The Cape Thompson region in Alaska is ideally suited for a nuclear blast. The nearest people live in Point Hope, 35 miles north of ground zero, and Kivalina, 40 miles south. The total population of both villages totals no more than 500. The coast is icebound for ten months of the year. No one lives inland from the coast. Except for some Eskimo handicrafts and polar bear and grizzly hunting, no industries exist, nor are there harbors, commercial fishing or roads.

The Eskimos do not live in one place, nor do they farm one plot, since the ground is permanently frozen: no pastures, no domestic animals. Permafrost. Over thousands of years they have found their precise niche in the intricate pattern of animal and plant life. They have learned to track the caribou, to catch the bearded seal on the ice, to spear the whale in offshore waters. They depend on the local biological environment for 80 per cent of their food and transportation.

The caribou, major source of food for the Eskimos, does not eat like the cow. The cow eats plants with roots in the ground. The caribou eats lichen—a rootless symbiosis of alga and fungus. Lichens absorb their mineral nutrition from dust in the air and they are more susceptible to fallout than other plants. The caribou have in their bones at least 4 to 8 times the strontium units in the bones of American steer. The strontium 90 content of caribou meat is probably considerably higher than that of any other animal used for food anywhere in the world.

Since the vegetation in the wetter, more protected slopes of the valley—including sixty-seven known species of lichen—supports voles and lemmings, the Arctic ground squirrels, and the caribou, it tends to maintain almost every other kind of life. Almost everything else, from the wolf to the man, consumes these herbivores. An increase in radioactive strontium gives rise to a certain concern.

The inhabitants of the Cape Thompson region, in an Eskimo Conference on Native Rights, voted to demand that the Department of the Interior revoke the Atomic Energy Commission's permit to reserve 1,600 miles of hunting land for Project Chariot. They claimed *Inupiat-Paitot* (Aboriginal Rights) to the land and transmitted their understanding of possible radiation diseases among their people.

The Atomic Energy Commission has initiated procedures demonstrating its concern for the region and its inhabitants. It has predicted the amount of vented yield (per cent of radioactivity which escapes to the air) in Chariot. A curve indicating only 5 per cent vented yield has been drawn, based on four previous underground explosions: Jangle U, Teapot-S, Neptune and Blanca. A curve equally valid could be drawn, based on these four points, producing an estimate of 26 per cent. The Atomic Energy Commission has measured wind velocities at Kotzebue, 210 miles southeast of Chariot site. Valley winds at and near ground zero are much higher.

Should *Inupiat-Paitot* be denied, Project Chariot would bring to the inhabitants of the Cape Thompson region harbors, canals, reservoirs and open-pit mining of ore. "The economic advantages seem clear . . ."

# China
A semitropical island situated north of the Philippines

and south of Japan and Okinawa. Including the Pescadores, China has an area of 13,885 square miles and a population of 9,675,000 (1957 estimate). The only territory remaining in the control of the Chinese Nationalist government after the successful advances of the Chinese Communists on the mainland; converted into a Nationalist military stronghold in 1949 and 1950. It is also known as Nationalist China, to distinguish it from the pretender to its seat in the United Nations, China, also known as People's Republic of China (estimated area 3,691,502 square miles, estimated population 660,000,000). Generalissimo Chiang Kai-shek on February 20, 1960, apologized to the members of the national assembly at Taipei for his failure to recover the mainland of China. From the time of the Nationalist government's move to Formosa Island, total United States of America economic and military aid to the Island of China was estimated at U.S. $3,-500,000,000.

**Christmas Island**  (from Latin *Christus,* from Greek *Christos,* anointed; plus mass, noun, from Latin *mittere, missum,* to dismiss)
A test site in the Pacific Ocean for the atmospheric explosion of nuclear bombs. The British, who own the island, lent it to the United States of America for a while for the purpose of nuclear-bomb explosions, explosions which the United Kingdom has in the past initiated with its own bombs. The Marshall Islands, which have acted as host for United States hydrogen bomb tests since 1946, were disqualified in 1962 from a geopolitical point of view. Although they are held under American supervision, the United Nations controls them as trust territories. Since a series of American atmospheric nuclear-bomb tests took place only in order to maintain the balance of power, such tests on United Nations territory would have unnecessarily alarmed the world and weakened the deterrent effects of American experiments.

**Clandestine Cache**
The supply of fissionable fuel and bomb material hidden within the borders of a nation that has pledged

itself to a disarmament agreement. A nation might prepare two clandestine caches; the existence and locality of one is leaked to the enemy's espionage; its discovery and confiscation avert suspicion of the other.

## Clean

Descriptive of a nuclear weapon with maximum blast and thermal effects (*qq.v.*) and minimum fallout (*q.v.*). Clean devices are suggested for limited nuclear warfare; they destroy property, installations and military personnel, but spare civilian populations behind military lines. They are also cited to calm those portions of civilian populations which are apprehensive about fallout from nuclear-weapons testing. Clean weapons are humanitarian.

At present, fusion reactions (*see* Fusion; Fission-Fusion Bomb) represent clean reactions as opposed to fission reactions (*see* Fission; Fission Bomb), which represent dirty reactions. (*See* Dirty.) But though it is true that fusion reactions produce only one radioactive product—tritium—and a rather slight one at that, the neutrons released by this reaction go on to radioactivate the environment significantly; for example, to the 1,900 pounds of radiocarbon (carbon 14) occurring naturally in the atmosphere, fusion reactions since 1952 have added over 2,000 pounds by virtue of neutron bombardment of atmospheric nitrogen. Also, fusion reactions require a fission trigger, which, when fired, is as dirty as any other fission reaction. "They [fusion weapons] can only be considered clean relative to pure fission weapons, much as gray might be considered light relative to black." (Dr. Triffet, U.S. Navy Radiological Defense Laboratory.)

## Colonialism

From *colony*, in turn from Middle English *colonie*, from Latin *colonia*. Used after the Roman practice to mean a farm, estate in the country. Used after modern practice in the biological sense to mean an aggregate of individual animals or plants, forming a physiologically connected structure, as the coral polyps; first used in 1872. Another and nonscientific usage is limited to property aspects of human behavior in the sociopolitical area. Thus, a hierarchy of power, influence and ownership is assumed in most contemporary definitions, in reference to the governing and the governed. Specifically, British Guiana is a *colony* of the United Kingdom and its citizens are *colonials;* a minor child is a *colonial* of his parents, and his developmental state, taken as a whole, is a *colony:* Colonialism subsumes the complexities inherent in both situations. Legally and morally the underpinnings of this reciprocal relationship ascribe to each member its particular roles, roles instituted for the mutual advantage of each one. The human organism, for instance, unable developmentally to provide for itself, must temporarily abandon self-realization in its need for protection, assistance and ethical guidance; the parent is committed to fulfill these requirements and to assume the responsibilities implied by his greater knowledge of the operations of the adult world. Unlike the biological definition, which imputes a mutual and equal interdependence of plants or animals in a *colony,* the nonscientific, or property, concept of Colonialism introduces complex variables into the higher nervous and ethical organization of human beings. The legal and moral bases of the concept have been recently called into question, with both members of the *colonial* situation unsure of their proper roles, or one of the members, usually the governed, rejecting the entire concept. Order in the twentieth century, in both familial and *colonial* relationships, has undergone serious challenges. (*See* Entropy.)

## Columbia River

The Columbia River has its source in Columbia Lake, British Columbia, and travels 1,214 miles to the Pacific Ocean. The Columbia River basin holds the largest atomic installation in the United States of America, the Hanford Works, covering 567 square miles in the western part of the state of Washington. The plutonium required to make nuclear weapons is produced at Hanford.

The Works are isolated; fewer than 55,000 people

live within 50 miles. The only other individuals who frequent the area are hunters and fishermen; the basin is popular for sports. In addition, many vegetables grow there.

Radioactivity from the Works reaches people through the river water, used for drinking at nearby Pasco and Kennewick; the river cools the reactors and the reactors bombard the river with neutrons. These neutrons change some minerals in the river into radio-isotopes.

Sometimes a reactor tube bursts and releases its radioactive materials into the river. When the water leaves the reactor it stays in retaining basins for 1, 2 or 3 hours and then flows on to the Columbia. The river disseminates materials, particularly phosphorus 32 from Hanford, to plants growing within it and upon its banks; the isotopes become concentrated in plant cells. The Columbia is a source of water for ir-rigation. As it flows onto the fields, its radioactivity eventually invades meat cattle and crops. Vegetables, wild ducks and whitefish that have trafficked with the Columbia carry the corruption farther.

Phosphorous 32 has a half-life of 14 days. A good measure of protection could be secured by fishermen and hunters if they kept their game frozen or smoked for about two months before eating it; they could also move some of the radioactivity from the flesh to the skin of whitefish by frying the fish, throwing out the skin, and eating the flesh, which tastes fine.

## Common Market
Term current in the mid-twentieth century to desig-nate a group of nations united for the furtherance of mutual economic interests. More specifically the Euro-pean Common Market, known also as EEC, European Economic Community, a dream of union, established in March, 1957, by Belgium, France, Italy, West Ger-many, Luxembourg and the Netherlands. After the historical nightmares in which political nationalism has played a determining role, the concept of a Greater Europe and an ultimate Federation of the World has stirred men of good will to act in concert for the pres-

ervation of mankind. In January, 1933, shortly before the Nazi seizure of power in Germany, Heinrich Mann insisted on the need for a supernational state, morality forbidding the continued existence of single countries, which a decent man could no longer serve. "Whoever says he can is lying."

The EEC lies geographically within the Outer Seven, another and similar grouping, from which it is distinguished by the name Inner Six. Austria and Switzerland, although $2/7$ of the Outer Seven, lie geographically inside the Inner Six. The other five of the Seven —Denmark, Sweden, Portugal, the U.K., and Norway —circle the Six. In a tradition reminiscent of pre-Renaissance unitary monoliths like the Holy Roman Empire, but based on twentieth-century concepts of democratic order, the EEC exists primarily to abolish internal tariffs and to establish one common external tariff structure. The Six also compose ECSC, as well as EURATOM; the Seven compose EFTA. All thirteen with the addition of Greece, Iceland, Ireland, Turkey and Spain compose OEEC, but Greece and Turkey may join EEC, and Finland, which belongs to nothing, may become a member of EFTA. OEEC may be replaced by OECD to include more countries including Canada and the U.S.A. in an attempt to work out closer relationships between EEC and EFTA. Portugal, however, a member of EFTA, is establishing its own "single market" with its own possessions. Unlike SEATO, NATO, CENTO and OAS, these organizations are economic, not military. In union there is strength.

| | |
|---|---|
| EEC: | European Economic Community (the Six) |
| EFTA: | European Free Trade Association (the Seven) |
| EURATOM: | European Atomic Energy Community (for peaceful development of atomic energy) |
| ECSC: | European Coal and Steel Community |
| OEEC: | Organization for European Economic Cooperation |

OECD:    Organization for Economic Cooperation and Development

SEATO, CENTO, OAS, NATO: *See* Free
World.

## Communications Satellite

It is safe to predict that this particular use of rocket vehicles
will have more direct effect on the man in the street than
any other development in space technology. He will now for
the first time be able to see, as well as hear, an English
cricket game, the shelling of Quemoy, the coronation of a
Pope.
—Dr. L. G. Dunn, President, Space Technology Laboratories

There could be few communities which would be unable to
afford one set (in Ceylon there are dozens of radios blaring
in every village) and when we consider the effect of TV
upon our own ostensibly educated public, the impact upon
the peoples of Asia and Africa may be overwhelming. It
may well determine whether Russian or English is the main
language of the future. The TV satellite is mightier than
ICBM.    —Arthur C. Clarke, English scientist and author

Some communications satellites are passive, like
Echo I, an inflated aluminized balloon. Echo I reflects
radio waves. When a radio message is sent out over a
great distance around Earth, it must bounce off the
ionosphere, a region from 50 to 250 miles above Earth,
which is capable of conducting electricity, making
long-distance radio communication possible. Sometimes, however, the ionosphere seems to develop empty
spots, holes, and the radio signals fade out. Echo I can
be used to plug up these holes by reflecting the waves
back to Earth. Other communications satellites can
rebroadcast messages, up to 600 at the same time. Television signals, which are high-frequency and zoom
right through the ionosphere, can also be relayed back
by communications satellites. Complete coverage of the
whole of Earth might be effected by three communications satellites in the same orbit but spaced 120 degrees
apart. Since the curve of Earth limits the range of surface transmitters to less than 100 miles, the contribu-

tion of three satellites, linked to each other by micro-
wave beams to provide television for the entire planet,
inaugurates a period of unexpected and soporific scope.

## Competitive Games

As a civilization becomes more complex, more variegated
and more overladen, and as the technique of production
and social life itself becomes more finely organized, the old
cultural soil is gradually smothered under a rank layer of
ideas, systems of thought and knowledge, doctrines, rules
and regulations, moralities and conventions which have all
lost touch with play. Civilization, we then say, has grown
more serious; it assigns only a secondary place to playing.
The heroic period is over. . . .
                              —Johan Huizinga, *Homo Ludens*

The Competitive Games are an effort to reintroduce
into contemporary culture an element of the playful,
the heroic. In Competitive Games, the players, business
prognosticators, economic planners, military prophets,
usually seated and equipped with writing materials,
choose from a finite list of possible actions a single
action, with no knowledge of other players' choices.
The outcome in each play gives the players their individual due of plus, minus or zero. Two kinds of
strategy usually receive attention: pure and mixed. In
pure strategy, a specific choice of action is made before
any plays take place; mixed strategy dictates a different course of action before each play, chosen in relation to statistical probability of usefulness.

Competitive Games contribute clarifications of conflict situations before the active crystallization of such
conflicts. Although many conflict situations involve
chance occurrences, Competitive Games, within the
old traditions of sacred play, assume that each actor,
or agonist, will act rationally in his own interest, that
is, abide by mutually understood, if unverbalized,
modes of the beautiful into which contest among men
is disciplined. (*See* War-Gaming.)

## Concentration Camp
From German *Konzentrationslager*. K.L., official contraction; K.Z., contraction used by prisoners.

*Der Tod ist ein Meister aus Deutschland.* Death is a master craftsman from Germany.                    —Paul Celan

A German prison system established by Goering in 1933.

As police chief of Prussia I arrested thousands of Communists. That is why I set up the concentration camps in the first place—to keep the Communists under control.
                              —Goering, 1946

Robert Darnau, an inmate of the concentration camp Neuengamme, found a human jaw in his soup. The kitchen supervisor and the crematory supervisor had an agreement: they would sell the kitchen meat to civilians and feed the prisoners on corpses.

**Confabulation**   *See* Lie.

### Cosmic Rays

The most energetic radiation presently observed by man, cosmic rays enter Earth's atmosphere from outer space and contribute 27 per cent of the ionizing radiation (*q.v.*) regularly found at Earth's surface. The passage of these rays through the atmosphere is equivalent to the penetration of a lead wall over a yard thick. It has been estimated that complete shielding against this radiation would require a laboratory with lead walls and ceiling over four yards thick. Wishing an experimental environment free of cosmic rays, one radiobiologist sought refuge in the Simplon Tunnel 8,000 feet beneath the Alpine crests. Opinion is divided over the effects of prolonged shielding from normal cosmic radiation. The average person on Earth is being struck by 30,000 cosmic rays each minute.

Cosmic rays were first suspected around 1911, when radiologists, pursuing a science barely fifteen years in existence, were surprised to find that background ionizing radiation did not disappear at sea, despite the absence at sea of normal terrestrial radioactive minerals; it was also surprising that ionizing radiation actually increased with altitude, as on the Eiffel Tower, the Alps, in a balloon. That solar eclipses had no effect on the rate of cosmic rays led to the conclusion that these rays do not originate in the sun. That the rays vary in concentration with the magnetic field of Earth indicates the electrical character of the particles comprising the rays. Indeed, cosmic rays are almost wholly electrically positive, being in the main protons and alpha particles. The speed with which these particles approach Earth generates an energy to which no terrestrial radiation is even remotely comparable. Entering the upper atmosphere, cosmic rays begin to transfer this energy to Earth's outlying atoms, stripping electrons which move on in brilliant showers. The cosmic rays are slowed down but continue, now colliding more frequently with atomic nuclei and smashing these into a debris of neutrons, mesons, beta rays and other nuclear particles that carry the energy Earthward as an incessant rain of secondary cosmic radiation. Fifteen miles above Earth's surface is the arena of greatest energy transformations.

Since cosmic rays are rather certain to be present at least throughout the solar system, their biological effects are pertinent to the problem of interplanetary travel. As regards these effects, opinion is chaotic. Fruit flies, mold, hamsters, shrimp eggs, mice, beans, cats and dogs are some of the life that has been sent aloft accompanied by photographic plates which register cosmic-ray exposure. Some things die, some don't; reproductive capacity is lost, but sometimes improves; cancer breaks out, but often it doesn't. However, one result is unfailing: cosmic rays turn hair gray. This effect is so intriguing, white mice are no longer employed.

The origin of cosmic rays is not known.

## Counterforce as Insurance
Also known as Insurance Against Unreliability. Although Insurance for Reliability, or Finite Deterrence (q.v.), structures a more dependable national posture than that represented by Minimum Deterrence (q.v.), some Finite Deterrers, mindful of the shortsightedness implicit in even the least Finite Deterrence, recommend the implementation of Counterforce as a necessary addition to the position of mere Finite Deterrence.

A somewhat greater amount of infinity subsequently characterizes the school of Insurance Against Unreliability: although prewar conditions of life will not be restored after a thermonuclear exchange, no position could be more absurd or more destructive of the human spirit than a denial of the possibility of normal and happy lives for the survivors and their descendants. As William Faulkner stated in his Nobel Prize acceptance speech, "man will not simply endure: he will prevail." (*See* Prevail.)

If, rather than 80,000,000 deaths, the total could be held down to, say, 40,000,000, no reasonable man, though aware of the tragedy in such alternatives, would abstain from the use of Counterforce as Insurance, including not only the ability to destroy the enemy on the ground, but also sheltering, sheltering plus anticontamination, active defense against bomber incursions, preparations to decrease the number of fatalities and injuries, limitation of damage, facilitation of recuperation, procurement of the best military result possible.

Many Insurers Against Unreliability, or Counterforce Insurancers, however, believe that no national strategy can be adequate which does not include Insurance Against a Change in Policy. (*See* Preattack Mobilization Base; *see also* Heart of Darkness.)

### Counterphobia

A compulsion to perform an activity which one actually is afraid of. The compulsion is a symptom of an anxiety about fear. The counterphobic is distressed at the passivity that the fearful situation invites. Passivity is more unbearable than danger, and the counterphobia converts this passivity into activity. Counterphobics are people who engage in pursuits which normal people are not afraid to be afraid of.

### Country A   (*See also* Country B.)

The way one gets 60 million casualties as a price one cannot afford to pay is by taking roughly one-third of the population. In other words, I have yet to meet an American who, after he thought about the problem 10 minutes, was willing to sign his name to a statement that he believed the United States would go to war deliberately, in cold blood, on any issue short of a direct attack on the United States, if more than half the people in the United States were killed on the Soviet retaliatory blow. It has to be less than half.

—Herman Kahn

The total SMA (Standard Metropolitan Area) from the point of view of its subsequent reconstruction following the annihilation of its every stick and stone. Country A, U.S.A., consists of 53 SMAs—New York and northeastern New Jersey, Chicago, Cleveland, Los Angeles, Dallas, Erie, Boston, Philadelphia, etc., which jointly contain about one-third of the population of the United States, a little over one-half the manufacturing capacity and wealth, and most of the technical and managerial services. Country A is the target on which the enemy is expected to place the highest priority. Pentagon specialists estimate that Country A, U.S.A., could be rebuilt from scratch in less than a decade. This estimate includes the usual slums and the GNP (Gross National Product). It omits luxuries like museums, universities, libraries, artists, theaters, archives, teachers, poets, medical centers, laboratories, historical architecture.

## Country B

We also believe that if you did nothing else but just kill one-third of the population of the United States, the other two-thirds would not commit suicide. They would bury their dead, go into a period of mourning, and then life would go on. It is just that simple. —Herman Kahn

That area of a nation exclusive of Country A (*q.v.*). Country B is the expansive, less populated, rural area of a nation. Its relationship to Country A is as a wealthy colony to a somewhat dependent mother country. Country B, U.S.A., contains two-thirds of the nation's population and little less than half the nation's manufacturing capacity. As a military target, Country B is predicted to have little priority, compared to Country A. The capability of Country B's rebuilding Country A, following a thermonuclear war, has therefore been of interest to military strategists. They have concluded that not only does the capability exist, but the rebuilding of Country A will take place in surprisingly short order. Among the many details that have been evaluated in this conclusion is the willingness of the surviving residents of Country B to take up the task. They are assumed to be willing. (*See* Dust Bowl.)

## Country C

Certain data were presented yesterday on ecological effects, these large fires and things like that. I think that data is a little premature. It probably does not correspond to a war of this sort, but a war maybe 5 or 10 years from now. But still you are doing things like that. You are burning large areas of the country. You are killing more insects than birds, and other things of that nature.      —Herman Kahn

One 10-megaton nuclear burst, exploded 50 miles above Earth, will produce approximately 5,000 square miles of scorched earth below, an area of total crop destruction. Those crop lands which were spared a destruction of this order of magnitude would be subject to the effects of fallout (*q.v.*).

Radioactive fallout dropping on agricultural land will contaminate the food chains through the soil, the crops and the animals. Most radioisotopes move into the soil by a percolating action with water, by slipping down through soil cracks, and through worm and animal burrow holes. The radioisotope most readily taken up from the soil is strontium 90 (*q.v.*); plants make almost no differentiation between radiostrontium and calcium, an essential nutrient element. Soil decontamination for radiostrontium will be required. For most crops and soils 1 per cent of strontium 90 in the soil is removed in a single crop. In farm areas run on a one-crop-per-year basis, 66 years would be needed to achieve 90 per cent decontamination of the soil. Some measures could be taken to reduce the waiting time.

The most effective method involves the removal of surface soil; the scraping of 2 inches of topsoil from freshly plowed surfaces will remove about 60 per cent of the contamination. The safe disposal of the fallout-ridden soil is a problem. Some contaminated lands could be used for non-food crops, like cotton or flax; the difficulty in such alternatives lies in the subsequent impossibility of removing the fallout after deep plowing or crop shifts. Thus lands originally used for the production of milk and vegetables would not be returned to these uses for many years.

The food chain, involving animals, is disrupted. Within two or three days, radioactivity is noticeable in considerable portions of the arthropod population of the area, including predators like spiders. In general predators are likely to obtain lower body burdens of radioactivity than herbivores. Plant-eating animals thus fall victim rapidly and disturb the food chain in which they are linked to man. In addition, severe beta burns could disturb the cyclical processes of the biome (*q.v.*). The cattle of Alamogordo (*q.v.*) were the first casualties of fallout and their beta burns the first lesions. All domestic animals have a similar response to total body irradiation. Very few die after exposure to 250 roentgens and few survive 1,000 r. Some animals, like the swine, recover more rapidly than others, like the burro; however, scientists believe that they have successfully induced leukemia in test swine. Permissible levels of radioactivity for animals have not been worked out satisfactorily.

The ecological effects of the thermal and blast components of nuclear bombs include far-flung damage. The destruction of forests by fire would create erosion problems lasting for decades.

A medium nuclear attack (*see* Hypothetical Attack) on the continental United States would probably affect, in the eastern part of the country alone, the dry oak and pine forests of the Appalachians from New England to Virginia. These forests would probably be wiped out, and so would the pine on the southern Atlantic and Gulf coastal plains; the agricultural lands of the Mississippi Valley would be overwhelmed.

Once erosion takes hold in forests dominated by species going back 400 or 500 years, it would take 1,000 years to re-create the forest. Removal of turf by fire and erosion on plains and prairies would create immense stretches of dust bowl (*q.v.*), expanding indefinitely. There is no effective way to check wind erosion.

In addition to fire, erosion and flood, plant and animal disease would intensify. Animals able to move into relatively uncontaminated areas would be survivors from "dirty" areas and probably be unfit for food. Insects, relatively resistant to radiation, and bacteria (*q.v.*), even more resistant, would move in and multiply without many significant checks. The combination of wind, water, flood, migration and rain emphasizes the continuous flux operating in land masses. An uncontaminated area will not remain uncontaminated.

## Covetousness

> but thorough daily care
> to get, and nightly feare to lose his owne,
> He led a wretched life vnto himselfe vnknowne.
> —Edmund Spenser

A passionate desire for something that another person already has. The covetous person lacks a sense of personal authenticity and seeks guidance in the choices first made by others. The insatiability of covetousness is the result of the inevitable disqualification of the person whose possession is finally attained. "How could he have been worth my efforts, if what he possessed has been achieved by someone as worthless as me?" Covetousness not only indicates a failure of personal independence; it goes on to demean the morality encountered in others. It is one of the deadly sins (*q.v.*).

## Crackpots

Counterintelligence agents' informal appellation for the atomic scientists in the Manhattan District (*q.v.*). The term combines disparagement of life style with acknowledgment of asset. The enlistment of crackpots in time of social emergency is an old story. Philoctetes, a Greek warrior, was shunned by his countrymen because of the offensive odor of a chronic, suppurating wound; however, he was a brilliant archer and was sought out by his countrymen when they needed his unerring bow. (*See* Creeps.)

## Cratering

A surface burst (*q.v.*) forms a crater in the vicinity of the burst: extremely high pressures produced by the nuclear explosion displace and vaporize matter at the site. Neutrons in the soil induce radioactivity in the crater over and beyond the radioactivity produced by the bomb material itself. The shallow crater formed by the surface burst exploded in 1945 at Alamogordo (*q.v.*) was fenced off from 1945 to 1961.

Even targets relatively immune to other nuclear explosion effects—such as aircraft runways, underground installations, shelters, subways—will be destroyed in a crater. A 10-megaton surface explosion will produce a crater 2,500 feet in diameter and 530 feet deep. The shattering and disruption of the soil within the distance of yet another crater radius would utterly devastate all structures in an area approximately one mile across.

## Credibility

As in Credible First-Strike Capability (*q.v.*); the Credibility of a certain military stance goes beyond the mere *possession* of specific Capability, or available means. The real degree of deterrence inherent in the Capability is reasonably irrelevant; if the enemy questions its potential efficacy, that Capability has no Credibility.

## Credible First-Strike Capability

Positional insurance against those weaknesses inherent in Insurance Against a Change in Policy; that stance through which a potential enemy will consider that certain political acts may provoke a First Strike. Although such a strike—if, for instance, delivered by the United States of America—would seem to go counter to traditionally established national policy not to start a war, the real purpose of a Credible First-Strike Capability is deterrence, not initiation.

If the American posture were such that the former

Capability were genuinely believed, the enemy would likely conclude that the risks were too high. It is important to know that a war in which the United States made the first strike would result, in the words of an expert (*q.v.*), "in more favorable conditions for us than would the wars that are generally considered." (*See* Preattack Mobilization Base; *see also* Heart of Darkness.)

**Creeper**   *See* Iodine 131; Krypton 85.

## Creeps
An appellation for counterintelligence personnel which was popular with the atomic scientists in the Manhattan District (*q.v.*). The term connotes repugnance mitigated by jocularity. It expressed both the hauteur and the resignation of the watched toward the watchers during the holy years of The Project. (*See* Crackpots.)

## Culture of Poverty
A subculture; a stable, traditional way of life; applied exclusively to individuals at the bottom of the socio-economic ladder. A culture of poverty usually comes about as a result of the transition between one stratified system and another, by the continued overlordship incident to imperial conquest, or as a result of tribal disintegration and subsequent movement to the slums of cities. Cultures of poverty, though they do not meet the needs for employment, personal integration, joy, personal privacy or sufficient food, maintain a high degree of specificity and survival and demonstrate man's capacity to construct long-lasting complex social entities out of almost nothing. (*See* Hunger.)

## Curie
Abbreviation: c. Named for Pierre and Marie Curie, the discoverers of the radioactive element radium, the curie is the conventional measure of the activity of radioactive materials. It is based upon the rate of particle emission from one gram of radium. *One curie is that quantity of a radioactive substance in which 37*

*billion radioactive disintegrations occur in one second.*
Some radioactive substances disintegrate at a slower
rate than radium; with such substances more than a
gram would be required to obtain a curie of radioactivity. Other substances achieve the radioactivity of
a gram of radium with less than a gram. For fallout
(*q.v.*) the conventional units are the millicurie (mc =
one-thousandth of a curie) and the microcurie (µc =
one-millionth of a curie). The micro-microcurie (µµc
= one-million-millionth of a curie) is also a subject of
current interest. (*See* Strontium Unit.) The curie is not
a measure of dosage or an indication of biological hazard. For these distinctions *see* Relative Biological Effectiveness.

## Cybernetics

A term covering the many ramifications of the study
and electrical engineering of messages as means of
constructing self-regulating machinery, such as compu-
tors. Also, the theory, as distinct from the technology,
of automation.

What seventeenth- and eighteenth-century mechanics
were to the subsequent industrialization of muscle,
cybernetics is to the current industrialization of mind.
It is cybernetics that has made it possible to speak of
the First and Second Industrial Revolutions. The historical division between these revolutions is World
War II. Since the mid-nineteen-forties, the vacuum
tube, punched tape and mercury column have been
added to previously unautomated mechanical and
managerial phases of industry with the result that
larger and larger aspects of human judgment are being
reduced to the level of brute labor. Automata of the
latter twentieth century are being designed and built
to compute both digitally and by integration, to perform cost accounting, to regulate factory systems, to
provide human-passenger locomotion, to render medical diagnoses, to translate languages, to make military
and political decisions, to amble vehicularly over
photoelectrified courses, to play complex games like
chess. Automata are capable of remembering, learning,
of audio, visual and tactile discrimination, and of a

level of self-maintenance that exceeds the level of analogous personal ministrations performed by most human beings.

The phenomenal domain of cybernetics is the message. A message occurs when information passes from a sender to a receiver. The transmission of information institutes a system, and systems may be physical or organic, machines or animals, in parts, wholes or groups. To the cybernetician, the human being is one example of a system; the neuromuscular operations of the human being are also systems, as are the eyes, the ears, the stomach, the mind. Groups of people are also systems; so are factories, telephone networks, business corporations. To subsume such diversity within one phenomenal domain requires certain unifying concepts of immense generality. Information is one such concept. Thus any phenomenon achieves the category of information if the phenomenon exists in any state of distinction from randomness: *these* holes on a paper tape rather than *any* holes; *that* ripple in a tube of mercury; *those* combinations and groups of vocal sounds; *this* length from here to there. Likewise, considerable generality is imparted to the concepts *sender* and *receiver*. A sender is any source of information; a receiver, any function affected by the information. It is axiomatic that an effect stimulated by a nonrandom cause, i.e., information, will not be random. Hence such an effect inherits the characteristic of information, i.e., nonrandomness, and can become, itself, an informant to another receiver. When a sender is also equipped to receive, and a receiver equipped to send, and the message is engineered, by either man or nature, to flow back and forth between the two, each mediating and controlling the other, a situation called feedback is born. It is feedback that perpetuates systems. The identity of any system, its purpose and function, is the result of the particular transformations of information that take place at the inputs and outputs of the feedback cycle.

Concentrating on the transmission of messages as the principle underlying all systemic activity, the cybernetician is liberated from such considerations as vitalism and spirituality and can interpret the world with an objective purity, as categories of communication. The analysis of how a person locates and removes one book from shelves of thousands leads to the possibility of a machine that will do the same sort of thing in terms of stored data. How a machine discriminates the differences in the colors of certain fruits before sealing them into cans leads to an insight into how animals or human beings make similar discriminations between objects in their world. Learning, computing, decision-making, listening, and the behavior that accompanies these processes are general events. The context of a function does not alter its essence. An electronic system the size of the Empire State Building and driven by the thunderous power of Niagara Falls—or miniature analogues—could begin to approach some of the more complex functions of the human brain.

From the preceding Industrial Revolution, the cybernetician derives strong mandates to explore his particular man-machine analogy. In the nineteenth century, the steam engine, viewed as a system that converts calories into work, led to a revolutionary view of the human organism as an analogous system that works by a consumption of fuel. The organism-as-engine has led directly to contemporary notions about, for example, human nutrition, its standards and pathogenic implications, which has been, as the phrase goes, all to the good. What far-reaching consequence in this, the Second Revolution with its organism-as-message network, what bold prosthesis in the interchangeability of man and machine, what deliverance from monotony, what new rules of conduct among men, what leisure, what entertainments, what novel comprehensions, what social forms—these possibilities lie buried in the mines of the future. The shafts are sunk.

# D

## Dachau

A town in Upper Bavaria, Germany, 8 miles northwest of Munich on the railway from Munich to Ingolstadt. Population (1939) 17,594. It has extensive fortifications, a castle and a museum of antiquities, and makes paper, sawmill machinery and beer. It formerly had a colony of artists.

## Dark Objects

Satellites which have never emitted, or have ceased emitting, signals. Such objects must be kept in perpetual inventory. A series of detection posts strung along the southern United States, Spasur (space surveillance), detects, tracks and identifies silent or dead satellites. Unfortunately, there is no way of determining whether a massive orbital device is a bomb carrier or not. The National Space Surveillance and Control Center is working on it.

## Deadly Sins

Of which there are seven and from which all other sins derive: Vanity, Wrath, Envy, Lechery, Covetousness, Gluttony and Sloth (*qq.v.*). Called deadly because they are held to lead to spiritual death.

A foggy mist had couered all the land;
And vnderneath their feet, all scattered lay
Dead sculs and bones of men, whose life had gone astray.
—Edmund Spenser

## Death Instinct  *See* Thanatos.

## Debriefing

A form of interrogation used by military, diplomatic and intelligence authorities to refresh the memory of persons who have been involved in an event, in an effort to clarify unanswered questions. The word is composed of the prefix *de* plus the noun *briefing*. The military term *briefing* is an instruction technique in advance of an action. The combining form *de*, in its various meanings, reveals the complexity and subtlety of the *debriefing* process. Men who are *briefed* subsequently find themselves *debriefed*. *De* may mean *down:* thus *debriefing* suggests bringing *down* the *briefing*, or preliminary instruction, to the understanding of those *debriefers* who may not have been the original *briefers*. *De* may mean *off, away:* thus *debriefing* suggests dispensing with the previous instruction technique in order to clear the mind for the consideration of experience subsequent to the *briefing*. Since the human mind occasionally wanders in the forest of non-causality, those military, diplomatic and intelligence authorities who had not been the original *briefers* may furnish assistance tailored precisely to their training. Thus, an ideal gam of *debriefers* would appear to include some original *briefers* and some *post-briefers*, all *debriefing* together.

## De Gaulle

all the General's voices soldier for the mourning of Paris the ancient cry of the blood the dignity of beaks the Ministry of Culture soldier for the return against the rapists of France Charles is Marianne. *We are all soldiers together. . . . It is a fact not only for the French but for the Germans, that they have never done anything great, either from the national or international point of view, without the military factor having an eminent part in it.* —*Le Livre des Morts*

The chief aim of General de Gaulle, President of the Fifth French Republic, is the resurrection, by way of nuclear nationalism, atavistic osmosis, curious alliances and magnificent rhetoric, of the glory that was France.

General de Gaulle was born in 1890. When he was more than 50 years of age, he symbolized for the victims of Nazi oppressions not only French resistance, but the effective potential of certain individuals for acts of memorable grandeur. Since that time, France has not been spared the final dissolution of her empire, the turbulence of parliamentary changes and the haunting memory of the power and brilliance of the court at Versailles.

## Dellwyn

One of a number of British merchant ships lying beneath the waters of the Mediterranean, off the coast of Andalusia, Spain. The *Dellwyn* was sunk by Italian and Spanish Fascists during the Spanish Civil War, in June, 1938, in sight of a British warship which withheld fire in the Empire's posture of neutrality and appeasement (*qq.v.*). This was the first recorded occasion when a British warship failed to respond on behalf of a convoyed sister ship. Since the sinking of the *Dellwyn* was not an isolated incident—eleven British ships had been previously sunk or damaged during that year in the Mediterranean—Sir Eric Drummond warned Count Galeazzo Ciano in Rome that unless these nasty incidents ceased, Neville Chamberlain's Government would fall beneath the indignation of the British public. In September, 1938, Chamberlain signed the Munich pact. In November, eleven more British ships were attacked in Spanish ports. By 1939, the British Government had exhausted its armada of interpretations.

## Delusion

An insistent, false belief, often of grandeur or persecution. Falsity, however, is only one criterion of a delusion. A second, and more important, criterion is the unacceptability of the belief to the deluded person's culture or immediate group. False beliefs which are collectivized and maintained en masse are more accurately called superstitions, prejudices, theologies, etc., and give comfort to the believer. Delusions, on the other hand, are maintained in isolation and loneliness, and, like any malady, cause suffering. Thus delusions are relatively harmless to the community at large.

## Democratism

Bearing a close, and therefore confusing, visual and

auditory resemblance to *democracy*, the term *democratism* refers not to a form of government but to a social process, the process wherein the exceptional is steadily assimilated by the usual. Deplored by social critics who are alarmed at the rate with which mediocrity replaces excellence, this process is merely another case of the tendency for systems, social or otherwise, to proceed in a direction that degrades hierarchy. (*See* Entropy.) Democratism normalizes wealth, literacy, manners, leisure, even protest. "Television is a vast wasteland"— an unexceptional protest, scorned by the usual, applauded by the usual, and leading to the usual consequences. Democratism insures that everybody has an equal and ordinary right to his own democratistic opinion.

## Denial

Of the various recourses for defending the mental apparatus from threatening stimuli, denial can be the most costly from the point of view of reality (*q.v.*). Whereas other defenses distort reality beyond recognition, this one simply evades reality by a withdrawal of attention. Indeed, denial may be regarded as an absence of recourse in the face of a threat. The energy usually available for attention to reality becomes available to the denying person as a restless, manic apprehension.

Except in very early childhood, denial never occurs wholly alone. It is orchestrated with other defensive maneuvers of mind and even finds a place in normal functioning. For example, the automobile accident rate has to be subjected to some amount of denial if one is to travel by car unanxiously; similarly air travel is feasible only through denial. Where to draw the line between adaptive and malignant denial is not always clear. However, one rather reliable indication of malignant denial is exuberance at the brink of disaster.

## Destruct

Variant form of *destroy*. A contemporary neologism in the vocabulary of space flight and missiles. The ultimate and penultimate consonants suggest the extraordinary flexibility of the American language for the formation of new words or variants more apposite to particular situations. The removal of the soft diphthong *oy* for the powerful *ct* reflects the requirements of a modern situation. A missile or satellite running an inappropriate trajectory must be exploded soon after takeoff with the command: "Destruct!"

**Deuterium**   *See* Hydrogen.


**DEW**

Distant Early Warning. A radar system, the DEW line is strung out along the northern edge of North America and gives two to three hours' warning time of enemy planes approaching. DEW is prone to error in discriminating planes, birds and stray radio noises. It is also insensitive to enemy frigates on the high seas.


**Dirty**

Used in opposition to *clean* as descriptive of a nuclear weapon for which no claim of cleanliness is made. (*See* Clean.) The dirt in issue is radioactive fallout.

Currently, *dirty* has acquired an additional sense. It refers to a weapon with minimum blast and thermal effects (*qq.v.*) and maximum fallout (*q.v.*). Such a radiological device is proposed for destroying civilian and military populations, while sparing property and installations. It is detonated upwind from the target. The dirt it produces then blows over the target on prevailing winds. The nuke (*q.v.*) of the Dirty Bomb is a fusion bomb. This nuke is encased in cobalt metal. The cobalt is vigorously radioactivated by neutrons released in the fusion reaction and goes sailing downwind.

On the other hand, Edward Teller reminds us that it is within possibility to use radiological warfare humanely. If a windless day were chosen for the explosion of a cobalt bomb, evacuation could be forced on the enemy without loss of human life. Also, materials other than cobalt may be employed for radiation effects of different durations and intensities. These effects, too, could be used in a humane manner.

# Doomsday Clock

Also, Clock of Doom. This clock has appeared monthly since 1947 on the cover of the *Bulletin of the Atomic Scientists,* a periodical founded in 1945 by a group of atomic physicists at the University of Chicago. Headed by Hyman Goldsmith and Eugene Rabinowitch, the group was soon to expand to include America's most distinguished atomic scientists, e.g., Oppenheimer, Urey, Bethe, Bronk, Compton, Franck, Morse, Muller, Rabi, Szilard, Teller, Weisskopf, all back from the atomic-bomb project and concerned with public ignorance of the realities of atomic energy.

Powered by the activities of mankind in respect to atomic energy, the Doomsday Clock ticks toward the world's midnight. In the specter of atomic war, the clock was originally set, and began ticking, at 8 minutes to 12. In October, 1949, following the official announcement of the Soviet's Joe I (*q.v.*), the hands of the clock crept several minutes forward. "The fact that the present development has been freely predicted by no means proves that we are prepared to meet it." Again, in September, 1953, when both atomic powers had successfully detonated thermonuclear devices, the Doomsday Clock moved ahead, now ticking at 2 minutes to midnight. "That time, when each major nation will hold the power of destroying at will the urban civilization of any other nation, is close at hand. . . ." In this nerve-racking proximity to Doom, the clock ticked on for the next seven years. During this period, the development of missile weaponry flourished, and that power, once merely close at hand, was finally grasped.

In January, 1960, to the relief of subscribers to the *Bulletin,* the Doomsday Clock was set back 5 minutes. This was the year Nikita Khrushchev made the pages of *Life,* a tourist in America, turning up on the movie set of *Can-Can.* "We are not succumbing to the facile optimism engendered by a change in the climate of our diplomatic relations with the Soviet Union. . . . We want to express in this move the belief that a new cohesive force has entered the interplay of forces shaping the fate of mankind, and is making the future of man a little less foreboding. . . ."

The clock remained stationary at 7 minutes to 12 through both the Russian and American bomb series of 1961 and 1962. The atomic scientists make no claim to being expert at running clocks.

## Doomsday Machine
A nuclear war-machine for restraining enemy nations.

A Doomsday Machine is an automated nuclear-weapons system which resides in the nation that has built it. Its behavior, however, is controlled by an enemy nation. Capable of annihilating all life on Earth, it is set to fire in all directions whenever the enemy transgresses any prohibitions which they have been informed of and which have been legislated into the machine. Thus, the enemy is provided with a clear list of restraints and is informed that the Doomsday Machine is now under the enemy's complete control. At the instant information of any transgression reaches the Machine, the Machine automatically discharges its destruction without further decision or assistance by the personnel of the nation that has built it. One prohibition that could be wired into such a machine might be: "You are not allowed to construct a Doomsday Machine." Herman Kahn (*q.v.*) estimates that a machine capable of destroying all life on Earth, plus the transgression monitor, could be completed in ten years at a cost of between $10 billion and $100 billion.

## Dust Bowl

"Would not the shock of the catastrophe so derange people that every man's hand would be against every other man's?" This seems entirely wrong.
　　　　　—Herman Kahn, *On Thermonuclear War,* 1960.

During the cold, clear morning of Armistice Day of 1933 a gale was blowing across the southern part of South Dakota. The sun began to dim formidably. Mid-morning was filled with a gray glare. By noon it was pitch-dark. Electric lights were turned on in the farm-houses, and families looked at one another, stupefied and frightened. Outside it was almost impossible for a person to keep his eyes open; tears made mud which caked the eyelids. Saliva turned black in the mouth. Even wearing a handkerchief over his face, a farmer would cough and spit up black. Inside the farmhouses dust began to collect on the floors so deep that ripples formed, while outside the wind continued stiff and howling. Soaked sheets and towels were stuffed against the window ledges to keep the dust out, but the anxious footprints on the dust floors faded almost as soon as they had been imprinted. By midafternoon the wind died, and again the sun blazed in the autumn sky. Farmers ventured outdoors: roads had disappeared; tall drifts of sand leaned against barn doors; tractors were buried; automobiles stood beneath formless mounds. Here and there eddies of dust swirled in the breeze. Dust trickled from the roofs and rain gutters.

The following day Chicago darkened under a dusty haze. The day after, the topsoil of the Great Plains had blown as far east as Albany, New York.

The American plains are a dry region. The mean annual rainfall varies between 10 and 20 inches as compared, for example, to the North Atlantic region, where from 40 to 50 inches of rain fall annually. Droughts are common. Months may pass without a drop of rain. This is a land where a farmer will pelt his roof with gravel to remind his young children what rain sounds like.

Prior to the twentieth century these plains were grasslands over which the winds blew, waving the grass like ocean water as far as the eye could see. The semi-arid topsoil clung firmly to the matted roots of grass and resisted the winds. This had been glorious cattle land, and, around the turn of the century, cattle kings unfenced their herds as though there were no end to nature's bounty. By 1905, windswept dust was becoming a nuisance on the American plains.

Homesteaders arrived, crop growers who joined the cattle in tearing up the grass. With World War I the demand for wheat loomed quite suddenly, and tractors were shipped out West, now to plow up in earnest the turf that for countless centuries had kept the soil fastened down. The nineteen-twenties were an era marked by industrialization. Industrialized farming came to the plains with a vengeance. Brooms began to do good business. So did shovels, which, toward the end of the twenties, were become standard equipment in some regions of Kansas for excavating plows and automobiles that might have been left standing in one place too long a time. By 1930 the construction of the Dust Bowl was completed.

The Black Blizzard of November, 1933, was the prelude to numberless dust storms in 1934, 1935 and 1936 that swept the American plains from the Texas Panhandle up through Oklahoma, eastern Colorado, Nebraska, Kansas, the Dakotas, Montana to the Canadian border. Farms became deserts; dunes shifted and crept everywhere; unmerciful winds carried dust into every crevice and aperture. The exodus westward began fitfully in 1934. By 1936 some areas were reporting 50 per cent of the farmhouses abandoned. Thousands of homesites were relinquished. Banks and speculators descended on the plains like vultures. It was in those days that you could sit by a window in Kansas and day and night watch the slow parade of family jalopies sagging beneath the weight of mattresses and noisy pots and pans, as all around the farms blew by.

The migration was toward California, a land lush with the green of farms and fruit orchards. On the way, the families of the American Dust Bowl found themselves dissolving in the larger migratory confusion of families unhoused by the economic upheavals of the farmlands of Alabama, Arkansas, Louisiana, Mississippi. Californians became aware of the increasing influx into their state of these shiftless aliens, filthy eyesores who glutted the labor market, who were prey to "red" agitation, whose hopeless laziness sponged the wealth which Californians had toiled to create. Roadblocks at the California border went up to regulate the traffic. Instances of hospitality were recorded, but these were rare. For the most, those refugees who straggled through were destined for camps of shanties without beds, water or buckets, or else slept on the roadside in and around their jalopies. Californians passed ordinances regulating the political and social activities of the new arrivals. They deputized armed guards to supervise and drive on the outlanders. Even vigilantes and night raiders were employed. To Californians in a time of peace, idealism and economic growth, these migrants, arriving empty-handed from the disaster-stricken heart of America, seemed entirely wrong.

# E

## $E = mc^2$

Doubtless the most widely known product of Albert Einstein's career, this expression is actually the last of four rather brief contributions to science which he published within the single year 1905. That particular year was the midpoint in Einstein's tenure as a Swiss patent examiner, an employment which apparently afforded him sufficient spare time, at least during that year, for a number of accomplishments.

In clearing up both theoretically and mathematically one puzzle—why an electric spark leaps across two charged terminals more readily in the light than in the dark—Einstein not only added to the explanation of light, but in a stroke established modern quantum physics. In explaining another puzzle—the ceaseless agitation of microscopic pollen grains suspended in a liquid—he supplied fresh mathematics and confirmation to the atomic theory of matter. Einstein's reputation could have rested here.

But shortly thereafter, in the same year, he went on to explain one of the most monumental failures in science: the failure in 1887 of the two American physicists Michelson and Morley to demonstrate by means of an ingenious experiment that, in different directions, light travels at different speeds due to the motion of Earth and the existence of "ether." But there was no difference in speed. Einstein's solution of this failure involved the acceptance of the fact, established by the experiment, that the speed of light was always constant irrespective of the motion of the source or the observer. At the same time, he abolished the idea of an "ether," a hypothetical fluid that filled space, and the idea of absolute space and time. He contended that space and time alter relatively with the motion of the observer compared to the constant speed of light. With increased speed, space shrinks, that is, lengths shorten, and clocks tick slower.

It was the extension of this concept of relativity to mass that yielded his fourth contribution of that year. It was known several years before that the mass, or weight, of an electron particle increased with its speed. The faster it moved, the heavier it got. Einstein showed that this increase in mass followed the same laws as the alterations in space and time relative to motion. Thus mass ($m$) has a definite relationship to motion, which is, in turn, always related to the constant speed of light ($c$). Carrying his calculations slightly further, he revealed that the mass of a body is also related to its energy content (E), and he developed these three factors into the simple and graceful relationship: $E = mc^2$, where E is the energy measured, say in volts; $m$ is the mass or weight measured, say in grams; and $c$ is the constant $3 \times 10^{10}$, which is 3-followed-by-ten-zeros centimeters per second (or 186,000 miles per second)—the velocity of light. Since $c$ is squared in this equation, even one pound of fuel ($m$) gives a tremendous quantity of energy (E), *if* the fuel is, of course, converted into energy. Thus, if one pound of coal *burns*, it will boil water for only a relatively brief amount of time. Burning is a chemical reaction, for which Einstein's equation is more or less irrelevant. But if one pound of coal is *converted* into energy, this equation is quite relevant, and, in fact, predicts that one pound of coal so converted would supply enough electricity for the entire United States for one full month. (The equation, however, does not tell *how* to do this.)

Subsequent experimentation since 1905 has verified Einstein's findings in all these matters.

Several years later Einstein left the patent office and joined the physics department at the University of Zurich.

## Earth—I

The fifth-largest planet and the third from the sun, not quite a perfect sphere; its diameter at the equator is 7,926.68 miles.

Earth's atmosphere holds gases—principally nitrogen (78 per cent) and oxygen (21 per cent), with traces of helium, neon, argon, krypton, xenon, radon, carbon dioxide and water vapor. For a height of approximately 180,000 feet the proportions remain essentially the same. The action of gravity in retaining the atmosphere makes Earthly life possible. (*See* Moon.)

The planet breaks down into three main parts: the outside crust; the mantle, occupying about half the diameter of Earth; and the core, also about half the diameter but much less than the mantle in volume. The crust varies from about 5 to 50 miles in depth. The mantle below lies to a depth of about 1,800 miles. Both are solid. The core is probably fluid with the possible exception of a smaller solid inner core.

Three-quarters of Earth is covered by water. Throughout the past history of the planet, the sea has been creeping over the land, washing away cliffs and soil. The process would bury all land beneath water ultimately were it not for the combat between surface forces and deep forces like volcanic eruptions, with their resulting widespread buildup of surface by cooling lava. Chemical weathering and disintegration of materials in rock cause a breakdown in the rocks, whose detritus is removed by a process of downhill creeping, air movements and water; the sea itself, however, may pile up sediment along coasts, which gain land from the water. The relative proportions of sea and land, the topography of the surface and of the sea bottom, change ceaselessly. (*See also* Blast Effects.)

. . . I have seen the hungry ocean gain
Advantage on the kingdom of the shore,
And the firm soil win of the watery main,
Increasing store with loss and loss with store.
        —William Shakespeare, Sonnet LXIV

Some limestone rocks about 3,000,000,000 years old contain structures apparently caused by the activity of some minute plants, algae. (*See* Aquarium.) This level of life seems to have continued uninterruptedly for almost 2,400,000,000 years. The period beginning about 600,000,000 years ago was suddenly characterized, according to all available evidence, by relatively advanced forms of marine life. Almost all life existed in the sea, and if a chemical change took place in the waters, creatures without shells or skeletons were able then to evolve such additions to their anatomy. If a chemical change did not take place, something else may have happened: it is possible that some marine organisms developed rapidly in small bodies of water. These organisms, at first restricted to warm shallow seas isolated from each other, would have the opportunity of spreading over larger areas as the melting ice caps returned water to the surface of Earth, raising the sea level. The wide dispersion of fauna in this period may have resulted from some such process. More sophisticated organisms have appeared since.

The manner of Earth's creation is a subject of debate. Some 5,000,000,000 years ago condensation of a vast spinning gas cloud created the planet: the solid particles formed in the process circled around the sun, building up into larger masses which attracted each other to form Earth by celestial accumulation. This may be what happened. If it is, Earth was cold at its beginnings and heated as the increasing pressure affected the interior; if it is not, perhaps Earth began as a spinning mass of hot fluid and developed a surface crust by means of which heat is slowly being lost. The amount of radioactivity within the planet is not known, but it may be sufficient to compensate for the heat loss. The variables are too problematical to allow for a wholly creditable theory.

The average temperature of Earth has shifted appreciably in the course of eons. Some 600,000,000 and 250,000,000 years ago, immense ice sheets covered vast areas of land. Earlier ice ages cannot be dated accurately. The last ice age occurred within the last 1,000,-000 years, and the world climate still appears to be colder than it has been through most geological periods. The present history of Earth seems to be taking place in the general context of the last great ice age.

## Earth—II
Earth, Pherecides teaches, is the primal element.

Of the four essential qualities—Heat, Cold, Moisture, and Dryness—Earth incorporates Cold and Dryness, and corresponds to the Humour Melancholy, which results from a disproportion among the four Humours, including in addition Phlegm, Blood and Choler. Melanelius, out of Galen, Ruffus, and Aetius, describes it to be a *bad and peevish disease, which makes men degenerate into beasts.*

Earth is the heaviest element. Like Water, it tends to go down. That explains its position in the center of the universe, toward which everything falls. Fire, Air, Water and Earth are arranged in giant concentric layers. Using the egg as metaphor, Fire is the shell, Air the white, Water the yellow, and Earth a little fatty drop in the middle of the yolk. At the point of greatest pressure lies the Abyss where Hell sits.

In a good man the elements are well mixed; Christopher Goodman has written:

Though the present condition of man be earthly, made of the earth, feeds on the earth, and is dissolved to the earth, and therefore the soul doth less discover herself by her proper actions than doth the material body; yet it is not unknown to philosophy that there is an ecstasy of the soul . . .

Earth is ornamented with stones, mountains, beasts and plants.

The diamond is a great stone, though no bigger than a filbert. It comes from India. The Greeks called it "the untamable force." The diamond when it is near iron counteracts the activity of the magnetic stone; it also discloses the presence of smallpox. Dioscorides teaches that the diamond is the stone of love and reconciliation. A woman who wears the diamond finds favor with her husband. If the diamond is placed under the head of a sleeping woman, it tests her faithfulness: faithful, the woman turns toward her husband; otherwise she rolls to the other side. When the diamond is carried on the left side, it protects against phantoms, bad dreams and the devils who sleep with women in the guise of men.

The magnetic stone, an iron-colored stone, is found in the regions in India where the troglodytes live. The magnetic stone attracts iron and glass. In Ethiopia there is a kind of magnetic stone which from one side attracts iron, and from the other repels it. There are mountains of magnetic stone that attract ships. The magnetic stone cures sickness in the spleen, and dropsy.

Certain parts of Earth are hollowed into caverns where the imprisoned winds occasionally rage. This, Aristotle teaches, is the cause of earthquakes. Where the east wind dominates is a region abundant in flowers and fruits. The west wind is cold and humid, less favorable. The north wind is cold and dry; that is why men of the North are tall and good-looking. The south winds make men timorous.

As for mountains, some say that at the beginning Earth was smooth and lacked them. Herbs from the mountains are better for animals than the herbs of valleys; fruits are less plentiful there than in other places, but excellent. Aristotle teaches that it rains very little on very tall mountains, because the vapors turn into rain before reaching the peaks.

It is good to remember the beasts, how they are. Certain animals were given to man for food—the deer and the sheep, for instance. Others were put on Earth to help him, like the horse and the camel; others yet, to amuse him, such as monkeys and dogs. Some animals remind him of his fragility: the flea does. And others allow him to remember the power of God: such are the bear, the snakes and the lion.

## Eatherly, Maj. Claude

American war hero, pilot of the *Straight Flush,* the reconnaissance plane which surveyed the target for the *Enola Gay* (*q.v.*). The explosion at Hiroshima may have shortened the Second World War and saved many combatant and noncombatant lives. Major Eatherly was so moved by "those who slept under the ashes at Hiroshima" that he forgot the larger purposes of the raid and its ultimate meaning in the termination of the war. Upon his return to Van Alstyne, Texas, in 1947, acclaimed for his service to the Free World (*q.v.*), he began to demonstrate symptoms of severe mental imbalance. Major Eatherly wrote to the municipal council of Hiroshima, recounting his part in the incident, and also wrote to the mayor of that city, addressing postal money orders for the use of children whose parents had been lost in the explosion. To a public pondering its own moral relationship to the events at Hiroshima, the name Eatherly was for a long time associated with the bombardier who had actually dropped the bomb. As the facts about Eatherly became clarified, the legitimacy of his claim to guilt was called into question.

After a four-year residence in the mental hospital at Waco, Texas, he was twice apprehended in criminal raids upon post offices and upon a shop cashier in Dallas. In each case, he was immediately freed through the clemency of authorities who dropped charges. He was recommitted to Ward 10, for incurables, in the Waco Hospital in October, 1960, after his obsessive desire to be found guilty for an act of patriotism was found to conflict repeatedly with the laws of Texas. In 1962, *Burning Conscience,* a collection of letters between Eatherly and Günther Anders, an Austrian philosopher, appeared in the United States, momentarily reviving Eatherly as a symbol of universal guilt. However, it still remains more consonant with the practical view of things to define Eatherly's guilt as merely the personal invention of an idiosyncratic mentality. A widespread assumption of public guilt does not conveniently derive from such a questionable model.

### Effective Half-Life
Another in a growing table of neo-measures, this one is the function of two classic measures: radioactive half-life and biological half-life.

The *radioactive half-life* is the time interval during which a particular radioactive substance loses half of its radioactivity (*q.v.*). The *biological half-life* is the time interval during which half of a particular radioactive substance which has gained entry into the body is excreted from the body. Radioactive half-lives range from fractions of seconds for some substances to many thousands of years for others. Biological half-lives range from days to years, depending upon the biological site of lodging; strontium 90, for example, which is absorbed by the bone structure, has a comparatively long biological half-life of 10 years, while cesium 137, which is absorbed by the quicker-metabolizing soft tissue, is eliminated at a high rate and has a half-life of 17 days. The radioactive half-life of strontium 90, it may be noted, is 28 years; that of cesium 137, 30 years. It should also be observed that though one half-life interval reduces a given radioactive value to 50 per cent, and two half-lives to 25 per cent, and seven half-lives to less than 1 per cent, and ten half-lives to .1 per cent, no amount of successive half-life intervals will reduce a radioactive value to absolute zero. This can turn out to be a significant characteristic of this kind of computation, for even an infinitesimal percentage of a large enough quantity of hazardous radioactivity can be noteworthy.

Now, *effective half-life* is a latter-day measure presumably having something to do with the above, since it is held out to be the time interval during which a particular radioactive substance loses half of its biological hazard value as a result of the combination of its rate of radioactive decay and biological elimination. The formula which expresses this relationship is:

$$T = \frac{T_b T_r}{T_b + T_r}$$

where $T$ is the effective half-life and $T_r$ and $T_b$ the radioactive and biological half-lives respectively. (All amplifications derived from this basic formula involve the concept of the Standard Man (*q.v.*), who enjoys a general state of radioactive equilibrium with his environment by taking in radioactive isotopes at the same rate that he eliminates them.)

However, though a numerology is evolving, it is often difficult to apply. Certain transformations are bothersome. For example, what sort of comparability can be established between cesium 137, which ruins several million germ cells in 7 or 8 days with its radioactive half-life of 30 years and biological half-life of 17 days, and strontium 90, which produces bone cancer or leukemia in 15 or 20 years with its half-lives of 28 and 10 years respectively? Moreover, wherever in the situation a mathematical simplicity does seem feasible, the feasibility is at once muddied by numerous existing uncertainties. Are the combined effects of simultaneous radioactive substances simply additive, or are they synergistic so that their total effectiveness is greater than the sum of each one taken separately? Also, does the physical departure of an organism from the Standard Man need to be adjusted for? And how? And in respect to what, the metabolic rate, the life span, etc.?

The computational spirit for mastering some of the vagaries of effective half-life is quite willing. Consider:

$$\Sigma E (\text{RBE}) \mathcal{N} = \sum_{i,j,K,m,n} \left[ f_{\gamma_i} \, E_{\gamma_i} \left( 1 - e^{-\sigma_i X} \right) \right.$$
$$+ \, 0.33 f_{\beta_j} \, E_{\beta_j} \left( 1 - \frac{Z^{\frac{1}{2}}}{43} \right) \left( 1 + \frac{E_{\beta_j}^{\frac{1}{2}}}{4} \right) \left[ N_{\beta_j} \right] + 10 f_{\alpha_K} \, E_{\alpha_K} \, N_{\alpha_K}$$
$$\left. + \, f_{e-_m} \, E_{e-_m} \, N_{e-_m} + 20 f_{r_n} E_{r_n} N_{r_n} \right] \, \cdots\cdots\cdots\cdots\cdots\cdots$$

But this is a peculiar mathematics, not because the quantities are still vacant, which is not unusual for a mathematics, but because the relationships are still uncertain. Such hastiness lends a quasi-spirituality to a discipline where precision has been the hallmark for centuries.

**Ego**  (from Latin *ego* = I)
Formerly to mean the self or person in some exalted sense; now commonly the self or person with emphasis on some quality of self-centeredness or esteem, as "He has *some* ego," or "This is a boost to my ego."

The term has acquired a technical meaning: The ego is that aspect of mind upon which are registered the conflicting demands of the instincts, the superego and reality (*qq.v.*) and which negotiates these demands, giving them expression or opposing them, according to the course of least conflict and maximum functioning for the organism. The ego's three petitioners are urgent, yet perilous. The instincts promise pleasure but threaten chaos; the superego offers love and approval but exacts a price of restriction and repression; reality holds out opportunity for emotional and material supplies but diminishes the individual's sense of narcissism (*q.v.*) and omnipotence. With respect to its three petitioners, the ego is at a singular disadvantage in that it is weaker than any one of them. On the other hand it is more adaptable than each of them. It alone possesses the powers of perception, reason and feeling, and while these powers are comparatively weak, they do enable the ego to promise, bribe and postpone its adversaries and also to make temporary alliances with any one of them to borrow additional power for temporary use against the others. The ego is fueled by anxiety (*q.v.*) which the ego in turn regulates. Too little anxiety blunts its sensitivity; too much cripples its scope.

The ego is the executive that administrates sanity. Its tenure is prey to a number of disasters. The ego may be constitutionally defective through a genetic flaw and will never administrate adequately; chronic insanity of some variety will sooner or later appear. The ego may be warped in its early development, especially in its treacherous infancy; one or several of a very large variety of disorders, from mild to painfully severe, will sooner or later appear. Temporary insurrections of instinct may flare up as at puberty, sending the ego topsy-turvy into the disorder of adolescence. The superego may grow fierce and vindictive as at the loss of some significant possession of the organism through bodily injury, the death of a loved one, or the involution of aging; depression is not uncommon in such eventualities. (*See* Mourning.) Finally, reality may undergo some dramatic alteration and overwhelm the ego's capacity to survive. But, perhaps, environmental disaster can be suffered and then forgotten. Memory is yet another function of the ego, a delicate function susceptible to obscure and troublesome quirks.

## Eichmann, Adolf

Nazi SS *Obersturmbahnführer* and bureaucrat, defendant in the case *Attorney General of Israel v. Adolf, son of Adolf Karl Eichmann* in the District Court of Jerusalem in 1961. Colonel Eichmann, technical director of transportation and emigration of millions of Jews to the gas chambers, was accused of direct responsibility in the Final Solution of the Jewish Question. Colonel Eichmann's defense was characterized by a firm philosophical foundation: the qualitative distinction, so often honored in the history of civilization, between *veranlassen* (to set in motion) and *tun* (to do). Colonel Eichmann fulfilled his assigned function: to set affairs in motion. He "never hated the Jews, was never an anti-Semite." He was concerned primarily with the advancement of his career and seemed to understand clearly the specialization of function which the modern state requires of its citizens. He also had a tragic intuition about the darkness threatening a high culture from within unless a constant and unremitting concern for order could assure continuity:

I couldn't hand out any information on my own initiative. Obviously, that would have been disastrous, and produced nothing but confusion, and would have led eventually to none of the people concerned knowing where they stood any longer, and endless questions of precedence would have come up, producing nothing but unpleasantness and chaos.

The Israeli psychiatrist called into the case considered Colonel Eichmann "quite normal . . . more normal than I feel myself after this examination."

Colonel Eichmann possessed a keen insight into the terrible tendency of some occupations to sap the moral fiber of men directly concerned with them. In this context, he demonstrated considerable sensitivity in his perceptions of a certain Höss, the commandant of the concentration camp (*q.v.*) Auschwitz, who "got quite a kick out of making the whole thing as horrific as possible for a man straight from his desk . . . he was quite brutalized, was Höss." Such an abdication from reason and orderly processes was not pleasant for Eichmann to contemplate. But, as he said, "I sat at my desk and got on with my job." Among his tasks, for instance, was the drawing up of a document authorizing another official to "conduct 150,000 Jews towards the *Endlösung* [final solution]." This extract from the trial records demonstrates Colonel Eichmann's punctilious regard for order:

EICHMANN: At this time I received an order from Heydrich, to draw up the following letter for Globocnik; Heydrich dictated to me: "I authorize you to conduct a further 150,000 Jews toward the *Endlösung*." I can't remember now whether he ordered the letter to be headed "Head of SS and Chief of German Police in the Reich Ministry for Internal Affairs" and signed "per Heydrich," or whether he wanted it headed "Chief of Security Police SD." I . . .

Q: But did the letter contain the words "conduct a further 250,000 Jews toward the final solution"?

EICHMANN: 150 or 250, I think, I really don't know.

Q: But that meant extermination and death?

EICHMANN: Oh yes, oh yes. These Jews were already dead, and Globocnik had them posthumously documented afterward. I think it must have been 250,000. I think so. Yes, Globocnik had it drawn up for a second time.

Q: And this second posthumous order also passed through your department, through your hands?

EICHMANN: *Jawohl, jawohl.*

Colonel Eichmann's position was consistent during the trial, and throughout his stay in prison he resisted the depression from which so many prisoners have suffered; he ate well and his health remained generally good. When the judges condemned him to death for crimes against humanity, the first death sentence in Israeli history, Colonel Eichmann's lawyer maintained that no man honestly concerned with the truth of the complex relationship of the individual to the modern state could deny the final appeal which he submitted to the Israeli judiciary.

Just before he was executed, *Obersturmbahnführer* Eichmann said:

After a short while, gentlemen, we shall all meet again. So is the fate of all men. I have lived believing in God and I die believing in God. Long live Germany. Long live Argentina. Long live Austria. These are the countries with which I have been most closely associated and I shall not forget them. I greet my wife, my family and friends. I had to obey the rules of war and my flag. I am ready.

**Electron**   (*See also* Particle.)

A fundamental subatomic particle having three defining characteristics: It is electrical; it is barely substantial, its mass being less than 1/1840 of a neutron (*q.v.*); though it can issue from a nucleus (*q.v.*) upon being born in the course of radioactive decay, it exists as an enduring entity in the external regions of the atom. The electron is generally thought to possess an electrically negative charge, a reputation based on the superfluity of negative electrons in this locality in the universe. Positive electrons also exist but not so abundantly here as elsewhere.

Discovered and named in 1897 by J. J. Thomson, the electron enlarged the concept of the atom to include internal relationships between subatomic parts; hitherto the atom carried on relationships only externally with other atoms. It is because of this insight that the electron must be considered a ranking discovery of the turn of the century, in a category with the discovery in those years of X rays and radioactivity.

It is usual to expound the electron's small size. The electron's restlessness, however, is less known. The electrons in the inner shells of light atoms like lithium or carbon vibrate about $10^{17}$ times per second. This number—$10^{17}$—may be comprehended perhaps if transformed into a time interval: $10^{17}$ seconds is a duration of 3,000 million years. In heavier atoms like gold and lead, the number of times the inner electrons vibrate in a single second exceeds the number of seconds that have elapsed since the beginning of the universe.

When flowing through a conductor as an electric current, or striking a metal grid in a radio tube, or involved in chemical unions between atoms, electrons are relatively benign. (However, *see* Beta.)

## Electron Volt
Often EV. In larger multiples, KEV, MEV and BEV (one thousand, one million and one billion EV).

Particles gain energy through velocity. One electron volt is the energy gained by an electron particle when it is accelerated by one volt of electricity. One EV is an exceedingly small amount of energy, since one volt of electricity does not boost the velocity of a particle very much.

Several thousand volts of electricity, however, do accelerate particles significantly, imparting KEV quantities to the particle. At higher speeds, particles attain MEV ranges; at yet higher speeds, BEV ranges. Particles attain these speeds naturally; electrons released in radioactivity travel in the KEV-MEV range, at which speed they are called beta particles; the natural radioactivity of radium releases rather heavy particles in the MEV range; cosmic rays are a variety of particles racing at BEV velocities. These speeds may also be attained artificially by introducing particles to long tracks of electricity. (*See* Atom Smasher.)

Artificial acceleration has already rivaled nature by driving particles into BEV ranges. This can be done in Geneva, Switzerland; Brookhaven, New York; and Dubno, U.S.S.R. Plans are afoot to exceed nature, as she is observed from Earth, with the construction of an accelerator that will drive particles into the trillion-EV range. The execution of these plans may ultimately require the financial collaboration of the United States and the Soviet Union. However, while money may be willing, there is a point beyond which nature is not. Particles cannot exceed a velocity limit which nature sets, the velocity of light. The BEV speed is close to it. The trillion-EV will be a mite closer.

## Elements, Man-Made

Prior to the early 1940s, the most complex structure of elementary particles that endured on Earth was represented by the atoms of the element uranium (*q.v.*). Since there are limits to simplicity but only resistances to complexity, it has never been beyond man's pale to increase, through his ingenious efforts, the complexities of nature as he finds them. One result of man's recent inquiries into atomic structure and energy has been a series of artificial elements of greater complexity than uranium. Nature does resist improvement in this direction (*see* Entropy), causing most of these elements to deteriorate into simpler structures rather quickly. Nevertheless, they are bona fide supplements to the scheme of things in this corner of the universe, perhaps even resurrections of primordial forms of matter which disappeared in the early history of our then barren planet. The first two in the series were named romantically: neptunium and plutonium. Sobriety soon took over: americium, curium, berkelium, californium, einsteinium, fermium, mendelevium, nobelium, lawrencium.

**Elugelab**   *See* Fission-Fusion Bomb.

**Energy**
That concept of substance which matter embodies, absorbs, releases and is activated by. Hence energy is inseparable from its expression through matter. Matter complies with this expression in a myriad of forms —heat, motion, mass, light—and though the various forms of energy are assigned to categories, e.g., mechanical, electrical, nuclear, radiant, chemical, gravitational, thermal, each form is transformable along fields of matter into any other form. Energy spills down these fields delivering vitality to every crevice of the universe.

Regarding energy there are two laws which have no exceptions. One is that energy is neither lost nor gained in any transformation. Dispersals of a given quantity of energy, however devious and far-flung, end up as no more nor less than the original quantity: energy is perfectly conserved. The other law describes a certain unconquerability of energy. Energy does not operate systems that are leakproof. In one or another form, energy leaks incessantly. Thus no system, however organized, can be perpetually self-contained. It is the nature of system itself to require external sources of energy for maintenance. Energy sets this requirement for its own existence. How the requirement is fulfilled is as varied as there are forms of energy and kinds of systems.

**Enola Gay**
Flying a B-29 on a daring day strike on Hiroshima, Honshu, carrying for the first time a type of bomb totally new to

modern warfare, he successfully dropped his bomb upon reaching the target city.

> —Citation accompanying the Distinguished Service Cross given to Col. P. W. Tibbets as he stepped from the *Enola Gay*.

My God!

> —Entry from the flying log of Capt. Robert Lewis, copilot of the *Enola Gay*.

Three B-29s left Tinian Island (*q.v.*) in the Marianas at 2:45 Monday morning, August 6, 1945. The bomb carrier, piloted by Col. Paul W. Tibbets, was named for his mother, Enola Gay.

The bomb, almost completely assembled, had been hanging in the bomb bay of the B-29 by late afternoon, August 5. Capt. William S. Parsons (*q.v.*), responsible for the technical control of the bomb, had been practicing its assembly all day. The burning crash of four B-29s at the end of their runways the previous day had convinced him that the final assembly should be made on the *Enola Gay* itself, rather than to risk any possibility of destroying Tinian.

At about 4:30 on the morning of August 6, Colonel Tibbets, worn out by the tensions and exertions of the mission, caught a short while of sleep. At 5:00 dawn appeared. At 7:10 copilot Lewis noted that, outside of a thin cloud layer, it was a beautiful day. At 7:30 Captain Parsons finished the assembly. At 8:30 a report was received from a reconnaissance plane, which had left an hour before the *Enola Gay* (*see* Eatherly, Maj. Claude), that Hiroshima was the preferred target. At 8:50 the *Enola Gay* reached Honshu, and at 9:11 it reached the initial point of its straight course to the target.

Japanese radar had picked up the *Enola Gay* and its two accompanying craft, but when no more airplanes followed them the alert was lifted. The last few minutes before the drop were utilized for the immediate preparations by Maj. Thomas W. Ferebee, of Mocksville, North Carolina, the bombardier; Capt. Theodore J. Van Kirk, of Northumberland, Pennsylvania, the navigator; and Sgt. Joe Stiborik of Taylor,

Texas, the radar operator. The target was unprotected. When the *Enola Gay's* burden (*see* Payload) had dropped to a certain point above the city of Hiroshima, it exploded, turning from a pinpoint of purplish-red light to a huge purple fireball 2,600 feet in diameter, which then became transformed into gigantic whirling flames, clouds and rings of fog. The resulting column of smoke turned into a mushroom, reaching a height of 50,000 feet.

Tibbets, Ferebee and Lewis, shaken and amazed, forgot to put on their protective colored glasses as the new light was born.

The blast of the explosion rocked the *Enola Gay*, at that time several miles from ground zero.

For 400 miles, the crew continued to see the dust and smoke.

Hiroshima, a city of 245,000 inhabitants, endured 80,000 deaths and 100,000 injuries, including almost all the doctors—200—and nurses—1,780—in the city.

After the Hiroshima radio station went off the air and the Tokyo telegraph center reported it could not reach the city, a young Japanese major flew over Hiroshima and reported the irrecoverable ruin of the city.

## Entropy
The mathematical measure of the amount of organization taking place when one form of energy is converting into another. Low entropy indicates high organization (order); high entropy, low organization (chaos). The mathematics of entropy are basic to thermodynamics, a branch of physics dealing with the relationship of energy to work.

This measure has been applied to systems other than thermodynamic ones, notably to communication systems where it is possible to regard information as a function of entropy. Thus:

ZBXQLTV RA BBLCSRN AQJP contains comparatively high entropy.

TRUTH IS BEAUTY contains comparatively low entropy.

While energy (*q.v.*) can never be lost, the tendency is

always for its entropy to increase. That is, systems, unless constantly maintained, simply run down into chaos.

## Envy

All in a kirtle of discolourd say
  He clothed was, ypainted full of eyes.
                    —Edmund Spenser

One of the deadly sins (*q.v.*). An indication of the voyeuristic source of envy lies in its etymology: Latin *in* = in, upon, + *videre* = to look. Envy begins in the child's observations of the liberties of adults, especially liberties involving what the child perceives as pleasure and excitement. As the child experiences a vicarious enjoyment in watching adults, this watching becomes complex and significant. Whenever there is intense looking, the object being looked at is experienced as purposely showing; this experience leads to resentment in the one who is looking. Envy describes the feeling: "I begrudge you what I see you have, for you possess it merely to torment me." The sin in Envy is its demand for license without qualification.

## Eros

One of two primal instincts (*q.v.*) attributed to man, the other being Thanatos (*q.v.*). The function of Eros is to maintain life, or, perhaps more accurately, to insure that the organism proceeds toward death on its own terms. Eros is constructive in the sense that it seeks to combine the objects of the environment into greater wholes and more complex organizations. This instinct is evident in the manifest energies of the organism in love and labor. Eros never functions alone. It is always fused, to a greater or lesser extent, with its primal counterpart Thanatos.

## Escalation    *See* Limited War.

## Expert
Related to the English *experience* and *experiment* by the Latin root *peritus* = experienced. With *ex* = out

of = *experitus* = out of experience. *Peritus* originates in the earlier Latin *periculum* (akin to *pirata* = robber at sea) = danger or risk. All meanings rendered neatly in its military (U.S. Army) application = the most skilled of three classes of riflemen, hence, a deadly marksman. Also:

> It is the hallmark of the expert professional that he doesn't care where he is going as long as he proceeds competently.      —Herman Kahn's friend (*see* Kahn, Herman)

> I sat at my desk and got on with my job.
> —Adolf Eichmann (*q.v.*)

> I was quite despondent. But when you look at it, we always sold many of these items—camp stoves, chemical toilets—for camping or summer-cottage use. We thought our way of bringing these items together in a display was the best way of serving our customers who have been asking for this type of merchandise. It's like setting up a model kitchen. I am a merchant, and I am in business.
> —Dominic Tampone, President, Hammacher-Schlemmer, on fallout-shelter merchandise

## Extrasensory Perception
Also ESP. An inadmissible mode of cognition in which an external event presents itself to none of the five known senses. Telepathy and clairvoyance are two common modes of ESP; the former is the extrasensory perception of the mental activities of another person; the latter is the extrasensory perception of events that have already happened, or that are happening, or that are about to happen. Though investigations of purported ESP phenomena manage to discredit most of them, they do not discredit all of them; moreover, there is a small body of experimental data strongly suggesting paranormal cognition in certain subjects. However, at this point ESP is more an embarrassment than a legitimate concern of science (*q.v.*). Like soup spilled at a banquet, it is seen but ignored.

## Eye, Simple
As opposed to the eye dots of annelids—red-blooded segmented worms—and the compound eyes of insects.

The simple eye is the visual organ in the higher creatures, consisting of the eyeball, the muscles that move
it, and the tear-inducing mechanism which keeps the
front moist. The eyeball is a sphere. A small bulge,
the cornea, projects in front of the eyeball, which has
three coats and three refracting media: the aqueous
humor, the lens, and the vitreous humor. The iris, or
colored diaphragm of the simple eye, is pierced to form
the pupil. The inner layer of the wall of the eyeball is
the retina, a transparent membrane.

A ray of light on its way to the retina must pass
through the cornea, the aqueous humor, the lens and
the vitreous humor, refractive and transparent surfaces
which bend light rays in order to bring them to a focus
on the retina.

Light enters the retina; it is somewhat absorbed by
the black pigment of the retina; it is somewhat reflected
through the pupil in the direction of entry: an image
is perceived at the same point in space as the luminous
object. (For distance receptors in the higher creatures,
*see* Central Nervous System.) The iris, a diaphragm,
moderates the amount of light coming into the eye.
(*See* Fireball.)

The mode of movement called light has been studied
with accuracy outside the body; its complex physiological effects in the simple eye, however, cannot be
stated with a precision equal to the observation that
red is produced by 392 trillion impulses on the retina
per second. The simple eye perceives a continuum of
colors from red to violet, with vibrations of 757 trillion
impulses per second. The unseen rays above the violet
include X rays and gamma rays. (*See* Thermal Effects.)

# F

## Fail-Safe

Also Positive Control. In a Fail-Safe military operation, bombers are instructed not to go beyond a certain point unless they receive positive confirmed orders to do so. This operation emphasizes the high Recallability factor in the use of airplanes as contrasted to the launching of missiles. The plane can be called back, or Recalled; the ballistic missile, once sent, is gone. In the event of an inconclusive warning of enemy attack, manned aircraft deserves, through Fail-Safe, a high priority rating. In addition, the plane, in flight, leaves the ground for the safer air. Fail-Safe may be contrasted with Safe-Safe, an operation in which the plane not only gets off the ground, but keeps going *unless* it is recalled. These operations are not to be confused with Fail, in which the plane is immediately destroyed.

## Fallout

Ceylon (Sinhalese), *vikirana seela rajo nipataya;* China, *yuan tzu chen;* Czechoslovakia Socialist Republic, *radioaktivni odpad;* France, *retombées radioactives;* Greece, *epiptosis radienergeias;* India (Hindi), *anoo dhooli;* Indonesia, *hudjan debu atom;* Japan, *hoshano kokabutsu,* also (colloq.) *shi no hai* (ashes of death); Jordan (Arabic), *tallouth el jo;* Laos, *kam-manta-pop-lang-si;* Lebanon (Arabic), *ghobar zirri;* Netherlands, *radio-actieve neerslag;* Soviet Union, *radioactivniye ossadky;* Spain, *lluvia radioactiva;* Sweden, *utfall;* Turkey, *atom bombasi radyoaktivite ceryanlari;* Yugoslavia, *padavina.*

Instantaneously, the bomb and everything in its vicinity is vaporized. The fireball appears. Then the shock. The fireball expands and soars, turning fiery red, then billowy white. It rises through the troposphere, drifting on the wind, hovering in the stratosphere, a huge, misty mass in the clean and drafty region high above Earth's weather. By now, local fallout is torrential. Global fallout begins later.

There are about 40 different ways for a uranium atom to fission; all of them are represented in a nuclear explosion. These 90-odd radioactive products of immediate fission are instantly joined by over 100 radioactive substances induced by the heat and radiation of the bomb. 200-odd radioisotopes are born in a fission explosion. The radioactivity of some of them will vanish in the next instant; the radioactivity of others will linger for thousands of years. Most varieties of this nuclear debris are solids at normal temperatures. They settle on the droplets of soil and steel condensing in the cooling fireball and fall to Earth in the vicinity of the explosion. These falling particles appear as a rain of glassy grains, pale yellow, green, brown. Indeed, the effect is of a mild desert sandstorm. The radioactivity emanating from this local fallout is lethal. Farther downwind from ground zero, beyond sight of the flash, local fallout occurs some hours later; here it descends as a fine white powder, almost invisible. It is also lethal. Within the day the local fallout has been deposited. Depending on the size of the bomb and wind conditions, "local" may include an area 500 miles around ground zero.

In the stratosphere, the remaining radioactive debris —microdust and vapor of some dozen radioisotopes— begins a windblown journey toward the polar latitudes, the stratosphere's gateway to the troposphere and Earth's weather. Most of the radioactivity of this debris has subsided; much hasn't. Henceforth for years, this debris falls out invisibly on soil, trees, plants, in the oceans, rivers, lakes, on city streets and buildings, on livestock and wild game, on humans; it is eaten, breathed, walked over, washed in; it gets in the hair, beneath the fingernails; it finds its way into the skeleton, the muscles, the glands, the bloodstream; it reveals only one discrimination: it has a preference for little children.

## Fascination

A mode of observation involving mastery without effort. The prototype of fascination is the infant's rapt gaze on what he desires to handle and control but cannot yet do for lack of neuromuscular development. He will lose himself in the sight and sound of some object or scene and, in so becoming one with it, experience the illusion of mastery. Subsequently, fascination may occur as a pre-stage to mastery. It is then followed by some intellectual or physical effort, as in an encounter with a fascinating poem which excites comprehension or with a beautiful boat that one then wants to rig and sail. Here fascination is charged with the vitality of surprise.

Fascination may also occur as an end in itself. Here it is invited for its own sake and is devoid of surprise. One places oneself receptively before an inconsequential though titillating object and enjoys a gratification reminiscent of infancy, i.e., mastery without effort. Fascination is then followed by self-recrimination and often hostility against the object one has lost himself in and swindled himself with.

## Fate

From Latin *fatus,* "that which has been spoken." Hence, declared, decreed, pronounced. Hence, a course of events beyond human control leading to a pre-determined outcome. (*See* Doomsday Machine.) The outcome usually bespeaks punishment, suffering and defeat. In varying degrees all human beings are susceptible to the experience that some kind of fate rules their existence.

The collectivization of this susceptibility in programs of destiny and prophecy leads to powerful justifications for significant social movements. Thus, "It is my fate to lead Germany and your fate to follow me." (Adolf Hitler) "The defeat of capitalism is not in our hands but in the prophecies of Marx." (Nikita Khrushchev, *q.v.*) Also, Manifest Destiny = the nineteenth-century doctrine that it is the destiny of Anglo-Saxon nations, especially the United States, to dominate the Western Hemisphere.

Now, a sense or notion of fate would seem likely to originate in our observations of those inexorable regularities and repetitions of nature, which are beyond our control, which we are nevertheless compelled to participate in, and which we sometimes dread. The most apt example might be death. But as likely as this assumption is, it is not a good one. Indeed, it proves to be a better assumption that it is we who impose a fatalistic view on nature rather than the other way around.

For one thing, a sense of fate simply does not visit especially those who are most exposed to the inevitabilities of nature.

However, a sense of fate, indeed, strong enough to produce painful feelings of doom and hopelessness, is regularly encountered in all mental illness. It is also worth noting that it is a feeling much more than a speakable thought. That it is especially pronounced among compulsive gamblers, addicts and promiscuous women gives a clue to its origins and dynamics.

These people not only share a strong sense of fate but some additional characteristics as well. To begin with, their distress is involved with some definite *activity*, rather than an inhibition, fear or thought. Moreover, the activity itself promises some kind of lasting triumph but inevitably results in disappointment: for the gambler, usually a loss or else an insufficient win that is subsequently played and lost; for the addict, a subsiding of intoxication and elation; for the erotomanic woman, abandonment by her lover or else her own loss of interest in him. In each instance, a repetition of the activity is required. Finally, the activity on which the hopes are pinned is never arbitrary nor can it be resisted. Thus, the sequence emerges: hope— activity—defeat—repetition. So predetermined is the sequence, so dependable the outcome, and so subservient the individual caught in it, that he is often said to be suffering from a neurosis of destiny. And he is likely to be the first to agree with the aptness of this label.

But since nobody is forced by current externals into this sequence, it remains to be answered what special inner mission these people are on. At the core of a neurosis of destiny is a defeat sustained in the deep past, emotional, vast and within the family unit, which was stricken from memory on the basis of an embittered threat: "I am helpless now. Let the matter rest. But temporarily, for I defer the conflict to the future when I shall be older and stronger (like the one at whose hands I am now suffering) and when I shall reopen it again and this time win." But years hence, with the memory thus obliterated, all that arises is the unspoken compulsion to act toward some exciting outcome. Mastery and the laying to rest of the original conflict are, of course, not feasible: the issue is no longer clear; the mighty adversaries of the helpless child have all grown old and are useless for satisfaction. All that now remains is the wound and the helpless child that now inhabits the body and the intellect of the adult. Fate is the emotional vapor that hangs over these remains.

And since all human beings have in common that helpless condition of childhood and have sustained to a greater or lesser extent the unspeakable injuries to feeling that this condition invites, some sense of fate is also held in common. Only its grip varies and the choice we make: we can be either its victim or its opponent.

Thus, Santayana: "Those who do not remember the past are condemned to relive it."

**Fat Man** (*See also* Fission; Fission Bomb; Great God K.)

Thin Man's sophisticated relation. A detonator for a fission bomb which uses plutonium (*q.v.*) as a charge.

The trigger for a fission bomb needs to perform two critical operations. It must bring together fissionable material in a precise quantity and shape in an environment of neutrons (*q.v.*). It must also coordinate the material so that the reaction does not impair the bomb before its full crescendo is attained. This material cannot be prepared for detonation before the target is reached, for once the material is in a critical (or supercritical) configuration, it can absorb a stray neutron provided by ever-present cosmic rays and go off while it is being flown to its destination.

The Fat Man is one solution to the problem. It is a hollow sphere of subcritical plutonium. At its center is a small but intense neutron source. Surrounding this arrangement is an ordinary chemical explosive which has been fitted into compartments. These compartments are machined so that when the chemical explosive is set off, it implodes (collapses) rather than explodes. The plutonium is compressed toward the neutron source. At this instant, it acquires a super-critical shape and the neutrons do their work.

The Fat Man was used in the first test at Alamo-gordo (*q.v.*) but because its reliability was suspect, the Thin Man was used in the Hiroshima bomb. The latter is a thin, tubular-shaped container with chunks of uranium 235 at each end. One of these subcritical masses is simply fired into the other, forming a critical mass.

The Thin Man was wasteful of fuel but it was certain not to fail. Once the first mission had proved a success, a more relaxed atmosphere prevailed, and the Fat Man was risked on Nagasaki three days later. It, too, was a success. (*See* The Great Artiste.)

## Fear

Often distinguished from anxiety (*q.v.*): in fear, the danger is known. That the danger is known, however, does not necessarily lead to action appropriate to the nature of the danger. Fear can so disturb the sensorium and viscera of the organism that objectivity is obliterated; the known danger might just as well be unknown for all the advantage that a person is able to take of this distinction. Flight, incapacitation and a host of transitory effects are well known in connection with fear.

A significant characteristic of fear is its unpleasantness. A clue to the source of this unpleasantness and perhaps to its basic meaning to the organism is found in the etymology of *fear*. *Fear* goes back to the Anglo-Saxon *fær*, which is related to the Old High German *fara* = to snare or to trap. Fear is the dread of loss of the most essential freedom of the organism: motility. Motility is the antidote of all frustration. When motility is lost, fear passes. Pain then occurs.

### Finite Deterrence

In an effort to deal with some of the problems posed by the posture of Minimum Deterrence (*q.v.*), peace strategists have evolved the concept of Insurance for Reliability: such Insurance, combined with such Deterrence, sires Finite Deterrence. Clearly, and unmetaphorically, experts (*q.v.*) tend to agree that reciprocal use of powerful U.S. and S.U. strategic forces would produce unprecedented catastrophe. Only a romantic imagination, however, awash in fantasies of mutual homicide, searching for simplistic solutions to problems of immense magnitude, will deny the significant differences between the unprecedented and the utter.

Peace strategists, then, rejecting the concept of the utter, and with it the notion of Minimum Deterrence, add Insurance for Reliability to the latter. The Insurance for Reliability should cover all situations that might require retaliatory strikes: for instance, airplane movements, submarine activity, missile launchings, carrier task forces.

The retaliatory capability stops short of Counterforce as Insurance, or Insurance Against Unreliability, a posture not typical of most Finite Deterrers. (*See* Counterforce as Insurance; *see also* Heart of Darkness.)

### Fire

Fire, Heraclitus teaches, is the primal element.

Fire is animate, and animates all living things. Fire is a process of becoming in which opposites are identical. *And it is the same thing in us that is quick and dead, awake and asleep, young and old; the former are shifted and become the latter, and the reverse takes place in turn. Good and ill are one.* Fire travels an Upward and a Downward Way; but *the Way up and the Way down are the same.* The universe is kept in existence by a tension between the two Ways. The soul, in its fiery state, is wise, and heeds orderly process in proportion as the soul is hot and dry.

Others teach that Fire corresponds to the Humour Choler, and incorporates Heat and Dryness. The property of Fire is to go up. Fire surrounds the region of Air, and mounts to the Moon. Beyond that lies the pure circle where the seven planets move. Beyond that, the firmament, turning perpetually from east to west. Beyond that, a heaven of crystal. Beyond that, the heaven from which the revolting angels were cast. Beyond that, the purple heaven, imperial place of divinity with all its secrets.

Fire is a kind of ennobled Air, more resplendent and fine, without a trace of humidity. Dry Air, drawn by the sun, is enkindled and burns.

## Fireball

> If the radiance of a thousand suns
> were to burst into the sky,
> that would be
> the splendor of the Mighty-One
>
> —*Bhagavad-Gita*. Purportedly recalled by Julius Robert Oppenheimer upon witnessing the first atomic detonation at Alamogordo on July 16, 1945

An apparent sphere of radiant gases formed from the bomb mechanism, the air and other materials in the immediate environment of an atomic explosion. The ingredients of the fireball are vaporized to luminosity in the billionths of a second during which the explosion releases its energy. Theory leads to the conclusion that the fireball is actually doughnut-shaped, the outer rim rolling and swirling, sucking up the environment and determining the subsequent pattern of fallout.

In the case of a one-megaton air burst, the detonation produces temperatures exceeding 100,000,000° F., rivaling the heat of stars; within one-hundredth of a second the diameter of the ensuing fireball is roughly 440 feet; within 10 seconds it expands to a mile and a quarter, rising upward at a rate of 300 miles per hour. This immense and rapid expansion forms a shock wave that illuminates the surrounding air into a fiery hoop; this shock wave ripples out over the target area to contribute to the blast effects (*q.v.*) of the bomb. Seen from as far away as 60 miles, the fireball appears 30 times brighter than the midday sun. This radiant heat represents some 35 per cent of the total energy in the explosion and is enough to combine the nitrogen and oxygen in the atmosphere into 5,000 tons of corrosive nitric acid, enough acid to make steam out of a billion pounds of water. The fireball of a one-megaton air burst may cause third-degree burns (complete destruction of the skin) to exposed persons 13 miles away. It will ignite light kindling materials within an area of 250 square miles. It rises nearly 25 miles, cooling as it goes, while materials like iron and stone condense into liquid and rain down on the earth below. The fireball is then the familiar mushroom cloud (*q.v.*).

### Firestorm

One of the effects of a nuclear explosion above an urban area: a general uncontrollable fire, so massive as to create wind velocities of hurricane force, and hence the sensation of a storm. The fire results from the ignition of kindling materials such as are commonly found in urban areas; this includes abundant supplies of fuel oil and gas. The burning uses up large quantities of air and sends warm currents upward; fresh air rushes toward the fire, promoting its spread. The vacuum over the flaming area draws this fresh air into the area at ripping velocities; physical destruction to the environment uncovers new fuel for the fire, which now burns with the intense roar of a vast blowtorch, and the storm becomes self-sustaining. The air supply to the sheltered population is depleted in a firestorm, so that if death does not come from incineration, it will come from suffocation. Since firestorms are bigger and better from nuclear explosions at high altitudes over urban areas, a well-sheltered urban population invites this type of explosion.

The models for this phenomenon were the firestorms of Hiroshima following the famous nuclear-bomb burst in 1945 and Hamburg, Germany, following the pre-nuclear incendiary air raids in July, 1943. In Hamburg some 60,000 persons were killed, almost as many as in the bomb drop on Hiroshima; temperatures reached 1,500° F., and wind velocities exceeded 150 miles per hour; days after the raids ended, there was enough heat remaining inside the shelters for the influx of oxygen to cause them to burst into flames when they were opened. The Hamburg firestorm, being pre-nuclear, was uncanny. That no firestorm developed at Nagasaki, however, is not uncanny. The city burned well; however, natural winds, carrying the fire into areas of low combustible density, spared Nagasaki a firestorm.

## First Column

The overseas political operations of the U.S. Central Intelligence Agency (CIA) are aimed at building what intelligence personnel refer to as first columns. The revival and protection of friendly regimes, support to anti-Communist underground movements, the training of foreign guerrillas all constitute first-column work. License to perform such masonry is given by the "additional services" and "other functions" clauses in the CIA statute. A most rugged first column stands in Iran, where the CIA in August, 1953, took part in the overthrow of Premier Mossadegh after his abortive attempt, with the Communist Tudeh party, to exile the Shah. Splendid first-column building is currently proceeding in Asia and Africa. On occasion, however, the CIA has come under criticism for running away with itself, as in Cuba in 1961, when the CIA, rubbing its palms and rolling up its sleeves, carried over trowels and shovels, but forgot to bring the stone. Indeed, since the Cuban incident a rule of thumb has been imposed on first-column building. When construction becomes so big as to be noticeable, the job falls to the Pentagon. The CIA will continue to erect those columns whose simpler designs can remain secret.

**Fission**  (from Latin *fissio* = a splitting or cleaving) This term acquired its original currency through biology, where it refers to the multiplication of living cells by division. But most of its current popularity has been gained through physics; here the term *fission* refers to the breakup of atomic nuclei into simpler parts. *Fission* was first used in this sense in February, 1939, in an article in the British journal *Nature*. It was so employed by Lise Meitner and her nephew O. R. Frisch, both, at the time, refugees from Nazi Germany.

Nuclear fission is a process of structural simplification. Hence it occurs most readily in atoms that tend to be overly complex and thus structurally precarious, like thorium, protactinium, uranium. In fact, in any arbitrary quantity of these elements spontaneous fission is going on all the time, though at a haphazard and practically unmeasurable rate. A stray particle in a mass of these elements is bound to be captured by a nucleus, giving up to the nucleus the energy of its velocity. Depending on the quantity of this captured energy, one or several of the hundreds of particles comprising the nuclear system of complex atoms may be released, or the nucleus may fission altogether into fragments of numerous new structures. This latter case can be likened to its biological counterpart in more ways than mere splitting; nuclear fission is conceived as a progressive elongation of a roundish nucleus with a thin waist forming between two ends; these ends swell once again into roundish shapes just prior to separating. This, of course, is how it goes with living cell division as revealed under the microscope. However, with atomic nuclei, the ends carry significant electrical charges, both similarly positive, and so repel each other toward a final burst of separation. Some mass is dissipated into energy. All this might have been pure conjecture, for in spontaneous fission not enough atoms are involved at any one time to bring the energy or the newly formed products into appreciable view. Over a billion uranium atoms, for example, would have to fission at the same instant to produce the fizz of a small pellet of gunpowder.

But the rate of fission can be increased artificially so that the phenomenon achieves visibility, so to speak, and can be verified and studied. Here the problem is to introduce numerous particles into numerous nuclei of a mass of, say, uranium. Moreover, the particles must possess that velocity which induces fission, rather than a mere limited alteration, of the nuclei. For this purpose only the electrically indifferent neutron particle is suitable; nuclei are poor targets embedded in

the remote cores of strong electrical fields; only an un-
charged particle like a neutron has a decent chance of
passing through these fields electrically unmolested.
At what velocities should neutrons be introduced into
a mass of fissionable material? This depends on the
particular material. In the late 1930s Enrico Fermi was
slowing down the velocity of neutrons by passing them
through water or paraffin wax, thereby wafting them,
rather than firing them, into minute, experimental
quantities of fissionable uranium. For some reason,
slow neutrons are readily captured by certain uranium nuclei, and fission occurs abundantly. Or at least
enough fission occurs to enable someone with patience
to pick through the specks of experimental debris and
locate traces of material lighter and more simple than
uranium.

With additional patience and plenty of money, you
can make a bomb. (*See* Fission Bomb.)

## Fission Bomb

Don't bother me with your conscientious scruples! After all,
the thing's superb physics!

—Enrico Fermi, before 1945

Also, A-bomb, atom bomb, atomic bomb, FF (fast
fission) bomb, nuclear bomb. A weapon first prepared
by the United States *sub rosa* in 1945, initiated by
alarm that Nazi Germany was developing a similar
device. (*See* Manhattan District.)

The fission bomb would not be possible were it not
that the fission (*q.v.*) of a uranium atom releases,
among other particles, neutrons (*q.v.*). Externally generated neutrons can induce fission in some atoms of a
mass of fissionable material, like uranium or plutonium. This in turn generates neutrons *within* the
mass, and other atoms fission, releasing additional
neutrons. Hence a self-sustaining chain of fission reactions is feasible. Indeed, eighty generations of fission
reactions might well consume a large mass of fissionable material within a millionth part of a second,
unleashing immense energy in the form of heat, shock
and radiation. (*See, for example,* Radiation Effects;

Blast Effects; Fallout; Fireball; Firestorm; Ionizing Radiation; Thermal Effects.)

The fission bomb rests on the solution of three practical problems. There is the technical problem of refining raw fissionable material into pure fissionable material. For every precious pound of uranium provided by nature, only a trace is that variant which is fissionable in a fission bomb, or convertible into artificial fissionable material. An entire town, like Oak Ridge, of sprawling factories and thousands of workers succeeds in extracting less than a palmful of this material in a month. There is the subsequent problem of determining that mass and shape of fissionable material which will absorb neutrons at a faster rate than they escape from the mass. (*See* Great God K.) Finally, there is the problem of designing and tooling a mechanism that will bring this mass of fissionable material together with such coordination that the chain reaction consumes the entire mass before the attendant explosion destroys the bomb and thus terminates the reaction in the remaining material. (*See* Fat Man.)

As the years go on, these problems are being solved by an increasing number of nations. (*See* Fission-Fusion Bomb.)

## Fission-Fusion Bomb  *(See also* Fusion.)

It is necessarily an evil thing considered in any light.
—Enrico Fermi, after 1945

So I confessed my sins to Fermi.  —Edward Teller

However, it is my judgment in these things that when you see something that is technically sweet you go ahead and do it, and you argue about what to do about it only after you have had your technical success.
—Julius Robert Oppenheimer

Over my dead body!  —James B. Conant

I am become Death, the shatterer of worlds.
—Sri Krishna in the *Bhagavad-Gita*

Also, H-bomb, hydrogen bomb, fusion bomb, super, thermonuclear bomb. With explosive yields in the megaton ranges, this bomb has reduced the Hiroshima-type fission bomb to the category of Nominal-Yield Weapons (*q.v.*).

The first super—Mike—was detonated by the United States on November 1, 1952, on Elugelab, a coral islet in the Pacific several thousand miles southeast of Japan. Its 3-megaton yield exceeded all expectations, including those of the MANIAC (*q.v.*). Elugelab vanished. At its site is a crater 175 feet deep and one mile long. Mike weighed a cumbersome 65 tons and was, therefore, technically not a bomb. Most of this weight was a refrigerator system which was needed to keep the hydrogen fuel—ordinarily a gas—liquid.

Ten months later, on August 12, 1953, the Soviet Union detonated a super slimmer and more agile than Mike. In seven months the United States caught up with a still more graceful super of 15 megatons. (For this, *see* Fission-Fusion-Fission Bomb.)

Super was actually conceived in 1942 in connection with theoretical ruminations about the fission bomb. Its practical materialization waited ten years upon two obstacles, one technical, the other moral. The technical obstacle was eliminated in 1945 with the explosion of the first nuclear bomb. This bomb offered the possibility of sufficient heat to fuse hydrogen nuclei. The moral obstacle was overcome in August, 1949, with the Soviet detonation of Joe I (*q.v.*). Being assured by the mathematical calculations of Professor Gregory Breit that the nuclear fusion of hydrogen on Earth would not set off a consuming global chain reaction, Edward Teller (*q.v.*) proceeded to oversee the successful construction of the first super.

Super is the result of the nuclear fusion between atoms of relatively rare variants of hydrogen, i.e., tritium and deuterium. The thermal requirements for this reaction are high but within the thermal range of a decent-sized fission bomb. Thus super is triggered by a fission bomb; hence super is basically a fission-fusion bomb. The refrigerator can be dispensed with if the hydrogen material is compounded with another element like lithium into a dry mass. All current supers are "dry" bombs. They are also apt to be something even more.

But even if progress, in all its fickleness, has already pushed Mike, that Elugelabian icebox, over the brink of obsolescence, the very same progress has insured Mike a vigorous progeny.

## Fission-Fusion-Fission Bomb (*See also* Neutron; Uranium.)

Our fate menaces all mankind. Tell that to those who are responsible. God grant that they may listen.
— Misaki, former fisherman on the *Lucky Dragon* (*q.v.*)

Also, FFF-bomb, H-bomb, hydrogen bomb, fusion bomb, super, thermonuclear bomb. Unveiled first by the United States on March 1, 1954, at Bikini in the Pacific, this is the bomb which finally appeased the technological appetite for truly large-yield weapons, thereby releasing the intellectual and financial resources for an earnest development of missile weapons. It is this bomb, combined with an intercontinental missile, that originally inspired the epithet *absolute weapon*.

Consider the immediate predecessor of this bomb, the obsolescent fission-fusion bomb (*q.v.*). This earlier thermonuclear bomb is ironically both productive and wasteful of an exceedingly precious by-product: neutrons (*q.v.*). A fusion (*q.v.*) reaction uncorks, along with plenty of energy, a burst of neutrons, which, however, are expended in the surrounding environment, contributing nothing to the blast and thermal effects (*qq.v.*). While it is true that these neutrons do convert atmospheric nitrogen into the hazardous, long-lasting radioisotope carbon 14, this sort of lingering fallout is not as militarily advantageous as the instantaneous blast and thermal effects and short-lived, more intense radiation. Free neutrons are hard to come by and should be put to better use.

The fission-fusion-fission bomb exploits these neutrons by intercepting them with an envelope of fissionable uranium. This bomb, then, is roughly a three-stage system: a uranium fission bomb triggers the hydrogen fusion reaction, which in turn releases abundant neutrons that go on to fission additional uranium. It all occurs practically at once, each stage adding to the bomb's total yield. Because there is relatively little restriction on the amount of uranium feasible in the third stage of the bomb—about a ton was used in the Bravo shot, the first Bikini detonation of 1954—the limits to the explosive yield of this bomb have yet to be established. Finally, this bomb is a master stroke of economy, for the neutron velocities of fusion will fission cheap uranium and thus allow the use of cheap uranium for the third stage. Third-stage uranium (isotope 238) costs $35,000 a ton, a pittance compared to the $10,000-a-pound uranium (isotope 235) in the trigger and in the old Hiroshima-type bomb.

At one time, in the early 1950s, a reservation existed about constructing a fission-fusion-fission bomb. There is such a thing as overkilling an enemy target. (*See* Overkill.) This is wasteful. However, the reservation was laid to rest when missiles came seriously into consideration. Slight aiming errors become magnified over intercontinental distances. A missile carrying an atomic payload aimed at the center of an enemy metropolis could well be imagined to land in the suburbs. In such an event, a fission-fusion-fission bomb will overkill the suburb, but will destroy the city proper as well. On the other hand, if precisely on target, it is true that a fission-fusion-fission bomb will overkill the city, but it cannot hurt to destroy the suburbs as well.

**Fock, Gorch**
A steel-hulled square-rigger. Arriving in New York City on May 7, 1962, the *Fock* is the first German naval vessel to visit that port since 1936.

**Folie à Deux**
Also, induced insanity. The communication and imposition of a delusional system upon a suggestible victim or group of victims, usually by a clever and

persuasive paranoic (*see* Paranoia), results in a *folie à deux*. This is common in family groups where a strong member falls mentally ill and gets the rest of the family to accept and live according to his or her personal delusions. However, a *folie à deux* is not unusual among larger, less intimate groups; cults and other groups wedded by magic rituals are often based on a *folie à deux*. The ultimate stability of the inspiring leader is usually at stake. The victim of a *folie à deux* never quite knows he is a victim; nor can he ever be persuaded that he is. Thus many people pass most of their lives in a *folie à deux* without ever having known it—though, perhaps, now and again they have vaguely suspected. But they have also vaguely realized they lacked the strength to abandon the leader.

**Form 1356**
A United States Government form, the repository of information on various structures with a protection factor of 100, and shelter capacity against radioactive fallout. Yellow-and-black signs will identify such structures. Protection against thermonuclear blast and thermal radiation or against bacteriological and chemical warfare is not a part of the Form 1356 program. Eventually, if there is enough time, the program may include such protection.

**Free World**
Antonym of Slave World (dial.). In distinction with the variously named half-free, neutral or balanced states; or in opposition to the variously named slave, totalitarian or Communist states: those states like Portugal, Iraq and the German Federal Republic which have allied themselves together in several groups for the purpose of retaining their autonomy and assuring the continuance of freedom. The Free World, although not an official ascription in any absolute sense, is usually considered to include NATO, CENTO, OAS, and SEATO. The member nations in each group are listed below:

NATO: Belgium, Canada, Denmark, France, German Federal Republic, Great Britain,

Greece, Italy, Luxembourg, Netherlands, Norway, Portugal, Turkey, United States of America.

CENTO: (formerly Baghdad Pact) Iran, Iraq, Pakistan, Turkey, United Kingdom.

SEATO: Australia, France, New Zealand, Pakistan, Philippines, Thailand, United Kingdom, United States of America.

OAS: The American republics.

Thus while no state belongs to all the four primary coalitions of the Free World, some, like the United States of America, the United Kingdom and Turkey, are signatories of three charters. In addition, other sovereign states, such as Spain, although not members of any coalition, clearly share the general feeling for self-determination characteristic of the Free World. It is difficult to place the neutral nations in one encompassing category, due to the rapid change of geopolitical events as well as to the significant differences in national purpose. Austria, Finland, India, Ireland, Spain, Sweden, Switzerland and Yugoslavia, for instance, are all neutral. However, some nations are more neutral than others.

## Fusion

The main source of energy behind the nightly pageant of the sky, fusion reactions generate all heavenly radiance and illumination.

Earth, like the moon and the neighboring planets, does not undergo fusion and is a dark, cold, lifeless celestial object but for the radiation filtering through the atmosphere from fusion on the distant sun. Recently, however, a number of fusion reactions have actually been touched off at various sites on Earth itself, and thus, for brief moments, Earth became self-illuminating—a planet with the pretense of a star.

On Earth, practically all reactions between atoms involve only the outer, energetic region of the atom, but not the nucleus, which is the comparatively stable, inert center of the atom. This is the case, for example, when fuels ordinarily burn, when aspirin works its effects on the body, when hydrogen and oxygen combine to form water, when green leaves employ sunlight to manufacture plant food. These are chemical reactions, simple or complicated, but chemical reactions nonetheless.

Fusion reactions, however, do involve the nuclei of atoms. Hence, these are not chemical reactions but rather nuclear reactions. As the name suggests, fusion is that type of nuclear reaction that involves the blending of nuclei, as opposed to the splitting of nuclei as in fission (*q.v.*), which is also a nuclear reaction. Compared to chemical reactions, nuclear reactions liberate immense energy. The difference is quite evident and impressive between, for example, TNT, which is a chemical explosive, and the hydrogen bomb, which is a nuclear explosive.

Why fusion liberates such astonishing energy is a question of atomic masses and what occurs when mass literally disappears. Consider the fusion of hydrogen atoms with each other. As it happens, two atoms of hydrogen forced into a fusion reaction create one helium atom, but some mass is lost in the bargain. The resulting helium simply possesses less mass than the sum of the two hydrogen atoms which created it. (This does not happen to any appreciable extent in chemical reactions, where the product always possesses the same total mass as its ingredients.) The lost mass converts into energy, and, as it turns out, a great deal of energy. (*See* $E = mc^2$.) Moreover, if a heavy variety of hydrogen is employed in such a reaction, like deuterium, which is about twice as heavy as ordinary hydrogen, or tritium, which is a very expensive and much heavier variety of hydrogen, there is a greater decrease of mass in the reaction and a significant increase in energy release.

But fusion reactions are difficult to produce. Nuclei are stubbornly reluctant to combine. Being electrical in nature and of the same charge (positive), they repel each other, and the nearer toward each other they are driven, the more vigorously they repel. No persuasion short of the kind of heat present in the sun and other stars will get them to fuse. Such heat strips the atom of its outer rings, exposes the nucleus and inspires it with immense trembling, sending it crashing against the resistance of its reluctant kin. Hence, a thermonuclear reaction. Such heat was at last achieved on Earth in the fission reaction of the fission bomb (*q.v.*). Indeed, on Earth, fission is the trigger for fusion. And on Earth, as on the older stars like the sun, hydrogen works out best as the fusionable material, especially those heavier varieties of hydrogen.

In all this there is an interesting mixture of contradiction and confirmation of some remarks made by the eminent British astronomer Sir James Jeans in 1933, in his Christmas Lectures at the Royal Institution. Speaking of the fusion reactions that went on at that time only on the sun and other stars, Sir James speculated:

It will never be possible to experiment with matter in this state in our laboratories—indeed, it would kill us if we tried. . . . Even a pinhead of matter . . . would emit its radiation in the form of a terrific blast against which nothing could stand. Quite close to the pinhead, the flow of radiation would produce a pressure of millions of tons to the square inch. . . . Even a hundred yards away from our pinhead, the blast of radiation would be so strong as to blow over any fortifications which have ever been built, and it would speedily shrivel up any man who ventured to within a thousand miles of the pinhead from which it issued.

But even with the materialization of a thermonuclear fusion reaction on Earth in the form of a hydrogen bomb, the distinctions between the errors and truths in these remarks are still controversial.

# G

**Gamma** (*See also* Radioactivity.)

An exceptionally energetic emission in radioactive decay, the gamma ray is distinguished by its lack of electrical charge, its very high velocity, its very short wavelength. In these respects it resembles X rays (*q.v.*) and can be thought of as a high energy variety of X ray. Like radio waves, light waves, and X rays, gamma rays are comprised of the variable and scarcely substantial photon particle.

Of the principal types of nuclear emission in radioactive decay (*see* Alpha *and* Beta), the gamma ray is the most penetrating. Its passage through matter is marked by a diffuse track, the result, largely, of induced, rather than direct, ionization. (*See* Ionizing Radiation.) Lacking an electrical charge, the gamma ray does not disrupt atomic structure by electrical attraction or repulsion; upon striking an atom, the ray transfers its energy to the particles of the atom; these particles, now agitated, play havoc with their surroundings. Whereas the heavy and highly charged alpha particle enters matter like a cannonball and is stopped dead almost upon entering, the gamma ray enters like piercing buckshot.

Gamma rays also endure over long distances. This characteristic, together with their high penetrability, creates particular hazard. Biological danger from gamma rays does not depend upon inhalation and ingestion of radioactive debris. Gamma rays can travel from environmental debris, like fallout (*q.v.*), and penetrate the organism from the outside in. These rays can enter at all sites and can reach all inner organs without needing to be conveyed to an organ specifically. Gamma rays can deliver whole-body radiation, which is, all things being equal, the most debilitating

form of radiation exposure; whole-body radiation in
ample dose leads to the most dreadful radiation syn-
dromes—marrow death, intestinal death, central nervous system death (*qq.v.*). In sublethal doses, gamma
rays are carcinogenic, and, even in conservative doses,
they are deft at penetrating and wrecking gene structure. (*See* Gene; Mutation.)

## Gene

The hypothetical biochemical unit in all living organisms which transmits hereditary characteristics by
influencing the chemical activity of the cells. Only the
reproductive sperm and egg cells possess solitary genes;
with the fusion of these two cells at fertilization, their
respective genes are paired, and all subsequent cells of
the new individual possess genes in pairs. Though
there are cells which lack genes—the red blood cells of
mammals, for example—such cells survive only a short
time and are incapable of reproducing themselves.
The genes are zones arranged along the coiled threads
within the chromosomes (*see* Nucleus, Cell). These
threads are bundles of fibrils; the fibrils are composed
of the submolecules that form the giant desoxyribo-
nucleic acid molecule (DNA). The location and se-
quences of the submolecular groupings within each
zone constitute the biochemical code from which the
anatomical destiny of the individual is translated.

Since genes occur in pairs, the control exerted by a
single gene is modified to some extent by its partner.
A gene is either dominant or recessive, according to its
power to assert itself when paired with a gene of an
opposing tendency. For example, a gene for brown
eyes, if paired with a gene for blue eyes, dominates
and will impart brown eyes; however, the recessive
gene for blue eyes is still carried by the individual,
and blue eyes may gain expression in some future gen-
eration. Some hereditary diseases are produced by
dominant genes, but, for the most part, pathogenic
genes tend to be recessive. Such genes will express
themselves in diseases only if paired by chance with a
similar recessive gene. However, none of this is to say
that recessive genes have no effect. Although not pro-

ducing blatant genetic disease, a pathogenic recessive gene does leave the individual more susceptible to the stresses and hardships of life.

Buried in the cell nucleus, genes are normally the most stable of all living units. However, they are not immutable. And though the spontaneous-mutation rate is quite low, certain chemicals, ultraviolet rays and ionizing radiation (*q.v.*) can increase the rate significantly. Most mutant genes are recessive and only very rarely beneficial. (*See* Mutation.) A mutant gene is as stable as any other gene and is not eliminated in the course of generations except by premature death of the bearer or reproductive failure. Such eliminations are called *genetic deaths*.

## Genocide

One of the observable constants in human history; first isolated, catalogued and named in the twentieth century; literally the word means the intentional destruction of national, racial, religious or ethnic groups. Genocide was declared a crime under international law by the Convention on Genocide, a crime which the contracting countries "undertake to prevent and punish." The declaration was voted by the United Nations General Assembly on December 9, 1948. The Convention, freely entered into by 55 nations unanimously, came into force January 12, 1951. It remained in force for ten years and is renewed in successive periods of five years for countries that have not denounced it. "Denunciation" is the term for the procedure of withdrawing from the Convention. Any country can give notice of such withdrawal six months before the expiration of the current period for which it is bound. If, as a result of such denunciations, there are fewer than sixteen nations bound by it, then the Convention will cease to be in force.

# Germany

וְשַׁבְתִּי אֲנִי וָאֶרְאֶה אֶת־כָּל־הָעֲשֻׁקִים אֲשֶׁר נַעֲשִׂים תַּחַת
הַשָּׁמֶשׁ וְהִנֵּה ׀ דִּמְעַת הָעֲשֻׁקִים וְאֵין לָהֶם מְנַחֵם וּמִיַּד
עֹשְׁקֵיהֶם כֹּחַ וְאֵין לָהֶם מְנַחֵם: וְשַׁבֵּחַ אֲנִי אֶת־הַמֵּתִים
שֶׁכְּבָר מֵתוּ מִן־הַחַיִּים אֲשֶׁר הֵמָּה חַיִּים עֲדֶנָה: וְטוֹב
מִשְּׁנֵיהֶם אֵת אֲשֶׁר־עֲדֶן לֹא הָיָה אֲשֶׁר לֹא־רָאָה אֶת־
הַמַּעֲשֶׂה הָרָע אֲשֶׁר נַעֲשָׂה תַּחַת הַשָּׁמֶשׁ:

—Eccles. 4:1–3

## Girl

In atomic-weapon parlance, a device that fails to explode. An atomic dud. In the hundreds of atomic detonations since 1945 no girls have been announced. The several abortive attempts to set off high-altitude nuclear devices in 1962 are not properly girls. The fault lay with the rockets, not with the bombs.

## Glory Hole

In the nuclear reactor (q.v.) at Los Alamos, a one-inch hole which pierces to the heart of the reactor. Materials can be inserted in the hole for radioactivation by neutrons in the reactor. Radioactivated materials are useful. (See Radioisotope.)

## Gluttony

Whose mind in meat and drinke was drowned so,
That from his friend he seldome knew his fo:
—Edmund Spenser

To the Glutton the World is a Feast, the people in it either Chefs or Waiters. Gluttony is one of the Deadly Sins (q.v.).

## Grandma's Pantry

A mythopoetic entity, set in the eighteenth or nineteenth century, emblematic of protection, warmth and the ample purveyance of essential victuals; in general, the term conveys overtones of amniotic reassurance islanded within a more hostile and competitive environment.

Thus a modern analogue contains eating utensils, two weeks' supply of paper plates and cups, canned milk and cereals for infants, basic storable foods, special equipment for the sick, ten-gallon cans for human wastes, battery radios with conelrad frequencies clearly marked, covered pails for toilet purposes, pocketknives and waterless soap.

## Great Artiste

Almighty God, Father of all mercies, we pray Thee to be gracious with those who fly this night. Guard and protect those of us who venture out into the darkness of Thy heaven. Uphold them on Thy wings. Keep them safe both in body and soul and bring them back to us. Give to us all courage and strength for the hours that are ahead; give to them rewards according to their efforts. Above all else, our Father, bring peace to Thy world. May we go forward trusting in Thee and knowing we are in Thy presence now and forever. Amen.

   —Prayer by Chaplain Downey, ending the briefing session preliminary to the bombing of Nagasaki

The *Great Artiste* left Tinian Island, in the Marianas, 6,000 miles from San Francisco, at 3:50 A.M. on August 9, 1945, piloted by Maj. Charles W. Sweeney, of North Quincy, Massachusetts. The aircraft, a B-29, bore no name on its silver fuselage; "#77" appeared there. The *Great Artiste* had unusually long, four-bladed propellers with orange tips.

The night was cloudy and threatening. At approximately 4:50 a storm broke around the plane, traveling at a height of about 17,000 feet. Outside the craft the temperature was about —30° F. Soon after 5:00 dawn appeared. The group of three B-29s that had left together made rendezvous over the island of Yakoshima, southeast of Kyushu, at 9:10 A.M. The aircraft went on to Nagasaki only after several other cities were by-passed because of cloud cover. The atomic bomb was dropped at 11:02 Japanese time. About 40,000 people, one-fifth of the population of the city, died.

The necessity of abandoning several targets, and the

wait for clouds to part over Nagasaki, placed a strain on the fuel reserves of the *Great Artiste*. It came so close to not returning that upon landing after the successfully completed mission, two of its motors stopped dead halfway down the runway.

For three hours and seventeen minutes the *Great Artiste* had wandered the skies over the Japanese Empire, looking for a good target.

This was the longest time any bombing mission had ever spent over the Empire.

**Great God K**   (*See also* Fission; Fission Bomb.)
The jocular deification by nuclear scientists of the awesome multiplication factor.

The introduction of neutron particles of controlled velocities into a mass of uranium or plutonium (*qq.v.*) induces fission in some of the atomic nuclei comprising the mass of material. Such fission releases fresh neutrons *within* the mass. Four possibilities exist for any one of these released neutrons:

1. It can escape through the surface of the mass into the surrounding environment.

2. It can collide with a nonfissionable impurity within the mass and dissipate its velocity.

3. It can be captured by a fissionable atom in the mass, but, because of unsuitable velocity, it will not cause fission.

4. It can be captured and cause fission.

If released neutrons undergo the first three possibilities in greater number than the fourth possibility, a self-sustaining chain of fission reactions within the mass of material is not possible. Any appreciable nuclear energy yield, as from a nuclear bomb, depends upon the majority of neutrons succeeding in the fourth possibility. The ratio of neutrons undergoing the first three to neutrons undergoing the fourth is called the multiplication factor and is designated by the letter K. A situation where K is less than unity (one) will not do for a chain reaction.

Certain mathematical, geometrical and technical rites exercised on a mass of fissionable material can coax the Great God K to reveal a stature greater than unity. The material can be refined to excruciating purity to prevent useless collisions. The surface of the mass can be shaped to minimize the opportunity for neutron escape. The inner volume and density of the mass can be adjusted to moderate neutron velocities. If these procedures are maneuvered with critical devotion, a mass of fissionable material with K greater than unity will have been designed.

Prior to 1942, the best value of K which any practical system had yet attained was estimated to be considerably less than unity—.87. On December 2, 1942 (see Atomic Age), Enrico Fermi and his associates at the University of Chicago managed, for what is thought to be the first time in history, to provoke the Great God K to reveal himself larger than unity. He loomed within Fermi's shrine under the grandstands of Stagg Field to a height of 1.007. This is all you really need.

### Ground Zero
A point on Earth's surface at the center of the A-ring (*q.v.*).

### Group
Beasts form herds and packs. They do not form groups. Groups are feasible only between creatures who, for better or for worse, have evolved a necessity to maintain ideals through an inner struggle with conscience and desire. Groups communalize ideals and thus provide refuge from inner struggle. In groups there is good conscience: man follows, leads, cavorts, studies, learns, pillages, murders, prays. There is no ideal for which a group cannot be formed. Of the individual the group demands obedience to the ideals. Of the group the individual demands perpetuation of the ideals. Even when struggle arises over these demands, it is never a struggle within the individual. It is outward and is therefore waged in continuing good conscience.

For the validation which groups provide him, the individual forgoes some commensurate portion of his privacy. This cannot be otherwise; privacy is the saboteur of groups; it is an opportunity for personal, contemplative adventure, out of which an individual may emerge with misgivings about the group's ideals. The family, the political party, the religious order, the military organization, the professional association all have overt methods of invading, to a greater or lesser extent, the privacy of members. In social groups and clubs, the methods are covert; they are based on the latent possibility of withheld good-fellowship and affection; in these groups, the individual is required to display conduct which affirms and reaffirms that what he does away from the group does not alter the ideals which have insured his standing.

There is ample evidence that man cannot do for very long away from groups; periodic relief from the burden of self-criticism seems to be vital; prolonged isolation from groups leads to various forms of madness. There is also evidence that prodigal affiliation with groups goes hand in hand with an impoverishment of moral stamina and a sense of alienation in the very midst of multitudes.

A group begins with three or more people. Two people cannot form a group. A group exists only when there is a chance for coalition.

## Guernica

An elder in a family of cities, some other members of which are London, Tokyo, Hamburg, Hiroshima. A small town of 7,000 inhabitants, largely Basque, Guernica is situated in a valley in northern Spain where the Pyrenees Mountains descend to the Bay of Biscay. Though not notably different in appearance from the numerous villages in the hilly countryside of the province of Vizcaya, Guernica does stand out in Spanish history. It is the site of Basque solidarity and integrity. It was to Guernica that the Spanish monarchs customarily dispatched their representatives, who swore to observe Basque rights and local liberties.

On April 26, 1937, at 4:30 P.M., the laborious church bells of Guernica announced an air raid. Ten minutes later, German Heinkels and Junkers, piloted by German aviators, began winging in at low altitudes, bombing the town and machine-gunning the streets. People from the town were followed up along the narrow roads by diving aircraft and were machine-gunned. Like clockwork, German aircraft arrived in waves every twenty minutes until 7:45 P.M. Methodically, the town was destroyed by blast and flames; 2,543 people were killed and wounded. "We bombed it and bombed it and bombed it, and *bueno* why not?"

The year before, on August 24, 1936, Germany had signed an agreement with England, France, Italy and Russia not to intervene in the Spanish Civil War. Accordingly, following the air raid on Guernica, Germany denied it—the Basques dynamited Guernica for publicity or German pilots had not been responsible, one or the other. Italy was concerned that British patience would be strained. Russia remained watchful of European relations. France was impassioned. England took immediate action; Anthony Eden told the House of Commons that the Government was considering immediately what could be done to prevent another Guernica. (*See* Dellwyn.)

## Guilt

O Rose, thou art sick!
The invisible worm,
That flies in the night,
In the howling storm,

Has found out thy bed
Of crimson joy;
And his dark secret love
Does thy life destroy.
—William Blake, "The Sick Rose"

One of the exclusively human experiences, hence a landmark of evolution. Guilt is an affect originating in the exploitation of anxiety by conscience, the pain of which is undone only by atonement, that is, by an equivalence of punishment. That reason fails to mitigate the pain of guilt lies in the fact that the ingredients of guilt, i.e., anxiety and conscience, are partially submerged beyond reason: anxiety is a reaction to an unknown menace; conscience tends to interpret anx-

iety arbitrarily as a signal of weakness toward a temp-
tation which it forbids. The forbidden may involve
thoughts as well as action, courage as well as stealth.
Hence guilt occurs throughout the range of human
existence, inciting also a range of atonements from
physical self-abuse, as in accident-proneness and suicide, to psychological self-abuse, as in depression and
obsessive rituals.

Since guilt is painful and its avoidance desirable,
strategies are evolved to cope with it. Some of these
are personal, others social. The personal strategies attempt to ward off either anxiety or conscience or both
in order to starve the process of its essential elements.
Certain atonements of minimal pain, possessing even
some practical value, are volunteered to the conscience
in the absence of guilt—volunteered as a bribe beforehand against subsequent activity likely to be forbidden.

The social strategies attempt a transformation of the
irrational aspects of guilt into rational ones: the forbidden is impersonalized in an orderly public code of
law, religious, ethical, legal; personal conscience, which
is not only arbitrary but inconsistent, is externalized
as priest, moralist, judge, who will act impersonally
without bias or caprice; and anxiety is converted to
fear wherein the menace—in this instance, the punishment fitting the transgression—is known. Consistent
with the scope of human functioning which guilt invades, social codes, administration and punishment
apply to thoughts as well as actions, to courage as well
as stealth.

# H

### Hardening
The kind of passive defense of which the typical World War II air-raid shelter is an example. It involves putting a shield between the objects to be protected, whether human or inanimate, and the explosion. Hardening against the blast, burn and radiation effects of nuclear weapons is harder. A distinction may be made, consequently, between *soft* hardening and *hard* hardening.

### Hard Landing
The opposite of soft landing (*q.v.*). A man-made satellite or rocket which lands on a celestial surface with no attempt at braking submits to a hard landing. Lunik II, for instance, guided to land on the moon, did so. Its radio signal stopped suddenly as Lunik II made a very hard landing, reducing the probe to a mess of splintered parts. Some hard-landed flights, in spite of tremendous concussion, are able to deliver goods: Lunik II released a pride of small medallions bearing the insignia of the Soviet Union on the surface of the moon.

### Hardware
Originally, goods of metal, ironmongery. Currently a term covering rockets, guided missiles, the technology and parts; fuel is not included in the category *hardware;* nor is the term applicable to the ceramic or metallic parts of rocket motors, or to such *software* as crew, cargo or passengers.

### H. E.
Abbreviation for High Explosive; nonnuclear explo-

sives. Usu. obs. (*see* Kiloton) except for poss. use in
Lim. Wr. (*q.v.*).

## Heart of Darkness

That place, unassigned locality, in Counterforce to
which experts (*q.v.*) have opposed the following additive, literalist progressions: Minimum Deterrence;
Finite Deterrence, or Insurance for Reliability; Counterforce as Insurance, or Insurance Against Unreliability; Preattack Mobilization Base, or Insurance Against
a Change in Policy; Credible First-Strike Capability
(*qq.v.*)

## Hospitalism

A clinical picture shown by infants who have been
separated from their mothers. So named because it is
frequently observed in hospitals and other institu-
tional nurseries. At first weepy, these infants soon
grow expressionless, dazed, faraway; they become pal-
lid, thin, febrile, insomniac, and tend to lose their
sucking habits. Thereafter, the only response which
can be elicited from them—and this only upon considerable provocation—is a scream. This condition
is reversible if the mother, or some adequate substitute
parent, is restored to the child within three months.
If not, the child reaches a point of no return and
wastes away into death. This fatal terminal condition is called marasmus, and once it is contracted, no
amount of human contact and warmth can cure it.

Since public tolerance of conspicuous neglect of infants is rapidly disappearing—as late as the seventeeth
century in Europe unwanted infants were tossed into
sewers and alleys as refuse, and in Dublin during the
latter part of the eighteenth century 99.6 per cent of
all hospitalized infants routinely died—the incidence
of hospitalism and especially of marasmus has dimin-
ished, making them difficult to study. However, opportunities for their study were again possible, being quite
adequately provided by the Second World War, which
created an abundance of infant war orphans and a
scarcity of nonmilitary personnel, a combination favorable for the development of these diseases.

## Hot-Spotter
A person who maintains one of two opposite positions as regards radiation hazard. (For his opponent, *see* Averager.)

Exposure to ionizing radiation (*q.v.*) and the biological incorporation of radioactive debris are known to occur nonuniformly throughout a population as well as within an individual. The high metabolic rate of children, compared to adults, especially as regards the skeletal system, favors a high rate of incorporation of radioactive debris, like strontium 90 (*q.v.*), indeed between 4 and 7 times higher. Moreover, different portions of the organism absorb comparatively different amounts of debris; some spots in the organism become "hotter" than others by as much as 60 times the whole-body average. In the population, local geographic differences, local dietary differences and local soil differences can create hot spots.

Hot-Spotters are those who focus attention on the points of highest, rather than average, radioactivity. It is their view that hot spots, rather than averages, should be emphasized when establishing standards for radiation protection, because hot spots, they contend, more than averages, are what produce biological destruction. Hence they invariably recommend stricter levels of protection against hazardous radiation. However, since bone cancer—to take one example that would test their position—requires 15 to 20 years to develop symptoms, it will not be before the 1980s that sufficient data will exist for determining the soundness of their current contentions.

## Hunger
An ache of a peculiar temporal pattern, for it is caused by certain slow rhythmic contractions of the stomach that appear in the absence of stomachic contents or at regular intervals by habit. Any substance introduced into the stomach to inhibit these contractions abolishes hunger. The alimentary experience of nausea, and the experience of the excretory processes, are simply internal perceptions, in terms of pressure or pain, of the states or processes to which they correspond. Hunger,

however, may exist in individuals who have ingested a sufficient amount of food to inhibit stomachic contractions. This order of hunger is often called malnutrition and results not from quantity but from kind of food introduced into the body system. This order of hunger exists in more than half the present population of the earth, approximately 1,500,000,000 people. The lack of any food results in a situation commonly known as famine. If the world population reaches the United Nation's minimum forecast figure of about 6,000,000,-000 people by the year 2000, more than 3,000,000,000 would then exist in a condition of famine or malnutrition. Among the main causes of the lag in food production are man's long abuses of natural resources, inefficiency of agricultural methods, and the occasional eruptions of wars during which territories were laid waste, livestock, forests, farm buildings, farm machinery and food-processing facilities were destroyed, some of the fishing grounds were closed and large numbers of fishing craft were converted to other purposes, and manpower for agricultural work was sharply reduced. *Kwashiorkor* in South Africa, *infantile pellagra* in Jamaica, *dystrophie des farineux* in France, *Mehlnahrschaden* in Germany, *m'buaki* in the Congo, *nutrition dystrophy* in India, *distrofia pluricarencial infantil* in Latin America all signify protein malnutrition in children.


## Hydrogen

One of the 92 natural elements. Abundant throughout the universe principally in the fiery material and incandescent atmosphere of stars, hydrogen, on Earth, conceals itself in combination with other elements to form numerous compound substances such as acids, protein, water, petroleum, bicarbonate of soda, etc. When separated from its compounds, it is a colorless, odorless, relatively calm, though combustible, gas. However, on Earth it is encountered in this form only rarely, issuing from volcanoes and lurking in the tiny pits of meteorites.

Hydrogen first appears in history in the sixteenth

century when the Swiss alchemist Theophrastus Bombastus von Hohenheim (alias Philippus Aureolus Paracelsus) gave a cryptic account of its preparation: an ignitable spirit bubbling out of the reaction of iron filings immersed in a dilute acid. However, it was some 200 years later, in the eighteenth century, that hydrogen was distinguished from other combustible gases. The English physicist Henry Cavendish prepared it, again, with metal and acid and went on to show that when it burned in air, it produced a vapor which, when condensed, could be recognized to be water. He showed that not all gases produce water upon burning; moreover, he demonstrated in this way the compound nature of water ($=$ air $+$ hydrogen) and thus dethroned water at long last from its position in the minds of scientists as an elemental form of matter. But Cavendish failed to distinguish air and hydrogen properly, deeming them merely variants of each other. It remained for his contemporary the French chemist Antoine Lavoisier to grasp the truth of hydrogen's elemental nature—indeed, Lavoisier named the gas (*hydrogen* $=$ water producer) —and to distinguish it from the element oxygen, which is the one gas in air that combines with hydrogen to form water. In this, Lavoisier went on to materialize modern chemistry out of its cloud of medieval nebulosity. (Since Lavoisier, in addition to being a chemist, was also a government tax collector, he was routinely hated by the French populace, who hauled him off to the guillotine in 1794—"The Republic has no need of savants!")

Now, the production of hydrogen by the reaction of an acid and a metal is expensive. But with the advent of electricity in the nineteenth century that followed upon the work of the Italian scientists Galvani and Volta, and with the revolution in industrial methods, hydrogen was transformed from an economically prohibitive laboratory curiosity to a commercially feasible product. For hydrogen can be generated cheaply and plentifully by passing an electric current through sea water; and also by passing steam over red-hot iron or coal. Commercially, it has a variety of uses: as a fuel, as a solidifier of liquid vegetable fats to produce oleomargarine, as a lifter of weather balloons and dirigibles, as a purifier of metals. It was also found that when hydrogen, burning with pure oxygen at full heat, was passed over a stick of lime, it produced a brilliant, dazzling glow that could be beamed in all the dingy music halls and theaters of the world. This was called the limelight.

Early in the twentieth century, hydrogen was combined directly with atmospheric nitrogen by the German chemist Haber to produce ammonia, which previously was eked out in small quantities from soft coal. Ammonia can be the chemical departure for a large series of products like fertilizers and explosives, and it was Haber's process that insured the capacity of the European Central Powers to wage war in 1914 by creating their independence from foreign sources of nitrogen compounds. (Haber was subsequently stripped of position and honors by the Hitler government for non-Aryan ancestry.)

But along with its commercial adventures, hydrogen was enjoying certain theoretical adventures within developments in the theory of atoms and elements. The Russian chemist Dmitri Ivanovich Mendeleev, for example, succeeded in locating hydrogen as Element No. 1 in an arrangement of elemental matter that proceeded from the most simple to the most complicated. In this scheme, hydrogen is the lightest and most simply constructed atom found in nature.

By 1932, these theoretical developments were sufficiently advanced to enable the American Nobel Prize-winning chemist Harold Urey and his associates to invade a still-deeper secret of the element hydrogen, the existence of its relatively rare variation called deuterium, a slightly heavier form of hydrogen occurring once in every 5,000 parts. Two years later, in 1934, a second variation was discovered, a still-heavier one, called tritium, occurring once in a billion parts. Since all three are really hydrogen, a new name was adopted to distinguish the lightest and most abundant variant. This is called protium.

Protium is what one means when one speaks of oleomargarine, bicarbonate of soda, balloons and the limelight. (For the uses of deuterium and tritium, *see* Fission-Fusion Bomb.)

**Hydrogen Bomb**   *See* Fission-Fusion Bomb; Fission-Fusion-Fission Bomb.

## Hypothetical Attack

The hearings on Biological and Environmental Effects of Nuclear War held by the Joint Committee on Atomic Energy of the United States Congress in June, 1959, received expert testimony of these effects based upon a hypothetical attack. The magnitude and quality of this attack upon the continental United States were specified by the Committee. It involved a striking force of 263 weapons reaching their destinations and furnishing a total of 1,446 megatons. The weapons came in five sizes: 1, 2, 3, 8, and 10 megatons. Seventy-one of the targets were concentrations of population and industry; they contained about 68 million of the country's population and received 567 megatons. The rest of the target areas—Air Force, AEC, Army, Navy and Marine Corps installations—received the difference, a total of 879 megatons.

The assessment of damage was computed by the Office of Civil Defense Mobilization, using a large high-speed electronic computer. All weapons were assumed to be ground bursts, causing fallout over considerable distances downwind from the detonations. Thus estimates of blast and thermal effects may have been substantially reduced by the lack of any air burst weapons. Nevertheless, the theoretical damage was sizable; the computations, based upon the 1950 census of 151,000,000, gave estimates of 19,651,000 killed the first day, 22,179,000 fatally injured and 17,191,000 injured nonfatally. The total of fatal injuries for this medium attack, extrapolated for the 1960 census, includes more than 50,000,000 people.

Six cities received two 10-megaton weapons each, the heaviest single assaults. Of those six, the estimate for the metropolitan area of New York City, for instance, included 3,464,000 killed the first day and 2,634,000 fatally injured; 2,278,000 were injured nonfatally. Boston lost 1,052,000 the first day, with 1,084,-000 fatally injured and 467,000 injured nonfatally. That would leave a population in the Boston area of 739,000, as compared with a living remnant of 6,806-000 for New York City.

Most of these facts have a great deal of judgment in them, sir.

—Dr. G. M. Dunning, Radiation Effects Specialist, AEC, testifying at the hearings in June, 1959

## Hypothetical Boy

An artificial person in the service of the United States Government, a resident of Washington, D.C., the consumer of about 55 pounds of food per quarter. Hypothetical Boy is 19 years old. He eats food purchased in conformity with the Department of Agriculture's moderate-income plan. Several cooks in suburban Bethesda receive a shipment every three months from food and drug scientists in Washington and cook it.

The Washington supermarkets supply one week's worth of food to the government shoppers—approximately 60 pounds. Although Hypothetical Boy eats only every thirteenth week, the sampling suffices for an analysis of the proportion of strontium 90 (q.v.) which it contains, both in what is cooked and in waste. When the seven-day meal is cooked, it is ground together with milk and water, and tested.

Scientists have found that the strongest concentration of strontium 90 is in bones. Other large amounts are found in vegetable and fruit skins, the source also of nutritionally beneficial elements.

Cooks in the clinic kitchens at the National Institute of Health place fruit skins, vegetable skins, bones and fat in the category of waste, unfit for Hypothetical Boy. Within this context, findings have been favorable with reference to the level of available strontium 90. Expected increases in nuclear tests will augment the proportion of strontium 90 in meals, and Bethesda cooks may have to make additions to the percentage of garbage in food purchased for Hypothetical Boy.

# I

### Identification
Here, an essential and elusive psychological process, especially vigorous in young children.

The nearest kind of behavior to which identification can be compared is imitation. But while identification does have something to do with imitation, its meaning is best conveyed by its difference from imitation: imitation is conscious; identification takes place almost entirely outside of one's awareness and control. Unlike imitation, which we are aware of doing when we do it and are in control of, identification is more like something which simply happens to us. It is as if when we imitate, we *behave* like another person, but when we identify, we *become* the other person, so that when we *then* go on to behave like the other person, our behavior feels to us like no one else's but our own. Consider the little boy who, before bedtime, steals about his room on tiptoe, in felt hat and bandanna, his toy pistol drawn. He is clearly *imitating* a cowboy, for when he is told to end the game and go to bed, he puts aside this costume and behavior and begins a series of actions he feels to be his own, e.g., dons his pajamas, brushes his teeth, washes, turns out his light. This latter behavior is based on identifications he has already made with his parents, and therefore it all feels to him like his very own behavior.

The advantages of identification are immense. By incorporating his parents and their way of life into the growing fabric of his own life, the child also takes in their commandments and supervision and makes these a part of himself. The authority that was once *external* is now *internal* (as a *conscience*), and the child has made a step toward independence from external authority. While much can go wrong with this—and often does—this much is always to the good: by beginning to become, so to speak, his own parent, the child begins to grow into a person in his own right.

Being as subtle and silent and as delicate and complicated as growth itself, this process is susceptible to innumerable injuries, many unwitting, most small, some tragic. Moreover, since identifications—especially those adopted early in life—are always more easily made than unmade, they yield more readily to affliction than to subsequent ameliorative processes.

## Identification with the Aggressor

In the usual course of growing out of infancy the child has unavoidable occasion to be impressed with the physical strength and absolute authority of his parents. His parents' comparative size is, of course, a constant reminder of their strength. Also, when they lift him up and carry him about, the child experiences their strength directly. As for authority, this, too, for a number of very significant years in the child's early life, is indisputably the parents' by virtue not only of who does the asking for, and who does the granting of, permission and favors but of who is clearly more knowledgeable about the ways of the world.

Two notions about all this begin to stir within the child. The parents' strength and authority protect him from a world he could not, on his own with his comparative weakness, survive in. But, also, he himself is in danger of becoming the target of that very power he needs so much to enlist and remain on the good side of. He could be injured and even annihilated by it were it turned against him.

Now, the sense of being dependent for survival on the very thing that is also dreaded is not an easy feeling to live with. It would be better for the child's peace of mind if he could somehow disqualify himself as a target. Naturally, he can be given assurances, which do help, but assurances go only so far in relieving his fears. Some *internal* change in the child is also required here.

One common and especially important way of meeting this situation goes by the name *identification* (*q.v.*). This is a process that is unconscious and that aims at altering one's conscience to accommodate the values of another person or group of people. When the process is employed in respect to an aggressor, it strives for the familiar logic: *If you can't beat them, join them, for they never turn on one of their own kind.* And since the validity of this is borne out—for, indeed, the more he acts according to the values of his parents, the less he *is* put upon—identification with an aggressor is filed, so to speak, along with other reactions of the child, ready to be employed in subsequent times of distress when he might find himself again exposed to danger, real or imagined, from a powerful and unmanageable aggressor from whom flight is not possible.

A grim example of this psychological defense came to light with the defeat of Germany in World War II and the liberation of the concentration camps. It was reported that prisoners, usually those who had lasted two or more years, would eventually take to wearing discarded Gestapo uniforms and would boast with satisfaction of how well they stood at attention during the twice-daily roll call of prisoners. Also, they would copy the leisure-time activities of their torturers, one game being who could stand to be hit longest without uttering a complaint. And often, a nonsensical rule, originating in the whim of one of the guards and soon forgotten, would be followed to its letter and with great pride by some of the veteran prisoners.

Thus, it would seem that oppression does not awaken the animal in us, as is usually supposed, but rather the frightened child.

**Illusion**   (*See also* Autokinetic Effect.)
An interpretation inconsistent with the actuality of a situation. If a straight glass rod is immersed in water, we have the illusion that the submerged part is bent from the water level. This is a visual illusion easily corrected by our tactile sense or by pulling the tube out of the water. However, not all illusions are as easily corrected; nor do we always want to correct those that are. The former include many of our social

beliefs; the latter include our certainties that there is infinite forgiveness of infinite error.

## Impulse

An act performed without due regard to the stimulus which releases it; the stimulus may be a mere approximation of that stimulus which customarily releases the act; or the stimulus may be one that is occurring alone at a moment when customarily it occurs as part of a series of stimuli. Thus an impulse is an act that is either inappropriate or meaningless, like a step of a ladder that, having been removed and isolated, has become merely a plank.

Impulsive behavior is observable in all animals. A sea gull standing on a beach may be seen to rattle its beak or ruffle its wing in a manner otherwise employed as part of a series of actions in nest building; it is as if one lock of a pattern of locks had been suddenly sprung by some stray key in the environment.

In a highly symbolizing creature like man, impulsivity is especially rampant. With his blurred instinctual sense and with his rich faculty for memory which urges a personal past on an otherwise blank present, man lives among numerous keys. Too many of them work. Meaning through behavior is exceedingly hard to come by. It is born of that fragile interaction between restraint and spontaneity, both involving plenty of regard for the stimulus (*see* Button).

## Instinct

A demand made upon the mind in consequence of the mind's connection with the body; hence that which resides between the mind and the body. In being neither mental nor physical, an instinct is best thought of as a pattern of behavior and is distinguished from other patterns of behavior, like reflexes and impulses, in involving the *entire* organism in a complex activity discharging a purpose. Instinct varies from species to species. Where mentality and physicality are less differentiated, as in lower species, instinct tends to be rigid and pronounced. But where mentality and physicality are more differentiated, as in higher species like apes, instinct begins to grow vague and diffuse.

In humans instinct is no less compelling than in other creatures, but it is most elusive and least adaptive, causing man to stride the earth with that awkward gait of one foot in and one foot out of nature.

**Insurance Against a Change in Policy** *See* Pre-attack Mobilization Base.

**Insurance for Reliability** *See* Finite Deterrence.

### Intelligence—I

The capacity to learn. Intelligence is a biological trait especially pronounced in organisms whose adaptation and survival emphasize neurological, rather than muscular-skeletal, functions. The presence of this trait is most remarkable in human beings. In fact, it is so remarkable that every human society addresses a comparatively large amount of activity to the cultivation of this trait. Such activity is called education; when cultivated, the trait becomes—and is then more properly called—intellect. Like any raw material, intelligence has no utility until it has been refined by society's ingenuity and labor.

A biological trait, intelligence conforms to all the laws governing such traits. Intelligence is subjected to heredity; high intelligence tends to be passed on by parents of high intelligence, low intelligence by parents of low intelligence, with all the susceptibility to mutation (*q.v.*) quite present. However, it is also in keeping with the principles of heredity that traits pull in the direction of the average. Thus it is observed that offspring of parents with low intelligence tend to be more intelligent than their parents, while offspring of parents with high intelligence tend to be less intelligent than their parents. As with any biological trait, the degree to which this particular trait exists can only be exploited. It cannot be altered.

### Intelligence—II

My God, this can't be true. This message must mean the Philippines!
      —Secretary of the Navy Knox, December 7, 1941

A category of news concerning foreign countries which is useful to personages of national power as a guide to action. This news may cover all phases of foreign capability and operation, with one lamentable exception: intention. Intelligence pursues, but can never quite extinguish, the unexpected.

Tradition recognizes three types of intelligence: *counterintelligence* denotes the efforts of one nation to thwart another nation's efforts to obtain intelligence; *strategic intelligence* refers to intelligence gathered in time of peace; *tactical intelligence* is intelligence gathered in time of war. Here tradition has grown moss; these last two distinctions have failed to obtain since the end of World War II.

In open societies like the United States, clandestine activities are offensive to the national self-image and much is made of the duplicity surrounding the gathering of intelligence. Espionage, however, accounts for less than 20 per cent of all intelligence; press, radio, documents, public reports, routine announcements, gossip, diplomatic relations, etc., are sources of over 80 per cent. Classic cloak-and-dagger activities have yielded to the more studious and methodical operations of the scholar.

Also in open societies there has been a tendency to use intelligence as a guide to *what* to do. However, intelligence may also be used as a guide to *how* to do what has been decided to be done in the first place. The invasion of Cuba under the auspices of the United States in 1961, albeit a fiasco, was an indication of the mid-century transition among live-and-let-live societies from one use of intelligence to another. (*See* First Column.)

American organizations which gather and provide intelligence include G-2, JANIS, ONI, ASJI, IAC, FBI, NSC, AEC, JIOA, the Washington *Post* and *The New York Times*. With the exception of the last two, these organizations have a relationship to the CIA, somewhat.

## Internment Psychosis

Sometimes, barbed-wire sickness. Imprecisely a psychosis. A mental condition found among refugees who are being cared for by a friendly country but who are at the same time restricted to special camps. Three phases are distinguished. There is an initial mood of overflowing gratitude. This gives way to an irritable and aggressive phase of behavior, which is soon followed by a mentality of indifference, passivity, moderate apathy and moderate depression. It is not unusual for this condition in one or another of its phases to persist even after release from internment and subsequent relocation.

Most susceptible to internment psychosis are those refugees who formerly lived entirely for their families and material possessions and were entirely rooted in their immediate physical surroundings.

## Intestinal Death

A radiation dose of 1,000 to 5,000 rad affects the gastrointestinal system. Severe nausea, vomiting, fever, weakness and diarrhea manifest themselves in the very early course of the pathology.

The dose range of 1,000 to 5,000 rad may cause permanent cessation of acid and pepsin secretion in the stomach. Ulcerations lead to infection and bacteremia; the injury upsets the balance between the host and the parasites. In addition body fluids are lost because the intestinal mucosa is impaired.

Effects in this dose range cannot be satisfactorily treated; the small intestine cannot recover from early damage. However, since the initial course of the disease cannot be differentiated from pathologies due to lower dosage (*see* Marrow Death), bone-marrow-cell injections may be therapeutically indicated. The true nature of the pathology will indicate itself by death within one to two weeks. (*See* Radiation Effects.)

## Intestine

From the skull to the pelvis, the body is made up of three cavities, the cranial (*see* Central Nervous System), the thoracic (*see* Lungs) and the abdominal. The abdominal cavity contains the stomach, the small and the large intestines. The small intestine occupies most of the central part of the cavity. Where it ends the large intestine begins, rising on the right side of the abdominal cavity, turning at right angles, crossing to the left, and descending. The large intestine encloses the small intestine on three sides and empties into the rectum at the base of the abdominal cavity. From the stomach down to the rectum, the tract is not attached except for the mesentery, a thin membrane which partly fixes it to the back wall of the cavity. The organs in the cavity, including the liver, kidneys, bladder, pancreas and the small and large intestines, are covered by a membrane, the peritoneum, which lines the walls of the cavity.

The greatest proportion of digestion takes place in the small intestine. The liver, pancreas and intestinal mucosa produce secretions which effect the breakup of food into substances which can be absorbed into the blood. These secretions in the case of the liver and pancreas flow into the first part of the small intestine, the duodenum.

The contents of the stomach gradually enter the duodenum through the pyloric sphincter. In the small intestine they are moved through by peristaltic waves; most of these waves move slowly and for a short distance throughout the 20-foot length of the small intestine.

Another kind of movement also occurs, rhythmical segmentation. Portions of the circular muscle of the intestinal wall contract regularly while others relax. As a result, food and digestive juices are thoroughly mixed. This segmentation also allows contact between material in the intestine and the mucosa, permitting the absorption of digested substances. Most bodily absorption of the end products of digestion—vitamins, salts, water, sugars, amino acids, fatty acids, glycerol— takes place in the small intestine, where the mucosa contains fingerlike extrusions, villi, which expose a large surface for absorptive operations. The villi move from side to side as well as up and down, movements effected by smooth muscles in their walls.

The muscles of the villi are not under centralized nervous control; neither are those which are responsible for the segmentation. The complex operations of intestinal digestion, charged with nourishing the body through osmosis and absorption, usually respond to specific nervous impulses which control their activity. Only in biological forms simpler than the sponge do muscle cells commonly contract in response to direct stimuli. This nervous independence is also present in the intestine, an atavistic reminder of simpler origins. (*See* Central Nervous System; *see also* Intestinal Death.)

**Intrawar Deterrence**   *See* Limited War.

**Iodine 131**

A radioisotope (*q.v.*) produced abundantly in fission reactions. Radioiodine was relatively ignored in the first decade of the Atomic Age because its radioactivity is short-lived. Iodine 131 has a half-life of eight days. (*See* Effective Half-Life.) By the time it falls out on dairy farms and gets into milk, it has spent most of its radioactive toxicity. Between nuclear-bomb testings it is practically nonexistent. However, events seem to require that the question of short-lived radioactivity be reconsidered. It has become interesting to take into account how much radioactivity remains, as well as how much is dissipated, in a radioisotope like iodine 131. In 1957, with bomb testing by the United States in Nevada, the Soviet Union in the Arctic, England in the Pacific, iodine 131 inundated the world's milk supply, especially the supply of the American Middle West, in amounts far exceeding government safety norms. This inundation re-occurred in 1958 and again in 1961 and 1962. There is no reason why it should not occur after any series of tests of significant tonnage. Countermeasures exist; nonradioactive iodine competes favorably with radioiodine in the body and can be introduced into the diet during hazardous periods; powdered and evaporated milk may be substituted for milk temporarily poisoned by radioiodine. These countermeasures have been indicated on at least three occasions in the United States. However, it will take some further time to determine which government agency is supposed to initiate and carry out the countermeasures. Government specialists have said that this will be ironed out by 1966.

In the meantime, iodine 131 is beginning to show itself in nuclear-reactor activity. A gas, something like industrial smoke, it leaks into the atmosphere during the removal of wastes from reactor fuels. Here it is called a "creeper." (*See* Nuclear Reactor; Krypton 85.)

Ingested principally with milk, radioiodine seeks the thyroid gland and accumulates there. The thyroid of children, which is small and very active, is especially vulnerable. The thyroid of fetuses is so small and so active that medical practice forbids the use of radioiodine in any amount during pregnancy. In pregnancy, the thyroid gland accumulates radioactive iodine in greater amounts than it ordinarily does, but in the pregnant state there are no symptoms of toxicity. (Medically, it is otherwise used in small and controlled amounts in the diagnosis and therapy of cancer of the thyroid.) Radioiodine emits beta and gamma radiation. It is known that chaotic exposure to radioiodine sooner or later leads to cancer of the thyroid (*q.v.*) in certain people. It is not known in which people until the disease appears.

## Ionization

The process by which one or several electron particles are stripped from the outer region of an atom or imparted to it, leaving the atom, one way or the other, electrically unbalanced (charged). An atom so charged is called an *ion,* after the Greek for *wanderer;* for an ion will drift excitedly through its environment in pursuit of an opportunity to discharge itself by acquiring stray electrons or unloading its excessive ones. Large-scale ionization in the atmosphere affects weather conditions, and farther out in the atmosphere ionization contributes to borealic and electrical manifestations. In living matter on Earth, ionized fluids are basic to the restless ebb and flow of vital functions.

## Ionizing Radiation

The numerous types of radiation may be grouped into two categories: ionizing and nonionizing. Examples of the latter are light waves and radio waves. The former category consists of alpha, beta and gamma rays, X rays and cosmic rays (*qq.v.*), and with the exception of cosmic rays, which occur only naturally, all ionizing radiation is both natural and man-made. The decomposition of natural radioactive deposits creates a steady leak of ionizing radiation all over Earth, while cosmic rays drizzle toward Earth continually. This omnipresent natural activity comprises what is called "background radiation." On the other hand, brisk local showers of ionizing radiation are man-made, as emanations from X-ray machines and nuclear reactors. Nuclear-bomb explosions unleash a veritable storm of this type of radiation.

All types of radiation affect matter. Ionizing radiation affects matter by reason of ionization. Like tiny bullets, this radiation penetrates matter, leaving a track of disruption in the atomic structure. These tracks vary from scattered to thick, and though they "heal," some amount of "scarring" remains. In living cells, this disruption may involve the liquid content of the cell—water, for example, becomes ionized and may re-form as corrosive peroxide, which poisons the cell; the disruption may involve the cell's reproductive apparatus—the chromosome material—killing the cell's reproductive ability altogether, or crippling its progeny for generations. Natural ionizing radiation is deemed a strong factor in the aging process of living creatures, whose cells are continual targets, slowly and ultimately worn out by an incessant barrage of penetrating background radiation. Sudden bursts of ionizing radiation disrupt so much of the atomic structure of exposed cells and loosen so many chemical bonds that flesh literally sloughs off, intestines fall apart, organs lose shape. And between these severe culminations and the uneventful aging process, ionizing radiation promotes many intermediate possibilities, e.g., leukemia, cancer, miscarriages, birth defects, eye cataracts.

Though damage from ionizing radiation is consistent with the level of dose, no level can be dismissed as harmless to human biology.

## Isolation

In keeping apart that which actually belongs together, e.g., an idea and its emotional connotation, a danger and its fear, the individual is spared from taking responsibility for what he actually feels. He need not recognize the source of his feelings and thus need not —in fact, cannot—do anything about them.

Isolation is frequently seen in individuals who are passionate about cold intellect and intellectual about powerful emotions. This results in sophomoric ideation and emotional shallowness. Isolation of the sensual and tender components of the erotic drives is also common. As a consequence the isolating individual finds himself in the painful predicament of having no desire for the person he loves and no love for the person he desires.

The normal derivative of isolation is logical thinking, where the continued elimination of emotional associations is carried out in the interests of objectivity. The mockery which isolating individuals make of normal logical thinking is revealed by a number of characteristics. There is the frequent gambit of pursuing logic to the absurd. Pedantry is common. A confusion between coldness and objectivity can be caught in the glee with which the gruesome is treated dispassionately.

# J

## Joe I

The first Soviet atomic detonation, in August, 1949. So named by American scientists for Joseph Stalin. It was Joe I that broke the remaining resistance among American scientists toward developing a thermonuclear bomb. (*See* Fission-Fusion Bomb.)

Joe I was discovered during a routine radiation detection flight over the Pacific by an American B-29 in late August, 1949, when photographic plates picked up anomalous streaks of atmospheric radioactivity. Since Joe I was not to have occurred before 1956 or 1960, if indeed it ever was to occur, Joe I was first thought to be the explosion of a clumsy atomic laboratory within the Soviet Union.

## Judas Hole

A peephole, as in a door or wall. Also, currently, for watching the gassing of naked prisoners, a small glass window in a shower room which has been converted from water to lethal gas.

## Jupiter

Of those planets orbiting around the sun, the largest, its volume 1,312 times that of Earth; Jupiter is the fifth planet from the sun, 484,000,000 miles distant. Not the coldest, it is nevertheless very cold; Jupiter's heavy, small solid center forms the core of a sheath of ice 10,000 miles thick. For 25,000 miles in all directions around the sheath, an atmosphere of hydrogen, helium, ammonia and methane encloses the planet. A temperature of —200° F. on Jupiter's surface keeps the atmosphere in a state of slush, reflecting the sunlight with an incandescence brighter to a beholder on Earth than that of any neighboring star.

The Great Red Spot in the cold twilight 484,000,000 miles away from the sun has been seen by astronomers since 1878. Almost no other features have been observed. Jupiter rotates very fast. Its day is less than 10 hours long. Whereas a point on Earth's equator moves at the rate of 1,000 miles an hour, an equivalent point on Jupiter's will move 22,000 miles an hour.

Jupiter's mass more than doubles the total mass of all the other planets. The resulting large gravitational field may be the cause of a celestial anomaly: of Jupiter's 12 moons, 4 travel from east to west, contrary to the motions of the great majority of the satellites, and of all the planets in the solar system. Jupiter may have captured four of the asteroids that traveled about the sun between Mars and Jupiter, and they may be running backward.

On or near Earth's surface, the only pressure comparable to the push of Jupiter's atmosphere exists in the depths of oceans; when the spaceship nears Jupiter, a landing on one of the satellites, rather than a dive into the planet's viscous mantle, may make its return to Earth possible.

## Just War

The kind of war permitted by St. Thomas Aquinas, fought for a just cause, and by permissible means.

The growing humanization in attitudes toward war, evident in theological disputations in the medieval period, reached a high degree of public concern in the era characterized by the origins of nationalism. The progressive decline in such activities as gladiatorial combat, branding and mutilation of petty criminals and festive public attendance at executions denotes a decrease in officially sanctioned acts of sadism and cruelty.

Nationalism may have ameliorated the more violent manifestations of war by subjecting it to discipline and various strictures to which many baronial landholders had not had to submit. The conduct of war in the twentieth century has become so devastating and threatening, not because of the absence of ameliorating rules—themselves the reflection of a growing humanity—but because the weapons of the military art have made it possible to inflict injuries and losses to an extent previously unknown.

The concept of Just War has appeared since Greek days. Among the Greeks, Just War was one against barbarians or one in which the Greeks succeeded, possibly a harbinger of analogous positions in the future. Among the early Romans, a war was Just when it was approved by the *collegium fetialium,* a corporation of special priests, *fetiales.*

The World Council of Churches, a modern corporation of divines, in 1958 sanctioned the ownership of high-potency nuclear weapons "for deterrence only and only in a discriminating way." The Council considers nuclear weapons, if used, an unjust means; if owned, but unused, a permissible means.

The anguishing paradox posed by the desire of the World Council to find in the modern period a proper application of the Just War concept has been resolved by other moral theologians in various ways.

Some medieval theologians considered the motives of war, as distinct from the causes, a vital criterion. In that line of speculation, Fr. John Courtney Murray considers that since nuclear war may be a necessity for the preservation of the Christian idea, if not of the Christian population, it must be made a possibility.

Later theologians unconditionally condemned the initiation of war. Pope Pius XII proclaimed that no nation could attempt to right a wrong by armed aggression. The atomic bombings of World War II were probably not aggressive activities since they occurred before the papal edict and incurred no condemnation. Also, the bombings of Hiroshima and Nagasaki shortened the war and saved the lives of many thousands of American soldiers, President Truman explained.

Thus a civilian life equals a soldier's life and nobody remains a noncombatant. This surprising turning in the history of Just Wars tends to reverse the effects of the Church's restraining influence, apparent after the Thirty Years' War, in 1650; greater compassion for the noncombatant population was evident and a great school of literature began in this period, some theological and some philosophical and legal, designed to improve and regularize the practice of war.

Some considerably subtle problems in moral theology, and some puzzles in the interpretations of the history of modern religious thought, impose themselves in the context of moral theology, as represented by St. Thomas, Pope Pius XII, Father Courtney, and Harry S. Truman. For instance, in the event of an accidental ICBM flight, in response to which defensive ICBMs take to space (*see* Button), some piercing concerns, beyond the problems raised by millions of deaths, cry out for definition and adjudication. Is such a defense, based upon necessary split-second reaction, aggression? Perhaps not. Since man is merely partipotent, the designation of such response as aggression would unreasonably punish him for not partaking in the omniscient Divine nature, for ignoring the true purposelessness of the incoming missile. Perhaps, however, an immediate armed reaction would itself arrogate to man the power of deciding in from 5 to 14 minutes whether he was involved in a Just War or not: such omnipotence might in its turn deserve theological imprecation.

Such imponderables, existing in a world of satellite warning systems and almost instantaneous armed reactions, cannot be underestimated. Until a reasonably clear-cut *and* universally accepted doctrine of Just War makes its appearance, the several powers most directly involved can act only on a gross and pragmatic level of operations.

Possibly the most significant contribution of war to organized societies lies in this desperate awareness by participants that even among the various possible Just War concepts, none may reach that mitigating absolutism which utterly frees one man to tear out another man's stomach.

# K

## Kahn, Herman

"Herman, you really shouldn't go around saying that people can fight and survive wars, because, after all, ten or twenty years from now you may be obsolete and it takes ten or twenty years to explain things to people, so let's start now." That is a judgment which I think (a) they have no right to make, (b) is wrong.     —Herman Kahn

It might literally be possible for human beings to blow the world into little pieces at some date within our expected lifetime, well within it, maybe. And it is clear that when that instant arrives, if you are going to fight a war at all, you have to fight it carefully, or maybe you cannot fight at all.     —Herman Kahn

He is one of the real experts. . . . If I could get Mr. Kahn not to talk as fast as he usually does, maybe we can follow him.     —Representative Holifield, Eighty-sixth Congress

He was born on February 15, 1922, in Bayonne, New Jersey. He took a bachelor's degree at U.C.L.A. in 1946 and a master's degree at Cal Tech in 1948, and stayed on in nearby Santa Monica, California, with RAND (*q.v.*), where he remained for twelve years coming into his own. He came into his own as a military strategist and operations analyst (*see* Operations Analysis), having exercised himself on the intellectual problems of the Pentagon (*q.v.*). As strategist and analyst, he has testified frequently, and possibly impressively, before numerous Congressional committees; he was consultant to the Gaither Committee, to the Scientific Advisory Board of the Air Force, to the Technical Advisory Board of the Atomic Energy Commission, to the Office of Civil Defense Mobilization; he was with the Center of International Study of Princeton University; he has given closed-circuit lectures before thousands to which Congressmen and generals have flown. His sundry routines were finally collected and set down in a ten-dollar book issued by Princeton University, *On Thermonuclear War* (1960). *OTW* rose rapidly to the rank of handbook in the military colony of the nation's capital. Its scope is broad: Estimated Genetic Consequences if World-Wide Doses Approached NAS 10r Limits; Radioactive Environment 100 Years Later; Estimated Production Capacity Surviving Destruction of 53 Standard Metropolitan Areas; Late Attack Against SAC and 150 Urban Areas; Flexible War Plans for a Defender; The Eight World Wars; A Possible 1975 Military Posture for U.S. or S.U.; Missiles Required to Attack a 1,000-Point Target System; Recuperation with Investment-oriented Policy. His subsequent book *Thinking About the Unthinkable* is similar in scope but is directed to the general reader. Unlike *OTW*, *TATU* was well received by a large portion of the liberal press. Does this alarm him? He is an indefatigable realist.

Since July, 1961, having left RAND, he has gone into business on his own. He heads the Hudson Institute near White Plains, New York, another of the new corporations, which, like RAND, researches problems for the American taxpayer. He is devoted to his product; he is doing well in New York. Even in his speech at the Centennial Celebration of M.I.T. in 1961, he talked shop:

> I can build a device—I think I know how to do it today, I doubt that it would take me ten years to do and I doubt that it would cost me 10 billion dollars—and this device which I could bury, say, 2,000 feet underground and, if detonated, it would destroy everybody in the world—at least all unprotected life. It can be done, I believe. In fact, I know it can be done.

Married, father of two children, gourmet, *bon vivant*, scientist to social scientists, social scientist to scientists, sincere patriot unrelenting over the clumsy posture of national security, he also has clearance.

**Kahn Energy**   (pl. *Kahn:* e.g., two *Kahn;* after a well-known expert, *q.v.*)

The quantity of fission energy required for the radio-active liquidation of the entire population of one major country with no shelters. The Kahn for the United States of America or the Union of Soviet Socialist Republics amounts to approximately $10^4$ megatons, or 10,000,000,000 tons; 300 Kahn equal one Beach (*see* Stockpile Energy; Beach Energy).

**Kennedy, John Fitzgerald** (1917–    )
Thirty-fifth President of the United States. From his father, Joseph, sometime Ambassador to Great Britain, he received early a confidence and a social place which made him no stranger to power; nor was he subject to the intemperate realities of hunger and need, which do not so much prepare a man for sacrifice as they often embitter him and reduce the scope of his ambitions for service to the state.

Of Kennedy, some would have it that he is essentially a technocrat. About such men, Chen Tzu-ang has written that they "are proud of their cunning and skill," but

They do not know what happens to the body.
Why do they not learn from the Master of Dark Truth,
Who saw the whole world in a little jade bottle?

Others, who stress the traditional difficulties impinging on a President, say differently. It is not wise to forget the pressures of old-line bureaucracy, the imponderables of relationships with legislative Houses, the old national split between isolationism and activity in foreign affairs. How many horses can a leader ride?

It is proverbial, and not for that reason any the less true, that power is not granted to the mild; Kennedy's success in attaining to the Presidency is a measure of his self-confidence and his forceful attention to relevant details, however slight, a trait for which he has been compared to Napoleon, who was rumored to know the names of 15,000 of his soldiers.

In the subways of water
the president
talks with his mice:

the trains are covered
with nets,
the mice never speak

writes Rothenberg. However well this noncommuni-
cating subterranean hierarchy may be said to characterize leaders in other, more absolutist states, it is not
applicable to Kennedy. His training in the Lower and
Upper Houses did no disservice in his perceiving and
appreciating the importance of appropriate concilia-
tion and tight organization. Though some do not re-
joice in his withdrawal from early denunciation of a
peer in the Upper House, one McCarthy, history in
retrospect grants such denunciation might have been
impolitic.

In 1957, he published *Profiles in Courage,* a study
of principled action under stress, which earned him a
high literary award in his native country.

At about this time, Kennedy undertook the formation of the planning and strategy group which would
make possible his eventual elevation to the Presidency.
Various members of his family were pleased to submit
themselves to the rigors of cross-country journeys, pub-
lic-opinion samplings and unrelenting organization in
the pursuit of his candidacy. He was 39 years old,
facing the difficult task of defeating the putative successor to an aged general much beloved by his countrymen and the recipient of many popular favors. The
nation was not in economic crisis; only in the pervasive communal forebodings of a doomed future was it
like the

. . . poor land of Tirol o poor cardboard horses
stamping and rearing in the dirty straw o poor
land of cabbage leaves under foot and mountains looking
    down
and no one left to walk suddenly into your houses o poor
clerks and poor bishop who have lost in your dossiers and
    bulls
all those poor people who came to doze in God's darkness

as Kelly writes.

In consideration of Kennedy's efforts in setting up
the Alliance for Progress to further interhemispheric

solidarity, his attempt to encourage democracy in Cuba, his wit and command of a wide range of information, and his fruitful avoidance of metaphysics in favor of "sophisticated and technical judgment," history will allow that he was, of modern leaders, not the least.

He has been no foreigner to the anguish bred by the making of decisions. In the face of a choice between the cancellation of nuclear testing and the corruption of the air, he showed again his habitual concern for some expert opinion, his retention of that empathy which first earned him high office, and the finality of his regrets. Nor had he lost the sentiment of solidarity with the apothegms of the system through which he had been so suitably elevated:

However remote and infinitesimal those [radiation] hazards are judged to be, I still exceedingly regret the necessity of balancing these hazards against the hazards to hundreds of millions of lives which would be created by any decline in our nuclear strength.

**KEV**  *See* Electron Volt.

**Khrushchev, Nikita Sergeyevich**  (1894–    )
Soviet political leader and chief business executive of the U.S.S.R., first secretary of the Communist party after Stalin's death in 1953 and Chairman of the Council of Ministers in 1958, the first Russian head of state since Stalin to control both the party and the state. Khrushchev said at the time of the 1936 Stalinist liquidations:

By lifting their hand against Comrade Stalin, they lifted it against the best that humanity possesses. For Stalin is our hope. He is the beacon which guides all progressive humanity. Stalin is our banner! Stalin is our will! Stalin is our victory!

Coincidentally with his arrival to power 20 years later, a series of important discoveries disclosed how ill-founded his old loyalties had really been. It became clear that by the gross misuse of his power, Stalin had managed to delude his closest colleagues and betray the Revolution; as soon as the relevant issues had been clarified, Khrushchev publicly denounced the *cult of personality* and called for a return to collectivism. The Chairman led the Soviet Union in a trend toward greater availability of consumer goods and increased trade through *peaceful coexistence* with the West, a position meeting with little sympathy from Mao Tsetung (*q.v.*). This emergence of a kind of "state capitalism," and of a new technical and managerial class, discloses curious analogies with the economies of some other very large states. The Chairman also had Stalin's embalmed body removed from the mausoleum in Red Square, where Lenin now lies alone.

During the period of his delusion, Khrushchev lent himself to various activities, signaled initially by Communist party membership in 1918; in 1938 Stalin sent him to the Ukraine to eradicate nationalist tendencies in that Soviet Republic, and during World War II he returned to the Ukraine as a lieutenant-general to coordinate its guerilla movement for some measure of protection against the invading Nazi ravagers.

In 1956, Chairman Khrushchev quelled a bourgeois uprising in the infant People's Democratic Republic of Hungary, in which roughly 15,000 people lost their lives, a figure totaling much less than 1/5 of 1 per cent of the Hungarian population; subsequently the imperative of staying abreast of the United States war machine forced the Chairman to resume unilaterally deterrent nuclear tests.

**Kiloton**  (archaic)
The explosive equivalent of 1,000 tons of TNT; once conveniently used to describe the yield of an atom bomb, now a nominal figure. (*See* Megaton; August 6, 1945; August 9, 1945.)

**Kiva**
A sacred ceremonial chamber of the Pueblo Indians, approached with greatest awe. Also, the remote-controlled laboratory where critical-mass experiments were conducted for the first fission-fusion bomb (*q.v.*).

This later kiva was observed by television a quarter of a mile away. (*See* Great God K.)

## Krakatoa

An island in the Pacific Ocean; the scene, on August 27, 1883, of the greatest known natural blast in the modern history of Earth, a volcanic eruption which increased the dust in the atmosphere sufficiently to cause a 10 per cent decrease in the intensity of solar heating as far away as France for a period of three years.

Calculations have predicted that one eruption per year like the Krakatoa eruption would bring back the ice age. In 1955, it was believed that it would take 100 nuclear explosions to approximate the dust pall of one Krakatoa. The Krakatoa eruption, however, may have been less fertile in long-range effects on the atmosphere than the 58-megaton nuclear explosion set off as a test by the Soviet Union on October 30, 1961.

REPRESENTATIVE COLE: How many Krakatoas did you say would bring about the ice age?

DR. VON NEUMANN: Usually it is believed about one a year.

REPRESENTATIVE COLE: One a year?

DR. VON NEUMANN: Yes; it would take a little while.

REPRESENTATIVE COLE: If the time ever should come that there would be nuclear or thermonuclear explosions to the point of a hundred a year, then in time we could anticipate the ice age?

DR. VON NEUMANN: We would notice real climatic changes after 10 or 20 years of that. But, of course there are other effects you would notice a great deal, long before that time.

CHAIRMAN ANDERSON: At least it has not done it as yet.

—From a Congressional hearing, April 15, 1955

## Krypton 85

A radioisotope (*q.v.*) of element 36. When 10 per cent of the uranium atoms in a nuclear reactor (*q.v.*) have fissioned, the by-products are sufficient to poison the remaining uranium. The uranium must then be removed from the reactor and decontaminated so that it can be used again. This is an extensive chemical process, during which krypton 85 turns up among the radioactive wastes. The collection and disposal of these wastes is not an easy task. Radiokrypton is a gas. Gas trapping is a harder task. That krypton is one of the half-dozen chemically inert gases on Earth and therefore cannot be manipulated by chemical reactions compounds the problem of disposing of it. In fact, the problem is maddening. Currently radiokrypton simply creeps away from reactor activity into the environment. Radiokrypton has a half-life of about 10 years. (*See* Effective Half-Life.) As it spreads, it hugs Earth's surface. (*See* Ionizing Radiation.)

**Ktenology**
The science of killing.

# L

**LASER** *See* X.

**Latent Period**
The time between exposure to ionizing radiation and the actual appearance of resulting bodily damage; leukemia (*q.v.*), eye cataract or other malignancies may not appear for several years; in milder conditions such as leukopenia (white blood cell deficiency), anemia (*q.v.*) or intestinal damage, the latent period may last from one to several days; the patient in either case will have a sense of well-being during the latent period and will, therefore, be able to function quite normally. Just as exposure cannot be verified by subjective means, neither can the distinction between the latent period and a period of normal good health; nor can the distinction be made by medical examination.

**L. D. 50**
Abbreviation for "lethal dose, 50 per cent"—itself a convenient statistical guide, which, when used in radiation studies, refers to the radiation dose which will cause death in 50 per cent of an exposed population within a specified time interval (usually 30–60 days).

Although the L. D. 50 for human beings varies, depending on the scientist consulted, from 300 to 650 roentgens, there is general but still not complete agreement that the range from "inconsequential effects" to death can be covered by the dose range 200–1,000 roentgens. Also, it has been suggested by one expert (*q.v.*) that such points as L. D. 10, L. D. 20, or L. D. 70 "are actually more interesting than the L. D. 50 specifically."

# Lechery

Yet he of Ladies oft was loued deare,
When fairer faces were bid standen by:
O who does know the bent of womens fantasy?
                                            —Edmund Spenser

One of the deadly sins (*q.v.*). In his fanatic preoccupation with sensual fulfillment, the lecher bruises himself against two pillars of civilization: (1) the emotional development of the child, proceeding through the parents' renunciation of sensual claims on the child; (2) the parents' example, constituting an adequate symbol to the larger adult community. In Lechery, whatever the chronological ages of the participants, their emotional ages and dispositions are such that a child is being violated by an old man behind a parent's back.

Of the seven sinners the lecher is most often cast as comic. A clown reminds us of not only the occasional folly, but also the presence, of our deepest wishes.

# Leukemia

That disease, invariably fatal, in which the number of leukocytes—white blood cells—multiplies to the greatest degree known in pathological blood conditions. In the course of the disease, anemia occurs, the spleen and lymphatic glands enlarge, and leukocytes proliferate in the liver, the kidney and other organs.

Where the total body is irradiated, leukemia is the most probable end result among the various types of malignancies. The actual dose required for the production of this blood cancer is not known; no reliable threshold has been advanced. Leukemia may be induced in animals by exposure either to large doses or to small doses stretched out over periods of years.

Study of leukemia cases in Japan, in six persons who had been about a mile away from ground zero in August, 1945 (*see* Enola Gay; Great Artiste), indicates that there is probably no threshold. They were subjected to radiation of no more than 100 r, possibly as little as 14 r. Another study has found a correlation between X rays of the pelvis in late pregnancy and the chance of the child's contracting leukemia: the conventional inspection dose does not go beyond 5 r. (*See also* Radiation Effects.)

## Lie

A false statement made with intent to deceive. Lies differ according to the psychology of the liar; some lies are more serious than others.

Among the most morbid are those lies put forth by some psychotics to fill the gaps of embarrassing amnesias. For example, in the Korsakoff psychosis (after Syergey Syergeyvich Korsakoff, Russian neurologist, 1854–1900) there is a defect in the recording and retention of current events. The defect is masked by elaborate lies borrowed from fantasy or reality. Such lies are called *confabulations* and are characterized by the easy suggestibility of the confabulator, who can be led on by interested questioning to make almost any statement no matter how contradictory. Also characteristic of confabulations is the steadfastness with which the confabulator sticks by his narratives. Alcohol is the most common cause of the Korsakoff psychosis. It may also be caused by lead, mercury or arsenic poisoning, a variety of infections, or any of the encephalopathies. Confabulation also occurs with brain injuries and senility.

*Pseudologia phantastica* is characterized by fantasy constructions that enlist some amount of actuality. This type of lying differs from confabulation in that the lie is dropped if challenged. Pseudologues look for approval and aggrandizement and are found abundantly in the "glamour industries" like show business. Severe pseudologia has its infantile roots and may be a revenge for having been deceived in childhood. Thus it ridicules what the pseudologue regards as grown-up society: "Since you lie to me in your way, I shall lie to you in mine." Pseudologia may also aim at something more desperate: "If it is possible to make people believe that unreal things are real, then those real things which menace me are possibly unreal."

*Psychopathic lying* (*see* Psychopath) is consciously opportunistic and is found among criminals and confidence men. Being well controlled and quite clear as regards intent, psychopathic lying is considered minimally morbid. Its morbidity resides in the lack of judgment of the psychopath, who will often lie when the truth will do just as well, and who thereby leaves himself open to the unnecessary risk of exposure. Here lying has the relatively benign quality of a habit, which is a self-sustaining form of behavior divorced from the motivation that originally set it in motion.

Individuals fanatically devoted to truth, like some social reformers and political and scientific theorists—individuals given to system-building—frequently falsify facts out of a sense of altruistic grandiosity: "I am the shepherd, you are the sheep. You are not as qualified as I to see the ultimate truth. You must see things as I see them and submit to my system." Such falsification typically involves subordinate but persuasive details. Challenging this type of liar provokes hostility and derision.

Premeditated, studied and principled lies, like those of the statesman in the interest of his country, are normal lies. Here we speak of fibs, white lies, prevarications, equivocations.

**Life Instinct**  *See* Eros.

**Limited War**
That war which may erupt into total war; or, that war which, since total war has now become impossible, remains the only type of combat presently possible. Greater stability in the military balance of terror has given rise to more sober considerations of the concept of Limited War.

A Limited War introduces Intrawar Deterrence by threatening Controlled Reprisal, attacks not aimed at utter destruction of the enemy but at the paralyzing of his will to a point of forced compromise or surrender. It also implements such Deterrence by reminding the enemy of the process of Escalation: the spread or intensification of a Limited Situation outside the active designs of the participants.

**Loss Sharing**
A plan to relieve American insurance companies of the need to pay off on their policies; a move by the

Federal government announced at the end of 1961 in an attempt to look beyond massive nuclear attack. Insurance policies which do not specifically exclude liability in nuclear war would face bankruptcy immediately if they tried to pay all claims. Through Loss Sharing the government would guarantee to pay, eventually, a percentage of the insured losses of individuals and corporations. The government has decided that individual Americans who survive in undamaged areas must take a back seat to keeping alive the national economy. Without the continued existence of insurance companies, a vital component of the American organization would no longer contribute to a high standard of living. The recovery and health of the nation is preliminary to individual redress. Roland Robinson, adviser to the governing board of the Federal Reserve System, said that since we would "all be in this kettle of fish together," the country's ultimate welfare would be better served if "the power of the government were used purely and coolly to restore economic solvency and if we did not try to indemnify for losses of health and ability to earn a living." (*See* Materialism.)

**Lucky Dragon** (*Fukurya Maru*). Also, Fortunate Dragon.
On March 1, 1954, several Japanese fishermen on the deck of the *Lucky Dragon,* a fishing trawler, saw a reddish-white flash on the horizon. Some minutes later, they heard a loud explosion from the site of what they later found out was the first fission-fusion-fission explosion.

Although the *Lucky Dragon* was 40 miles outside the danger zone, the wind direction from Bikini had shifted in an unexpected manner, and the fishermen lay in the path of radioactive fallout. (*See* Atomic Accident, Bikini.)

Three hours after the blast, the fishermen began to see and hear the faintly audible, white, radioactive dust falling upon their ship. For five hours the rain of the white dust fell.

The boat, the men, the fish were covered by the dust.

The men's footprints left their marks in the dust on deck. They decided to go back home. The trip took 13 days.

They were good seamen, and washed down their ship. It was well that they did: the whole crew had been exposed to anywhere from 200 to 500 r, the latter figure a dose fatal to half of those exposed to it.

On March 14, suffering from abdominal pains, nausea, blisters, fever, conjunctivitis, they arrived at Yaizu.

Within several days all 23 fishermen were in hospitals and Japanese scientists had boarded the *Lucky Dragon,* where they found some of the white ash. Laboratory tests disclosed the presence of radioactivity in the unbought tuna; it was ordered confiscated. About 100 customers had previously bought some of the *Lucky Dragon's* catch. But since the fish had been dead at the time of the explosion, only the skins were affected, and the skins were removed before eating.

Aikichi Kuboyama died on September 23.

The Japanese Foreign Minister paid his respects; the United States gave Mrs. Kuboyama $5,600, and the Japanese nation $2,000,000 in reparations for the injury sustained by the Japanese fishing industry and the fishermen on the tuna trawler.

## Luna Car

A moon rover locomotored in bug-legged fashion and bearing gifts for the man in space, the lunar-logistics carrier precedes man to the moon and awaits his arrival. Man parks his vehicle in a lunar orbit and descends to the moon's surface by space ferry too small for food, water, oxygen, instruments. Luna Car, radio-controlled, crawls toward the earthlings—unless it is jammed against some obstacle such as a protuberance on the moon's terrain. In this event, a radio beam locates its whereabouts, and the visitors go toward it. Either way, the meeting is significant; not only are the visitors in contact with vital supplies; they are also comforted by the knowledge that their excursion, at least to this point, is go. If the capsule that landed them is unable to return them to their orbiting vehicle, Luna Car will sustain them until they are rescued.

The lunar-logistics carrier replaces previous plans to put a mechanical robot on the moon before sending up human astronauts. This robot, called a Prospector, would have probed the lunar situation with more care than the television satellites and impactors now being hustled up in advance of man. The robot is a step that must now be bypassed. Time is essential.

## Lungs

Two saclike organs forming the respiratory organ in the higher creatures. Inhaled air travels from the nasal cavity to the lungs through the trachea, which divides into two bronchi; one goes into each lung. The bronchi are structurally similar to the trachea, but smaller in diameter. They ramify into 25,000,000 delicate bronchial branches, about $\frac{1}{2}$ mm. in diameter each. Each branch then rays out into from 12 to 20 terminal branches, every one ending in an air-sac. In the finest bronchioles the walls become very thin and cartilage disappears.

A layer of columnar epithelium—surface tissue composed of closely packed cells—lines the inner walls of the bronchial tubes. Many of these cells form glands active in the secretion of mucus, which lubricates the breathing passageways and contributes to a continued moistness in the environment of the surface cells. The columnar cells also give rise to fine, hairlike processes, cilia, which move continually back toward the trachea; they forbid the passage of particles like dust into the lungs. (*See* Radiation Effects.)

Each air-sac has a number of little chambers, lined with a single layer of epithelial cells. The lung contains hundreds of millions of capillaries which lie immediately adjacent to the chambers. The respiratory gases diffuse through the thin walls of the chamber and the capillary to yield oxygen to the blood; in an exchange process taking about one second, the red blood cells from the capillaries give up their carbon dioxide, for expiration.

At the instant of birth, the lungs, in a deflated condition, contain no air; from the time of their first expansion they are never again completely deflated.

The space between the lungs and the chest wall, the intrathoracic cavity, is almost completely occupied by the lungs and contains nothing but a thin film of fluid. With an increase of fluid or in the quantity of air in the intrathoracic cavity, breathing slows or stops: intrathoracic pressure rises and the lungs deflate. (*See* Blast Effects.)

## Lunik

The first Russian moon rocket. Lunik took about two days to travel the 240,000-mile distance to the moon. However, since it passed the moon at a distance of about 5,000 miles, it was not near enough to submit to lunar gravity and go into orbit. From that point in Lunik's adventure toward an orbit around the sun, the Soviet Union changed the satellite's name to Mechta, *dream.*

## Lunik II   *See* Hard Landing.

## Lunik III

A Soviet satellite which in October, 1959, passed behind the moon and then returned toward Earth. It took the first photographs of the dark side, and radioed the pictures back to Earth. The dark side looks very much like the other side.

# M

## Macmillan, Harold

Mr. Macmillan, when he first became a Member of Parliament for Stockton-on-Tees in 1924, was one of 17 members of his family then serving in the House. In 1920 he had married Lady Dorothy Evelyn Cavendish, daughter of the ninth Duke of Devonshire; the Cavendishes exist in the nucleus of the power elite that governs the Conservative party. Previously he had been present at Eton and at Oxford, where he did well.

Despite his central position in the hierarchy, Mr. Macmillan, also connected with the reputable publisher of the same name, took on the role of rebel during most of his political career, although he served with administrative distinction in the roles of Resident Minister in North Africa, Minister of Housing, Secretary of State for Foreign Affairs and Chancellor of the Exchequer. Mr. Macmillan wrote a book in 1938. It was called *The Middle Way;* in it he offered a policy of *rationalization* as a countermeasure to radical political drives for nationalization. Power, housing and fuel industries should be reorganized by the Government, which would also attempt to so implement such welfare services as to put an end to extremes in poverty. This daring proposal earned him the opprobrium of British Tories.

During the same period, and reaching back into the 1920s, Mr. Macmillan continued to represent the most disciplined and gratifying positions in the Tory world view. His forceful demeanor in the face of a solid phalanx of millionaire businessmen Members of Parliament demonstrated his authentically deep antagonisms to the incursions of commerce into a delicately articulated world. This rebellion against the spirit of the time marked him again as a man to watch.

He spent approximately 20 years out of the centers of power, but his hard intelligence and his obvious integrity ultimately claimed a justified attention. Mr. Macmillan has been Prime Minister of Great Britain since January, 1957.

Mr. Macmillan is a member of Athenaeum, Carlton, Turf, Pratt's, Buck's, and Beefsteak, all clubs, some quite old; he has served as president of the Game Research Association; he has rendered service as a trustee of the Historic Churches Preservation Fund; Mr. Macmillan was wounded three times as a member of the Special Reserve, Grenadier Guards, in World War I.

## Madison Avenue

Henry Clay, speaking of James Madison, fourth President of the United States and eponym of the institution deriving its name from the street called by his name, said that Madison had more judgment and common sense than Thomas Jefferson, who was a visionary and a theorist. Madison, said Clay, was cool, dispassionate, practical and safe. Madison's personality, adds the *Encyclopaedia Britannica,* was "perplexingly vague."

This separation of men into two such general types is not unfamiliar. The advertising profession, too, has on occasion been harassed by accusations of "vagueness" and "other-directedness," to a degree that would deny to it the status of a profession; but it is well to recall that President Madison himself was not without his supporters: the common sense and judgment, the practicality, of the advertising profession will withstand intense examination. And perhaps even its visionary capacities deserve their share of attention.

The search for methods of reaching other people, of communicating, is no new process. The modern world, in its common accusations against the advertising profession, ignores the antiquity of similar efforts. Were not the prophets concerned primarily with communication? Did they not develop the best means available to them—an original poetic style—for the diffusion of their ideas and passions? No one will easily say that there is a Jeremiah at B.B.D.O., but the links of the advertising profession with a highly respectable line of work should not be dismissed.

When the Food and Drug Administration seized 132 food products in 1961 because of short weight or improper labeling, Henry Abt, president of Brand Names Foundation, said of government efforts to provide additional legal protection for the consumer, "The characteristic competition between brand names is the most severe discipline that has existed in any economic system and, under any circumstances, is a greater guarantee of consumer interest than any that could be added by redundant legislation." Mr. Abt could not have risen to his executive position without a deep involvement in matters not only of practical utility, but also of value; his statement is typical of the determination in the advertising profession to emphasize its self-policing aspects and the free workings of the society in which it moves.

The "negative image" of the advertising profession, the philosopher N. H. Strouse (*see* Materialism) has said, presents many problems for his agency. Many college graduates do not consider advertising because of this "negative image." Some agencies have tried to solve the problem by raiding others, but this merely increases "the personnel instability of our business . . . one of the most serious factors in our growing costs and decreasing profits." In how many professional associations will such candid self-analyses be presented?

The seriousness of the issues facing the advertising profession and the probity of individual responses are symbolized by the action of several agencies to purify the language of the tribe: the word *creative,* mercurial ally to an easy self-glorification, has become the object of attention. In recent years agencies have put on creative efforts run by creative account executives and assisted by creative art directors. This misuse, cheapening the current coin, will end in the reversion to a greater asceticism. As S. H. Katz, president of Leber, Katz, Paccione, Inc., says, "It's silly for an agency to call itself creative. The word can be used correctly only to define specific function. I have no quarrel with the title 'creative department' for example."

## Manhattan District

Established on August 13, 1942, as a district in the U.S. Corps of Engineers. *Assignment,* Project DSM, Development of Substitute Materials—i.e., atomic energy for military purposes; specifically, the equivalent of 500,000 tons of TNT, an amount capable of devastating Germany's military and industrial machine. *Available Material,* scant; specifically, 4 grams of uranium metal owned by Westinghouse. *Required Material,* tons. *Plant Facilities,* none. *Personnel,* full priorities. *Cost,* large but in line with other military expenditures. *Prognosis,* according to theory and recent experimentation, excellent. *Estimated Time,* three to four years. *Security,* top secret. *Officer in Charge,* Brig. Gen. Leslie R. Groves (variously, "Greasy" Groves, "Gee Gee") of the Corps of Engineers.

Within three months of its formation the Manhattan District created a metallurgy for uranium which had been absent for centuries and accumulated 3 tons of the metal, while insuring a future rate of delivery of 500 pounds per day. Enlisting the services of a dozen chemical and engineering corporation giants, the District drove the price of uranium down from $1,000 to $22 per pound. Under continuous advisement of a priceless staff of scientists and technicians, which was soon to be headed by Julius Robert Oppenheimer (*q.v.*), the District secured enormous tracts of prime industrial real estate in Tennessee and Washington for the immediate construction of miles of engineering works to produce fissionable plutonium (*q.v.*) and uranium 235 (*see* Uranium). On this land the atomic cities of Oak Ridge, Tennessee, and Hanford, Washington, were built from scratch in the most daring manner in engineering history. Time forbade the prior construction of pilot plants; this was especially hazardous in view of the absence of previous engineering tradition for such plants. The Hanford Engineering Works, which was soon approached by an eight-lane highway, turned out to be the fourth-largest city in the state of Washington; in full swing, Hanford had a population of 60,000. In addition to these feats, the Manhattan District put together the best-equipped scientific laboratory in the world atop a mesa at Los Alamos, New Mexico. Here it convened the most distinguished group of scientists in the world, having ransacked American universities and Western European centers of learning. At the peak of its frenzy, the District had set in motion over 150,000 workers and was spending an amount of money rapidly approaching $2,000,000,000. A virtual army of counterintelligence agents slaved around the clock guarding what turned out to be the war's best-kept secret.

Within three years the Manhattan District succeeded in squeezing sufficient fissionable material, gram by gram, out of Oak Ridge and Hanford to effect the construction at Los Alamos of several atomic bombs. The first bomb was detonated on July 16, 1945. (*See* Alamogordo.) As if momentum had gathered which no man could resist, a second was fired within a month. And then a third. . . .

For the Manhattan District the rest is anticlimactic. Oppenheimer resigned two months later to return, ostensibly, to campus life. He was followed by others, who departed the Hill of Los Alamos in family cars and trailers burdened with trunks of household effects, books, souvenirs. In the haste of Project DSM, files were left chaotic, inventories in a shambles. The Hanford Works, once a self-contained community with stores, theaters, schools, deteriorated into a ghost town as security relaxed and workers were released to take up postwar residence in nearby cities. The former autonomy and insulation of the District was destroyed by the politics and legislation of peace. On December 31, 1946, the District was turned over to the civilian Atomic Energy Commission.

Embedded in history, the Manhattan District is a majestic symbol of the awesome capacity of a very great nation to concentrate its wealth, material resources, intellect, and determination in the defense of its sovereignty. They still make bombs at Los Alamos. But it can never be the same.

## MANIAC

Acronym designating "Mathematical Analyzer, Numerical Integrator and Computor," an electronic calculator designed and so named by John von Neumann, the famous mathematician-physicist and practical jokester. MANIAC was rushed into existence by von Neumann in 1951 to facilitate the astronomical calculations requisite for the construction of the hydrogen bomb. It reduced months of mathematical labor to mere hours and was thought to be as indispensable to the creation of the hydrogen bomb as Edward Teller (*q.v.*).

## Manned Space Station

At the proper distance outside Earth's atmosphere an artificial satellite will remain relatively stable in a continuous orbit as long as it does not encounter resistance from wisps of air slowing it down to a descent of burning destruction into Earth's atmosphere. A manned space station is a manned artificial satellite constructed to serve as a scientific research station, a home for weapons systems, a place to live in space, a provisioning area for the transfer of people, hardware and cargo to and from space vehicles, an orbiter with a controlled atmosphere, communications and pressurization systems, and gravity simulation.

One of the first scientific plans for the building of a station in space was put forward more than 35 years ago by Hans Oberth, the Rumanian father of space flight. The coming need for filling stations in space triggered much interest in early speculations about manned space stations. The developments of military rockets, particularly ICBMs, has led into satellite science, and many of the pioneers in rocketry have interested themselves in the concept of manned satellites.

The forerunners include Gen. (now Dr.) Walter Dornberger, formerly commanding general of Nazi Germany's Rocket Test Station, later missile design consultant for Bell Aircraft; Professor Wernher von Braun, formerly technical director at the same Rocket Test Station; Dr. Eugen Sänger, formerly in charge of the German Air Force's rocket research establishment at Trauen; Krafft A. Ehricke; Kurt Stehling. They agree that space stations are important, can be constructed, and most of them are now helping the United States of America to realize their dream. Many of these men have also helped the United States to build larger and more dependable IRBMs and ICBMs. (*See* Rocket.)

The first stations will probably be built—as early as 1969—in segments loaded onto rockets and delivered to the site. Workers in space suits, or in small one-man spaceships furnished with metal arms, will assemble the segments in orbit. After a number of decades, or centuries, the station, hooking up to new laboratories and segments, would constitute space cities. The station will require its own air-conditioning system, as well as supplies of food, water and movies, all of which could be delivered by distributing rockets.

From the station, spaceships using the satellite as a launching platform to various planets or other stations would need less fuel than a departure from Earth would require; the ships could be assembled at the station from parts conveyed by ferry rockets.

These, of course, are only primitive possibilities. Ultimately the construction of artificial worlds may siphon off a great percentage of Earth's population. The small asteroid, for instance, which symbolizes the possibilities implicit in man's use of space (*see* Asteroid Bomb), could provide the foundation and structural materials for the construction of manned space stations or *asteries*. Since there is very little likelihood of life on asteroids, such ventures could not intelligently be called colonialism (*q.v.*) but, more appropriately, asteroidism (*q.v.*).

## Mao Tse-tung

Chief of state in a country of some 700,000,000 people, the most heavily populated on Earth, Mao Tse-tung has been undisputed leader of the Chinese Communist regime since 1934, a record unequaled in any other powerful state.

The ancient Emperor Yao, who is remembered in the *Fountain of Old Songs,* wrote a simple Confucian "Warning," good for the humble, and particularly appropriate for the mighty in the millenial succession of Chinese dynasties:

Tremble, be fearful,
Night and day be careful,
Men do not trip over mountains:
They fall over earth mounds.

It is also said that the Emperor Yao, walking in the
country, heard some peasants singing:

We work when the sun rises,
We rest when the sun sets.
We dig wells for drink,
We plow the land for food.
What has the power of the Emperor
    to do with us?

The vast agricultural communes, and the intransi-
gence of Mao's revolutionary Leninism, were born out
of the harsh conflict between the old common needs
and the immense traditional realities of imperial pressures.

Mao was dismissed from the Politburo and the Party
Front Committee by 1927; he had propounded the
view that a successful revolution in China would only
take place within the peasantry, not in the urban pro-
letariat. His deviation from conventional Marxist theology set him apart from 1928 onward; from that date
he forged the groundwork for the party in China, not
without the admitted sacrifice of at least 800,000 de-
viant co-citizens from 1949 to 1954.

Heresy fathers the orthodox. The notion of freedom
in Mao's China does not readily square with Western
ideas on the subject. Mao, in the 1950s, set forth a
policy of letting "a hundred flowers blossom and
a hundred schools of thought contend." The clarifica-
tion of his statement by Chou Yang, the vice-chairman
of the All-China Federation of Literature and Art Circles, explains:

When we let a hundred flowers bloom, poisonous weeds
may appear in the guise of fragrant flowers. Therefore, letting a hundred flowers blossom and a hundred schools of
thought contend necessarily involves two opposite and inter-
related aspects: letting a hundred flowers bloom and eradi-
cating the poisonous weeds.

Conditions for the exercise of restrictions of free thought in the West take less simple forms.

To what degree the Confucian inheritance plays a role in the People's Republic is not clear to the West; how soon China will join the nuclear club cannot be precisely estimated: very few curious travelers have entered the giant land mass. Mao himself has never moved out of Communist territories: the darkness in communication in the mid-twentieth century has fertilized mutual suspicion and emphasized an impressive lack of sympathy between the People's Republic and the West. Neither is prepared for the emergence of China as one of the three most powerful states in the world.

Like the Emperor Yao, but on occasion with a different voice, Mao is a poet. He has written:

The hills on the plains are shining elephants.
I want to compare our height with the skies.

## Marrow

The soft tissue that lies in the hollows and spaces of bones. This may be mainly fatty (yellow marrow) or may be red. Red marrow is one of the principal blood-forming agents of the body. In the young it is also a site of new bone formation. The three most important constituents of whole blood produced by marrow are: the platelets, which are an important factor in blood coagulation; red blood cells and the oxygen-transporting medium (hemoglobin) which invests them; and white blood cells, which are the body's defense against infection.

The inaccessibility of bone marrow is in keeping with the importance of its function and its need for protection. Thus the body may suffer various mechanical injuries as well as a wide variety of diseases without disturbing the balance of blood elements or the process of bone formation in the young. (However, *see* Marrow Death.)

## Marrow Death

A whole-body radiation dose in the range 300–1,000

rad will affect the blood-forming organs. A dose of 400–500 rad will result in the death, within 30 to 60 days, of about half of those exposed.

Initial symptoms are nausea, vomiting and possibly diarrhea, appearing within hours of exposure, often lasting several days, and accompanied by feelings of great fatigue and overexcitability of reflexes.

The next phase reintroduces a feeling of well-being. The white blood cells, however, continue to decrease to very low levels and tissue damage progresses. A similar decrease, though less severe, affects the red cells (*see* Anemia). The victim has a tendency to bleed.

During the second or third week, the height of the disease, continued high fever and extreme exhaustion take place, accompanied by loss of weight, loss of hair, reddening of the skin, hemorrhages in the skin, ulceration of the mouth, throat and intestines. The protective mucosa of the mouth and intestinal tract is lost; this symptom increases the vulnerability to infections already initiated by the drop in white blood cell count. Such infections may often cause death. If no fatal infections develop, the bone marrow produces cells for about two or three weeks and stops: marrow death occurs.

There are no specific therapeutic agents against radiation disease, but victims of radiation in the range 300–1,000 rad may profit from the injection of bone-marrow cells taken from unirradiated donors. Whole-body exposure to substantially more than 900 or 1,000 rad, however, creates an irreversible situation. (*See* Intestinal Death; Radiation Effects.)

## Mars
The red planet.

To our eventual descendants life on Mars will no longer be something to scan and interpret. It will have lapsed beyond the hope of study or recall. Thus to us it takes on an added glamour from the fact that it has not long to last. For the process that brought it to its present pass must go on to its bitter end, until the last spark of Martian life goes out. The drying-up of the planet is certain to proceed until its surface can support no life at all. Slowly but surely

time will snuff it out. When the last ember is thus extinguished, the planet will roll a dead world through space, its evolutionary career forever ended.
—Percival Lowell, *Mars as the Abode of Life*

Lowell, an American astronomer who died in 1916, and the Italian Schiaparelli are the most closely associated with the theory that Mars is an abode of life. In 1877 the Italian astronomer announced that the surface of Mars was incised by *canali,* or channels. He never stated that these *canali* were artificially constructed, but he never denied that they might have been built by intelligent beings. Lowell, adventuring much further, saw the lines on the planet connecting two points in the shortest possible way in instance after instance; he assumed they were originally built to pipe water to great Martian cities from distant areas and composed a great Martian irrigation system. Schiaparelli saw the lines joining dark regions which he called lakes, but Lowell, convinced that Mars had been without large bodies of water for hundreds of years, called these areas "oases." The great Martian cities, doomed because the planet, in its old age, was losing its water supply and its free oxygen, were reduced to these "oases," located for survival at the meeting points of various canals. Gigantic pumping systems throughout the planet served to circulate the water derived from the melting polar caps, whose change in size in accordance with the seasons was readily apparent through telescopes. Very few, if any, modern astronomers currently agree with Lowell's theory. No definitive conclusion has been reached even in regard to the existence of the *canali.* W. M. Antoniadi saw such lines when a small telescope was used under fair conditions, but a more powerful telescope, used in conditions of good visibility, assured him the "canals" were nothing but a series of dots, the basis for an optical illusion. The question remains unresolved.

Mars, the fourth planet from the sun, comes to within 35,000,000 miles of Earth at its nearest approach. Its diameter is 4,220 miles, a little more than half the diameter of Earth, its day about the same as Earth's, 24 hours and 37 minutes. Mars is rusted: the planet has absorbed a great deal of oxygen and thereby derives its redness. The amount of free oxygen left is so small that it cannot be measured from Earth. The rest of the Martian surface is various shades of green, a coloring probably due to the existence of some primitive vegetation, moss or lichen, which can survive in such extreme Earthly climatic environments as Siberian cold, on desert rocks and on denuded mountain heights. Moss or lichen could survive in the Martian temperatures, which range from 80° F. at noon to about —150° F. at night. The planet's atmosphere contains very little water vapor and cannot store heat; thus as soon as the sun sets on Mars the temperature sinks.

Mars has two moons, very tiny. One, Phobos (Fear), the inner moon, is 10 miles wide and may, unlike Earth's moon, be irregular in shape and craggy, as if a mountain had been hurled into space. The second, Deimos (Panic), is only 5 miles in diameter. Phobos rotates very quickly, going around its planet three times each Martian day. If Mars has other tiny moons, an astronomical possibility, their existence will most likely not be ascertained until voyagers from Earth travel the 35,000,000 miles between the two planets.

**Mass Defect**  *See* Packing Fraction.

## Materialism

Philosophically, the doctrine that all existence is ultimately reducible to matter in motion. Traditionally, a term denoting values subversive of 2,000 years of basic Christian assumptions, and in that sense carrying the meanings of barbarism, atheism, or polytheism, inquisitorial practices, willful and unnecessary destruction of human life, and the installation of force as ultimate reference and as base of inequity—concepts opposed to the Western way of life. Opposed to idealism, philosophically the doctrine that all existence is ultimately based on thought. The most representative philosophers of the materialist conviction include the Ionian pre-Socratic Greek philosophers, immediate forerunners of the great age of Athenian civilization, while the main stream of nineteenth-century European philosophy is German idealism, seen in Kant, Fichte, Schelling and Hegel. Marx is a materialist, but has been called an idealist by those materialists who use the term in a nonphilosophical context. He is also an idealist, agreeing with Hegel in a strong emphasis on world process; however, his materialism rejects Hegel's view that the world process is the unfolding of a design or idea in the experience of an absolute mind or spirit. Materialism, used pejoratively in the Free World (*q.v.*) in the twentieth century, appears in such phrases as "dialectical materialism" or "godless materialism" or "atheistic materialism." Other uses of the term demonstrate some commingling connotations suggestive of cross-cultural exchanges: "Let's face up to the fact that frank and honest materialism is not a weakness. It is a symptom of strength. . . . What we need more than good taste, mannered restraint and higher cultural values is to maintain the American stance as one of a red-blooded, full-hearted, two-fisted scrapper." This use of the term by the philosopher Norman Strouse, president of the J. Walter Thompson advertising agency, indicates the modern exfoliation of its possibilities.

**Matter**  (from Latin *materia* = solid; earlier, timber or wood; earlier, the hard part of a tree; so perhaps from *mater* = the trunk, which produces the branches; therefore, perhaps, from *mater* = mother)
Formerly, and now loosely, matter is that which occupies space and has weight. Formerly, also, matter was one of two components of the physical universe, the other being energy. From another point of view, matter is one of two realities, the other being field. However, these distinctions are only quantitative. Matter is those regions of a field where the concentration of energy is great.

## Megaton
The explosive equivalent of 1,000,000 tons of TNT (*q.v.*); currently in use to describe the yields of thermonuclear weapons; for theoretical reasons (*see* Fission-Fusion-Fission Bomb), *megaton* could, like *kiloton*

(*q.v.*), soon become archaic. (*See also* Doomsday Machine; Asteroid Bomb.)

**Menticide** (from Latin *mens* = mind, and *caedere* = to kill. *See* Brainwash.)

## Mercury

Mercury is one of the original "wanderers" identified long before the invention of astronomical instruments, although she is very difficult to identify without such instruments: Mercury is the smallest of the planets, with a diameter of 3,100 miles, 93,000,000 miles mean distance from Earth and 36,000,000 from the sun. No planet comes nearer to the sun.

When Mercury makes her closest approach to Earth, only her dark side is presented and she looks invisible. The planet has a *captured rotation;* her year and her day are equal: she turns around on her axis in exactly the time it takes to complete one revolution around the sun.

The eccentricity of its orbit and the slight alteration in its elliptical course moved the astronomer Leverrier to authenticate a planet, Vulcan (*q.v.*), in order to account for discrepancies between Mercury's movement and the predictions of Newtonian gravitational theory. The difficulty was cleared up, and Einstein's theory of general relativity further justified, when that theory demonstrated that the ellipse of a planet described an expectable, slightly shifting pattern around the sun.

The same side of Mercury always faces the sun; on the bright side the temperature is high enough to melt lead, antimony and thorium; sulphur and mercury become gases. Light gases like ammonia and methane, well represented on such large cold planets as Saturn and Uranus, would have left the planet. Heavier gases like carbon dioxide, oxygen and nitrogen will probably have moved from the bright to the dark side, where they may exist in frozen or liquid form, diffusing away from a temperature of 770° F. to one of –450° F.

The extreme temperatures on Mercury probably

prohibt any life similar to the carbon- and water-based life on Earth.

**MEV**  *See* Electron Volt.

**Mike**  *See* Fission-Fusion Bomb.

## Minimum Deterrence

The concept that no sane national leaders would initiate hostilities against a state equipped with an adequate number of thermonuclear weapons. The only variables remaining in need of attention within the context of Minimum Deterrence include a definition of *sanity,* a definition of *adequate,* a clear expression of *the-point-beyond-which-the-state-could-not-be-pushed,* and a reasonable concern for the intrusion of irresponsibility, miscalculation and accident. (For a conceptualization designed to meet the challenge of these variables, *see* Finite Deterrence; *see also* Heart of Darkness.)

## Minutemen

A last line of defense in the United States against the Communist advance. Discussions on outdoor survival in the event of nuclear war convinced Robert Bolivar DePugh that most American citizens were not equipped to face potential armed invasion, internal revolution or nonviolent political take-over of the United States by the Communists. The resulting organization, the Minutemen, may be taken as broadly representative of a number of groups including the Loyal Order of the Mountain Men Society (later affiliated with the Minutemen) and the Gulf Telephone Company guerillas; W. F. Colley and John Snook, respectively, head the two organizations. DePugh, Colley and Snook have willingly placed themselves in a position of personal hardship and renunciation attendant upon their minority position.

Ralph Waldo Emerson, commonly the philosopher connected with theories of individualism, says in his *Journals:*

All the mistakes I make arise from forsaking my own station and trying to see the object from another person's point of view.

Having asumed the responsibility of free will, the paradoxes implicit in personal choice, DePugh, Colley and Snook take their place within this line of thought, a line also occupied by Tom Paine and the original group from which the Minutemen borrowed their name. At what point, for instance, must a man hold a position outside the Establishment? When do higher moral imperatives exist? What role remains for individual assertion? In answer DePugh, Colley and Snook agree that ultimately man must proceed from a position determined by his own experience. A basic Minuteman document states:

We must be willing to continue the fight for liberty even though we no longer have the legal support of established authority and prepare ourselves to take any action—no matter how brutal—that may be required to renew the protections of the United States Constitution for future generations.

Article II of the Bill of Rights of the Constitution states: "The rights of the people to keep and bear arms shall not be infringed." State laws have qualified this article to such a degree that it is now almost inoperative for the majority of citizens. Mr. Snook maintains enough automatic weapons to furnish arms for a guerilla unit formed by the 23 girls in the employ of the Gulf Telephone Company of Foley, Alabama, a firm owned by the Snooks. His initiative in attempting to restore eighteenth- and nineteenth-century individual liberties extends to active leadership on field maneuvers of the guerilla unit. The Minutemen, on their maneuvers, employ Browning machine guns, Browning automatic rifles, M-4 rifles, a 60-mm. mortar and a 57-mm. recoilless rifle; they plan to use the Minute Mask, mass-produced, against the dangers of nerve gas and bacteriological warfare. The Minute Mask is a plastic body-hood with chemical-filled breathing tubes. The group also had a number of bazookas as instruction pieces, but those were taken back by the government, from which they had been stolen by Richard Lauchli, a regional Minuteman leader.

Lauchli was placed on probation for two years; his continued membership illustrates the open nature of the Minutemen's admission requirements. Essentially the movement is open to anyone unconnected with a subversive organization. "Even a felony record is not a bar to membership," Mr. DePugh has stated, "if the person appears to be now a good citizen."

The club has not been free of certain internal power struggles, principally between W. F. Colley and Troy Harold Houghton for the California regional chairmanship. Colley, who was requested to submit to the removal of his reproductive powers (orchidotomy) as a consequence of a conviction in three counts of sexual molestation of young children, yielded to Houghton, who was convicted of indecent exposure, with no request for removal.

Critics of the movement have demanded that the Minutemen surrender their autonomous status and join presently organized Civil Defense units.

## Mirage IV

Part of the arsenal of the Free World (q.v.). A French jet bomber designed to carry nuclear weapons. M. Pierre Messmer, a defense minister of France, has defended his government's plan for a nuclear striking force by arguing that it would reinforce NATO.

France has been testing nuclear devices in the Sahara Desert since 1960, in order to develop effective weapons for its Mirage. (See Orbiting H-Bomb.)

## Missiles, Ballistic

The ICBM is heavier, goes farther up and out than other missiles. The two great American ICBMs are the Titan and the Atlas, rocket-propelled, shooting up nearly 800 miles into space with a range of over 5,500 miles at a speed varying from 15,000 to 20,000 miles per hour. A ballistic missile receives its guidance at the time of blast-off, whereas a guided missile is controlled throughout its flight. The ICBM can carry a nuclear warhead whose destructive power has 250 times the force of the bomb that destroyed Hiroshima;

it can travel its 5,500 miles in less than 30 minutes. After the empty fuel tanks and hot motor airframe of the first (booster) stage separate and burn out, the warhead continues its journey in free, ballistic flight. It subsequently re-enters the atmosphere toward its target, nudged only slightly off its course, if at all, by possible winds and gravity.

Navaho, which has the range, accuracy and armament of Titan and Atlas, could go up only to 100,000 feet; thus it was not a full ICBM. However, Navaho furnished much information for the ICBM-IRBM program, and had been called the "know-how" missile. Although the Navaho program, in its eleven years of life, ending in 1957, cost $690,000,000, its place within the continuous progress of ballistic missilery was primarily one of suggestive assistance.

Thor and Jupiter are IRBMs, effective for mid-range missions. They have a range of more than 1,500 miles, a ceiling of 250 to 300 miles and a thrust of 150,000 pounds, about 250,000 pounds less than Titan and Atlas.

Thor and Jupiter, like Atlas and Titan, are surface-to-surface missiles. But the United States has a splendid underwater-to-surface missile, the Polaris, which is in the IRBM category and ranges out to 2,900 miles. A submarine carries 16 Polarises. Some of Polaris's advantages consist of the following: it can be launched from underwater; a highly mobile launching platform, the Polaris-carrying nuclear submarine, is very difficult to detect or intercept; Polaris uses a solid propellant and thus can be fired instantaneously. (*See* Propulsion.) Polaris, unlike the liquid-propellant rockets Thor and Jupiter, is America's first true push-button IRBM; it is one of the very good rockets.

But not as good as Minuteman. By 1965, Atlas and Titan, although they are two of the excellent rockets, will have yielded to Minuteman: the U.S. Air Force plans on 834 ICBMs; more than 600 will be Minutemen. If the Polaris is a fine underwater missile, Minuteman constitutes, in its 84-foot hole, a motionless, expectant comet. Most Minutemen are waiting in Montana.

The Minuteman ICBM is available within 30 seconds; it may travel more than 6,200 miles, and it operates, like Polaris, on solid fuel: such missiles are more reliable and take less time in countdown. Solid fuel also makes missiles more mobile, although this in Minuteman's case may not be relevant. Minuteman constitutes, according to construction chief Brigadier General Goldsworthy, a missile most trustworthy.

Minuteman's guardians guard below ground. Four subterranean keepers must agree on the receipt of a signal to launch and must perform certain coordinated and related actions. The man in charge of pressing the firing keys is highly experienced, qualified and closely supervised. If he were not absolutely right for the job, the Air Force screening program for mentally disturbed men would most probably have found him out. He must not only be screened by healthy commanders of atomic-weapons units; he must also have graduated from high school. Air Force psychiatry has observed that such individuals as have not thus graduated tend to become bored more easily and to yield to impulse more readily than alumni of high schools, junior colleges, technical schools, colleges, universities, graduate schools and professional schools.

The classification of such new weapons is a matter of some difficulty in the rapid pace of modern technology. What is an IRBM? Can some comparison be made between its functions and more traditional categories? The Army has held that the IRBM is long-range artillery; the Air Force believes the IRBM to be a form of pilotless bomber. Although the first successfully tested IRBM was the Army's Jupiter, the Defense Department has assigned it to the Air Force. The IRBM is a form of pilotless bomber, most likely.

The services differ also in the categorization of missiles. The Army and Navy divide *their* missiles into seven categories determined by the location of the launcher and the location of the target. S stands for Surface; U stands for Underwater; A stands for Air; M stands for Missile. No SUAM has yet been developed; nor has the Defense Department authorized any SAUMs, AUSMs, ASUMs, USAMs or UASMs. The SAM, the ASM, the AUM, the SUM, the SSM, the

USM and the AAM, however, do exist. Air Force designations are according to missions. S stands for Strategic; I stands for Interceptor; T stands for Tactical; G stands for Guided; A stands for Air or Aircraft; R stands for Rocket; M again stands for Missile. The Air Force owns GAMs, GARs, IMs, TMs and SMs. The IRBM and the ICBM are SMs.

## Missiles, Human    *See* Translation; Blast Effects.

## Mob
A group (*q.v.*) in the worst sense.

## Monger
Before the sixteenth century, a dealer, trafficker, trader; now rare, except as a combining form: scandalmonger, rumormonger, etc. Currently one who carries on a petty or disreputable traffic. (*See* Hardware.)

## Monte Carlo
A method of sampling used when the procedure of taking a real physical sample cannot be effected; thus, a simulated sampling. A hypothetical population is structured to take the place of the real world of specific objects or people. A sampling is then made from the hypothetical universe through the use of a random number table. Such procedures can be very helpful in an attempt to establish probable eventualities where sampling presents reasonable difficulties, such as statistics of possible fatalities in thermonuclear adventures, complicated by many associated variables.

## Moon
On Earth's moon there is no atmosphere to produce winds; no rain falls; no waves grind down the surface. The moon approaches to within 222,000 miles of Earth and has a diameter slightly more than 1/4 of Earth's. Its period of rotation around Earth is the same as its period of rotation on its axis: the same side always fronts on its planet.

On the bright side, temperatures rise higher than 212° F., the boiling point of water; with the end of a lunar day, the temperature drops to $-243°$ F. When the sun is eclipsed by Earth, the temperature on the bright side of the moon falls 260 degrees within one hour. These temperature shifts produce erosion by the crumbling and cracking of rocky eminences. Meteors, unimpeded by the friction of an atmosphere, may strike the lunar surface full force; this also produces erosion. Only meteors and temperature extremes change the topography of the moon.

The surface of the moon includes five categories of formations: craters; large smooth plains, *maria,* so called under an early and mistaken apprehension that they were seas; elevations; long clefts and ridges; and starlike extensions radiating from some of the craters. No single theory has been completely able to account for the variety of features, but a cogent hypothesis assumes the initial coalescence of several large fragments of matter into one mass. The heat output produced by this merging reduced the mass to a semifluid state. Then a crust, struck repeatedly by fragments of galactic matter, hardened as the bombardments created craters. As the lunar mass cooled, quakes and volcanic activity threw up irregular eminences; the surface cracked, covered and smoothed large areas, and flooded a number of the existing crater formations, after which a ceaseless rain of meteorites continued to pit the surface of the moon.

Atmospheric and tidal erosion have largely obliterated the observable continuum of geological history on Earth; the moon, untouched by comparable forces, will present to visitors a relatively virgin topography, a museum of massive transformations.

## Mountain, or The Mountains
Modern symbolic term in politics. The genesis is obscure. Used affirmatively, as: "Castro waits in the Mountains; he's a revolutionary." Used interrogatively, as: "The revolutionaries in Portugal failed to unseat Salazar; have they reached the Mountains yet?" Used imperatively, as: "Hurry! To the Mountains!"

## Mourning
A reaction to the loss of a loved object. Though usu-

ally a person, the object may also be a part of the
body, a material possession, or an abstraction like one's
nation. The degree of the reaction is consistent with
the degree of attachment to the object. And quite often
the degree of the attachment to the object is realized
only from the degree of the subsequent reaction to its
loss.

Mourning is complex. Initial disbelief followed by
grief and melancholia are its most renowned manifestations. Bitter self-recrimination for prior abuses to
the lost object is a regular feature of mourning and
lingers on long after the initial manifestations. Other
persisting effects include resentment, shame, loneliness
and anxiety. Nightmares, delusional disruptions of
solitude, momentary confusion of strangers with the
lost object, and other hallucinatory phenomena are
not uncommon.

The duration of mourning varies and, like all emotional states, cannot be hurried. Mourning is thought
to come to an end when the mourner's emotional in-
vestment in the lost object is redistributed among
other objects. This, however, is a never fully realized
ideal, for, in truth, no mourner ever completely succeeds in obliterating that final nostalgia which hovers
over the memory of lost objects. Indeed, more often
than not, mourning gives way to an unnoticed and
indelible alteration in the mourner's vitality, as if existence has faded a shade grayer.

No age group is immune to mourning. All things
being equal, recovery from mourning appears to be
most favorable between the ages of 19 and 26. In
younger people, mourning inflicts permanent lesions
to feeling and intellect. In the very young, it can lead
to death. (*See* Hospitalism.) In the very old, it quite
frequently leads to death.

## Multistable Deterrence
A deterrent situation with built-in three-way stability.
The situation as defined by experts contains significant insurance against first strikes because the potential retaliation remains catastrophic. Secondly, the
situation contains significant stability in relation to
extreme provocation; since both sides own a Credible

First-Strike Capability (*q.v.*), neither will easily start anything. Finally, since Point Two will lessen tension, Point Three involves the reduction in the possibilities of accident: more tension, more possibility of accident; less tension, less possibility. If a thermonuclear accident *were* to occur, it would probably take place in a more agreeable international context than would otherwise have been possible.

## Mushroom Cloud

The hallmark of a nuclear burst. Truly a cloud: it is wet, cool and sometimes capped with crystals of ice. The fireball (*q.v.*) has expanded so rapidly that its temperature falls to a point where the water vapor in the air that has been updrafted condenses into droplets. These droplets are too misty to create rain, but they are large enough to reflect the white light of the sun. The mushroom shape has been formed by the initial column of material sucked up beneath the burst and the material's outward swirling once within the fireball. The shape is fixed momentarily against the surrounding shock front. The cloud, now a billowy cumulus, passes upward through the subfreezing temperatures of the tropopause, being blown slowly shapeless by the winds. An amorphous mass, it reaches into the stratosphere. The heavy particles of the burst are far below, falling in the vicinity of ground zero. The cloud now contains the radioactive microdusts and gases of subsequent global fallout (*q.v.*).

## Mutation   (*See also* Gene.)

A mutation is a sudden variation in the chemical makeup of a gene. Mutations can occur in any cell at any time in the life cycle. Some forms of cancer are manifestations of somatic-cell gene mutations. However, mutations in the reproductive sperm and egg cells invite special concern because these mutations are transmitted to future generations.

The causes of natural mutations are not well understood, but it is known that even the smallest doses of ionizing radiation (*q.v.*) can give rise to mutant genes. While the precise quantity of ionizing radiation re-

quired to alter a gene has not been established, no
dose is considered "safe."

Mutations beneficial to the individual and the
species are rare, occurring about 3 times in 1,000 mutations. About as rare are visible mutations which
are not clearly detrimental to the individual. Approximately one-third of all mutations cause death to a large
percentage of their bearers before adulthood is reached.
The remaining mutations—about two-thirds—exert
their influence subtly by altering internal physiological
processes and undermining the individual's resistance
to disease and to the wear and tear of life. Because
these subtler mutations lower only slightly the chances
of the bearers' reaching adulthood, the chances of these
"mild effects" being eliminated by reproductive omission is also lowered. Such mutations parade through
generations, precipitating disease, infection, suffering.
The proportions of beneficial, slightly deleterious, semi-
lethal and lethal mutations seem to remain fixed; no
matter how much external sources increase the mutation rate, genes go on mutating in the same respective
proportions.

The apprehension that the nuclear age with its
radioactive wastes will produce monster children is
fanciful. It is more consistent with the present facts
to predict an increased incidence of miscarriages from
defective embryos, abortions due to malformations of
the fetal braincase, limbs and jaws, degenerative diseases, congenital absence of hands and feet, cleft palate,
hemophilia, harelip, albinism, cretinism, hardening of
the arteries, diabetes, high blood pressure, balding.

Yet, there is a hopeful side to these considerations,
even in the event of a nuclear war with its upsurge of
ionizing radiation. Here we may obtain clues to unknown genetic possibilities and inherit opportunities
for creative racial development. Dr. R. R. Newell,
testifying before the Joint Committee on Atomic Energy of the United States Congress in 1959, summed up
this facet with eloquence:

Fortunately the human race has the power to go on, leaving
the fallen behind and cleansing itself gradually of the ge-

netic injuries inflicted. We can even draw an ideal picture of the survivors of worldwide irradiation, emerging as a bigger, stronger, wiser, gentler, healthier race than would otherwise have developed. The price would be: A large or major fraction of the population killed or dying within a few months; survivors carrying many radiation-induced mutations; high infant and adult mortality for many generations, straining the naturally high fecundity of women to maintain the population. Then as populations begin to build up again, would come the opportunity for conscious eugenic management, with large families limited to parents of superior native endowments.

# N

## Narcissism

From Narcissus, the gorgeous youth in Greek mythology for whom Echo died of unrequited love; Nemesis, in anger, caused him to pine away for love of his own reflection on the waters of a pond and then transformed him into the narcissus flower. From *narcissus* comes the prefix *narco*, pertaining to the stuporous or sedative effects of certain drugs.

This term was adopted by nineteenth-century sexologists to denote perverse self-love, an extreme of which would be masturbation devoid of fantasy before a mirror. This sense of the term is now obsolete. However, common usage retains some of this sense, the term being employed often as a florid synonym for selfishness. However, so loose has the term become in common usage that its etymologically absurd variation *narcism* frequently occurs.

Currently *narcissism* has acquired a fresh precision: it denotes that early period of infancy, during the first months of life, when the child has only a vague and shaky cognizance of the autonomy of objects around him. His world view is omnipotent; the environment is merely an extension of his body and exists solely for his pleasure; acute contradiction of this view, as in slight delays in feeding or fondling, induces immediate rage. As the first year of life draws to an end, narcissism has begun to suffer defeat by maturation and education.

A subsequent return to this mode of relating to the environment is a susceptibility of the human psyche throughout life. A strong tendency toward narcissism is revealed in the person who falls repeatedly in love, each time with the untamed optimism that the situation cannot possibly possess anything but that which is desired; rage and embitterment increase as the situation, like a dissolving mirror, grows transparent and reveals the reality behind it, which is that the other person is an individual in his own right. Narcissistic characters are incorrigible overestimators of both good and bad fortune and are inclined either to stake everything or to risk nothing on the basis of flimsy odds; they are demanding, manipulative, histrionic, full of moods, and in their unvarying choice of pleasure over reality is the dynamic of their chaos and defeat. However, some amount of narcissism is indispensable: it is a deep source of enthusiasm and hopefulness.

## Navigation Satellite
A ship outfitted with the proper radio equipment will be able to obtain accurate information about its position from a navigation satellite. In case of serious damage to navigation networks on Earth, such weapon bearers as the Polaris submarine could still be guided to their targets. Four such satellites promise worldwide coverage. In the future only ships without special radio apparatus will be able to get lost.

## Nehru, Jawaharlal (1889– )
In 1920 Nehru joined with Mohandas Gandhi in a Movement for Indian Independence; he spent a total of 16 years in British Jails for such Activities. Since September, 1946, he has been the Prime Minister of India.

Morality in International Politics, like a poor Woman of some Probity, can seldom resist that aspect of its Ground which is called Expediency. As it is hard to Condemn a Creature moved to inconsistent actions by her own Nature and its Environment, even so little righteous Judgment can be applied to a Statesman who occasionally, trapped in a thicket of Imponderables, avails himself of what he usually Detests. If Nehru has said that nonviolence was "a new message which our people were destined to give to the world"; of Gandhi, that "nothing would displease his soul as much as to see that we have indulged in any small behavior or violence"; that "if a major war is not to be permitted, then minor wars which may lead to major wars should not be allowed to occur"; that, in view of a choice between Negotiation and War, "we shall negotiate and negotiate and negotiate to the bitter end. Any other approach is anti-Gandhian and against our fundamental principles"; if he has for so many years spoken in this Manner, and so Essentially given himself to Nonviolence against some of the Genius in his own Temperament, no Person, although aware of the Indian Conquest of Goa in 1961 and the great Passions over Kashmir, but would be Foolhardy and Uncharitable to demand of the Prime Minister that Unexceptionable Chastity in Conduct which, were it absent in a Religious, especially in consideration of her more constricted Sphere of Activities, would in that event be the desideratum justly expected by a Man of Reason.

## Neptune

Neptune is so far from Earth that it cannot be seen without a telescope. The planet is 2,800,000,000 miles from the sun and is the eighth-farthest away, only Pluto moving in a farther orbit. Like Jupiter, Saturn and Uranus, its structure has a central rocky core. Around it a layer of ice 6,000 miles deep constitutes the second, and final, solid mass of Neptune. The atmosphere around Neptune, composed mainly of methane, may have a depth of 2,000 miles. Its temperature, lower than that of Jupiter, Saturn and Uranus because of its greater distance from the sun, is perhaps about —346° F. Neptune's existence was postulated before it was observed. When the motion of Uranus, its neighbor, was seen to be irregular in relation to prepared astronomical tables of planetary movement, the only hypothesis that could explain the existence of such irregularity was the existence of an ultra-Uranian mass. The heavens were searched in September, 1846, and the planet was found. Two men, Adams of Great Britain and Leverrier in France, share the priority of discovery. Perhaps Leverrier holds a greater percentage of the priority: his speculations were published and communicated to the French Academy November 10,

1845. Although Adams had sent his results to a colleague on November 1, 1845, a certain amount of scientific opinion, especially in France, held that publication constituted a more dependable proof of discovery. The French received with great favor a suggestion that the new planet be called Leverrier but the British were cool. The planet was named Neptune.

## Neurosis
Also, psychoneurosis. A clinical condition of mind and behavior resulting from a compromise between two conflicting emotional choices: one choice is known but not wholly favored; the other choice is unknown but preferred. The resulting neurosis serves the purpose of sparing the remainder of the personality from disorder by the conflict.

## Neutrality
An old demonstration of animal cunning. Of the onager, or wild ass, it is said that

this animal brays a dozen times on the equinox, March 25. It is from sadness, stating that night and day are equally long, because the wild ass prefers night to day.
—Philippe de Thaon, 12th century

## Neutralization of Satellites
A problem of extreme difficulty. (*See also* Orbiting H-Bomb.) Military reconnaissance satellites launched by unfriendly powers would pose a serious threat to security. (*See* Orbital Spies.) Neutralization of such vehicles as they intrude on the space overlooking a state's territory is a vital matter of security. To determine the orbit of a strange satellite, the satellite must be detected. This problem is almost impossible of solution, since it is relatively simple to make the vehicle nonreflecting to light and radar. If such detection can be made, however, and the orbit determined, an unmanned missile could be fired into an intercepting orbit. Unfortunately an attacking state could use a great number of decoy satellites to confuse the defenses; attacks on every one of them would put a

severe drain on the economy, particularly if atomic warheads are used in the interceptor. The neutralization of satellites is a problem of extreme difficulty.

## Neutrino

Another candidate for cosmic primordialism, this atomic particle is a catalyst in the endless decays and re-creations of the subatomic order. The neutrino was postulated in the nineteen-thirties to justify slight discrepancies in energy during certain transformations of nuclear particles. (*See* Atom, Twentieth-Century.) Calculations soon required an antineutrino. Currently, a twin for each neutrino has become necessary. For example, the neutrino which is involved in the birth of an electron when a neutron decays is the reverse of the neutrino which is involved when a muon, or mu meson, materializes in a pion decay. (For mesons *see* Particles.) Other processes insist on twin antineutrinos. While they carry definite quantities of energy, neutrinos possess neither mass nor charge and are the only entities in the physical universe not subject to gravitation. They have a close proximity to nothingness. That all four varieties carry similar quantities of energy and yet do differ from one another suggests that there are different kinds of nothingness. It has been estimated that a neutrino can penetrate 100,000,000,000,000 miles of lead before colliding to a halt, give or take a few miles.

## Neutron

This chariot glides past the gates of hell and is consumed therein.                                                        —Homer

Amid the multiplicity and vagaries of subatomic particles (*see* Particle) the neutron is a pillar of conviction. Discovered by Sir James Chadwick in 1932, the neutron ascended almost at once to the category *nucleon,* a category of nuclear particle indicating fundamental and enduring reliability. The only other nucleon is the proton, and together the neutron and proton are fixed points in the fluctuating theory of atomic-nuclear structure.

The various properties of the neutron suit the speculation that the neutron is part of the original, primordial matter of the universe. The neutron is electrically neutral, and its mass is approximately the sum of the two fundamental electrical units—the positive proton and negative electron. Its hard center is encased with a melting softness. Thus a pre-electrical, preatomic era of the universe is thought to have given way when the neutrons cooled, shedding clouds of electrons which were held fast in an atomic arrangement by the protons resulting from this emission. The low temperatures of the current universe still undermine any exposed neutron, for within 12 minutes after escape from the shelter of an atomic nucleus, the neutron decays into a proton, an electron, and an evasive antineutrino (*see* Neutrino).

Neutrons can be isolated from nuclei in a number of ways: certain types of radioactive decay liberate traces of neutrons; particle bombardment of targets like beryllium is a source of neutrons (*see* Atom Smasher); uranium fission liberates considerable amounts of neutrons (*see* Nuclear Reactor; Great God K); and fusion reactions liberate colossal amounts (*see* Fission-Fusion-Fission Bomb).

When isolated from atomic nuclei, neutrons cause havoc in all matter. Being electrically neutral, the neutron is capable of bypassing the strong, restrictive electrical forces of the atom and reaching the nucleus. Colliding with the nucleus, the neutron unsettles the distribution of nuclear forces and instigates radioactivity (*q.v.*); neutrons unleashed from a fusion reaction convert, for example, inert atmospheric nitrogen into radioactive carbon 14. If the energy of velocity is precisely right, the neutron can fission (*q.v.*) certain types of atoms. In fact, it is the only particle that can. For this reason, the neutron is called the key that unlocks the energy of the atom.

In this last capability, neutron rays have established a social influence equal to light waves and radio waves.

**Neutron Bomb**   (*See also* Neutron.)
A weapon which takes ideal advantage of two signifi-

cant characteristics of neutron particles, their ability to penetrate and radioactivate matter.

Used in an antimissile device, a neutron bomb creates a thick environment of neutrons in the path of an oncoming missile; the neutrons detonate the intercepted missile warhead prematurely.

Used on a cosmopolitan target, the neutron bomb unleashes an assault of neutron radiation, which annihilates, through whole-body irradiation death, the exposed and semiexposed population and traps the deeply sheltered population beneath a city of intense, long-lasting radioactivity. If the bomb is designed to minimize its thermal and blast effects (*q.v.*) and to maximize its neutron production, the real estate and building installations can be spared destruction while the population is wiped out. Such a bomb is detonated in the air over the target and produces an immense, muffled glow. Its lethal aftermath is silent, theoretically.

**New Humanists**   *See* Probe.

**Nike-Zeus**
In the last 1, 2, 3, 4 or 5 minutes of an enemy ICBM flight, the Nike-Zeus, aided by four cooperating radar systems, will intercept and destroy the ICBM. The radar systems must track the enemy, single out decoys as they sweep in among the company of real missiles, figure out a course, launch the Nike-Zeus, and guide it to a meeting.

**Noah's Syndrome**
From Noah, the Biblical patriarch who was commanded by God to build the ark on which he, his family, and two of every kind of creature rode out and survived the Flood. Noah's syndrome begins with a forewarning of disaster of some sort, which impels the individual to prepare against it, whereupon he falls into the obsessive hope that the disaster will come to pass. In severe cases, the individual actually goes on to encourage and abet the disaster against which he originally prepared. In this he expresses his hatred

against those in the unprotected environment who remained indifferent to his original anxiety.

## No-Cities
A U.S. military strategy intended to preserve society. Until the U.S. or the S.U. attacks a city, no city will be attacked.

## Nominal Bomb Shelters
The phrase used to describe an era (*c.* 1950) of government planning for civil defense. Shelters were planned to be maximum strength for key personnel and facilities important to the community in an emergency; moderate strength for urban masses; improvised for small-group and family protection in residential areas; all were to be effective against blast effects and local fallout—presumably from a nominal bomb delivered to its target by manned bombers whose presence would sound a warning alert from those who saw them first: the Ground Observer Corps. (*See* Orbital Spies; Missiles, Ballistic; BMEWS.)

## Nominal Target, Hiroshima
A castle within the circle marking 500 meters from ground zero, headquarters of the Imperial Japanese 5th Division, which was, on August 6, 1945, preparing plans for the defense of Kyushu—one of the home islands of Japan; the destruction of this division's planning facilities was the official mission of the *Enola Gay* (*q.v.*).

## Nominal-Yield Weapons
A generic classification; an atomic bomb with an explosive yield of 20 kilotons, more or less, or, according to the U.S. Public Health Service system, "low yield"; specifically, the weapons exploded over Hiroshima and Nagasaki.

## Non-nuclear Club
A voluntary organization, whose members either have or do not have nuclear weapons and the capacity to manufacture them. Those victims of inferior technol-

ogy who do not have such capabilities may belong to the Non-nuclear Club as a token of intention and concern; they may also not belong to the Non-nuclear Club as a token of ambition, national pride and concern. States in the Nuclear Club—the United States, the Soviet Union, the United Kingdom, and France— are equally candidates for membership; in their case a decision to join would involve more than a declaration of intention.

A good number of states may soon be offered a pragmatic choice. An inquiry into the nuclear capabilities of various powers produced the conclusion that 11 nations were technically able to embark on successful, independent nuclear-weapons production in the near future and that 8 others could follow soon after. The alphabetical list includes Australia, Austria, Belgium, Canada, Czechoslovakia, Denmark, East Germany, Finland, Hungary, India, Italy, Japan, the Netherlands, People's Republic of China, Poland, Sweden, Switzerland, West Germany and Yugoslavia.

## Nth Country

Any state not presently categorized as an advanced nuclear power. This includes mostly everybody except the S.U. and the U.S.: the great company of potential nuclear adventurers.

After the large-scale future dissemination of nuclear weapons to great numbers of states—through alliances or independent technological advances—experts look to the adoption of a different term for the small remaining subculture: DECAYth, ARCHAIth, PRIMth; or Dth, Ath and Pth Countries.

## Nuclear Reactor

A machine for the controlled release of the energy of nuclear fission (*see* Fission) for uses other than explosions.

Reactors are designed to moderate between fission-inducing neutrons and a fissionable fuel like uranium or plutonium, so that the resulting energy can be drawn off at a steady, nonviolent rate. Usually in the form of heat, this energy can be applied, for example, to water to produce steam which can then run electric-generating turbines.

Moderation is one of the central problems. Neutrons are "started up" in a reactor by juxtaposing chunks of fissionable fuel in appropriate quantities. The amount and velocities of these neutrons are moderated by intercepting the neutrons' paths with some substance capable of controlling neutron behavior. Carbon in the form of graphite is one such substance. Hence a "graphite reactor" is built by piling cubes of graphite one on top of the other, some cubes containing fissionable fuel, most cubes not. This results in a massive blend of fuel and moderator. Rods of neutron-absorbing material, like cadmium, can be inserted in the graphite latticework to slow down fission, or can be withdrawn to increase fission. Suitable casing protects the environment from radiation and reflects escaping neutrons back into the reactor. The use of moderators less cumbersome than carbon has been tried with success; also the fuel itself has been tried in a water-soluble form with good results. These efforts diminish the size of reactors appreciably. Reactor portability is an important goal. Reactors are wanted for spacecraft.

Reactor fuel is expensive and it soon falls into disuse by contamination from its own by-products in the course of its being used; the fuel then needs to be removed and re-refined, which is also quite expensive. The reactor parts themselves succumb to the destruction of heat and neutron bombardment and need to be dismantled and replaced periodically. Radioactive wastes created by neutrons have to be disposed of safely; currently they are being stored in tanks (see Nuclear Thimbles) or are encased in concrete and dumped into the oceans; these are admittedly temporary, makeshift solutions; a suggestion to launch these wastes into space is being entertained. Radiation hazards to employees are not yet clearly defined; what constitutes safe and unsafe levels of radiation exposure is still disputed, some specialists insisting that no level is safe. How to insure that reactor fuels will not be diverted clandestinely to weapons in the event of a serious international disarmament endeavor grows increasingly baffling as reactors multiply all over the globe. (*See* Zero-Zero.) But visions of the immense possibilities of nuclear reactors have unloosed an unhesitant courage, typical of man's response to technological revolutions. The distractions of developing other sources of energy less costly and less hazardous can now be ignored in the face of the new challenge. Problems and dangers will certainly be dealt with somehow, sooner or later.

The level of civilization of a nation, which is commonly measured against such progress as the humanization of its penal code or the universality of its literacy, is now also measured against its attainment of nuclear energy. As one official put it, "Without radioactivity we'd have less to think about today. Without radioactivity, as a matter of fact, we'd have nothing to think about—we'd all be slime in the primeval swamp."

## Nuclear Thimbles

Tanks with a capacity of 103,000,000 gallons of radioactive waste, which have been constructed by the Atomic Energy Commission at each of its three largest atomic-energy installations, at a total cost of $60 million. Each is more than half full of high-level radioactive wastes and the level is rising.

## Nucleus, Atom

That locality in the universe where energy is most bound; hence, matter par excellence. (*See* Matter.) Conglomerations of this substance form all the material bodies that move within the writhing void of the heavens. If stripped of external electrons and packed sufficiently, nuclear substance would exceed a weight of 130,000,000 tons per cubic centimeter. However, material of such density is not likely anywhere in the universe. In cold bodies like Earth, atomic nuclei are separated by relatively vast spaces; even the most dense material like lead and gold is puffed with far more space than matter. Where nuclei occur somewhat more packed, they form "hot" bodies like the sun and begin to release the energy hitherto immobilized in their existence.

Nuclei nestle in the cores of atoms; they are surrounded by a thick electronic cloud. Although the nucleus bears most of the atom's weight, it is a comparatively small part of the atom; a nucleus is as hard to come by as a grain in a bale of cotton. The existence of nuclei dawned on the imagination in 1911 when Ernest Rutherford observed that while most rays from radium passed through a metal foil unswervingly, some few did come out of the other side at a peculiar angle as if they had ricocheted off a small dense particle. The notion of the atom as a nucleus with planetary electrons descends from this observation. In succeeding years, atomic nuclei have been probed with a variety of rays at various velocities (*see* Atom-Smasher), and a picture of strange and complex forces emerges; these forces are born of the very proximity of particles in the nucleus, of the spins and rotations of these particles, of their grave weight, and of their solitude in the vast atom, which shields them from the agitation of an incessantly energetic universe.

Occasionally nuclei succumb to invading forces and make some rather slight accommodations, as when hydrogen nuclei transform into helium or exceptionally complex nuclei like uranium slip into more simple nuclear structures. (*See, for example,* Fission; Fusion.) These accommodations are very rare and consume very trivial amounts of the nuclear substance. Fission, for example, releases about 1/1000 of the mass of a nucleus; all the rest is conserved in a new arrangement. Free energy is the fuel of creation; nuclei are only the ashes. Despite the awesome responses of mankind—a mischievous and frail growth on a waning planet—very few of these ashes have any real spark left.

### Nucleus, Cell

The cell constitutes the essential structural and functional unit of plant and animal life. The nucleus in a gland cell, in an amoeba, in a bone cell or in any other cell—with the exception of a sex cell—follows much the same archetypal life cycle.

The cell nucleus is a small particle surrounded by a nuclear membrane and suspended in cytoplasm, a gelatinous material surrounded in turn by a semi-permeable membrane. The nucleus is the site of the division of the cell. A segment of cytoplasm removed from its nucleus will not be able to generate new cells by division; the segment will die. The cell nucleus, by mitosis, the fundamental process of division which engenders new life units, undergoes a transformation from relative solidity to the creation of chromosomes. These small bodies, bearing the genes (*q.v.*), carriers of hereditary determinants, divide longitudinally into precise halves. The original nucleus becomes two, each group of chromosomes shrinks back into a compact, clear, fluid central unit, a nuclear membrane surrounds the unit, and each of the two new cells exists independently.

In sperm cells, the chromosomes do not split up. Half go to one new cell, half to the other. After one subsequent mitotic division, each of the four new cells changes its shape, to appear as sperm. The nucleus becomes the head and neck and the cytoplasm the tail. When the sperm cell fertilizes the female egg, the tail is discarded and the nuclear material merges with the nucleus of the egg, which also carries only half the ordinary burden of chromosomes. The merging produces a new organism. (*See* Ionizing Radiation; Mutation.)

## Nuke

Diminutive of *nucleus*. The innards—mechanism and fuel—of any "atomic bomb."

## Oedipus Complex

From Oedipus, son of Laius, King of Thebes, and of Jocasta. Fated to be killed by his son, Laius gave the infant Oedipus to a shepherd to be left on Mount Kithaeron to die. The shepherd, compelled by great sympathy, brought the infant to Polybus, the childless King of Corinth. At puberty, when Oedipus was told by an oracle that he would kill his father and marry his mother, he fled Corinth in an effort to spare his alleged father the cruel prophecy. But in his journey Oedipus met Laius; they quarreled, and Oedipus slew Laius. Shortly thereafter, Oedipus married Jocasta. When he finally discovered who Jocasta really was, he blinded himself by grinding jewels into his eyes. Jocasta hanged herself. In his blind wanderings with his daughter Antigone, Oedipus was finally killed by the avenging Eumenides.

This myth concretizes the vague emotionality of all individuals at a late phase of infancy when a definite quantity of erotic energy is directed, with complex interest, toward the parents. The Oedipus complex is inevitable in a creature like man whose sensory and motor apparatus have grown disparate in the course of evolution; at five years of age the human child is susceptible to a higher pitch of desire than his neuro-muscular system can fulfill. This is unique in nature: at this relative point in the life cycle all other creatures are sexually mature and begin to reproduce, while the human being is still an infant and has a long way to go. His reconciliation to this tragic journey is the hallmark of all his subsequent humanity.

## Operational Analysis

A branch of applied psychology aimed at achieving a smooth continuum between a machine, such as a spacecraft, and its human operator. The operational analyst studies attributes of the human organism, such as motor reactions, with a view toward informing the engineers of complex equipment how to design those features which the human operator will be working. Where, for example, a signal is needed to alert the operator to the necessity of adjusting a particular control knob, a decision must first be made as to whether the signal should be auditory, visual or tactile; data on these senses assist in the making of such decisions. These data would also indicate the subsequent refinements of a particular signal system: if auditory, how loud the buzzer, hum, bell, chimes, horn, siren; if visual, what color and how bright the blinker, arrow, picture, number, symbol; if tactile, how pleasant or painful the nudge, massage, heat, cold, vibration, shock, stab, pinch. Likewise, the postural characteristics and manual reactions of the human organism will dictate where to position the knob, its size, its frictional opposition to movement. The lag between a sensory stimulus and the operator's response to it will determine the gear ratio between the knob and what it does elsewhere in the equipment: if the lag is only slight for a particular operation, the gear ratio can be enlarged to slow down the performance of an operation; if the lag is long, gear ratios can compensate accordingly. The dream of the operational analyst is to discover the repertory of human reactions and to translate its variability and complexity into a series of mathematically linear inputs that can be guided by compensatory mechanical systems in such a way that human error is filtered out in the output of the equipment the human operator is operating.

As could have been predicted, this technical activity has begun to spill over into some of the continuums between the everyday citizen and his everyday equipment. It has been learned, for example, that the average American toilet and seat are all wrong, from an operational analytic point of view. Current design of this piece does not allow the muscles of the calf and thigh to participate optimally. The toilet and seat should be elevated and tilted slightly forward.

## Operation Paperclip

The procurement and importation into the United States of German armament theorists and technicians following the defeat of Germany in 1945. The Nazi Air Ministry and armament industry were ransacked and personnel were hustled off to America, either under contract or under protest. The United States answered the criticism that Operation Paperclip, in doing business with Germans and avowed Nazis, was morally indefensible with the argument that the Russians were already kidnaping the best brains in Germany. In this the United States was correct. The Russian counterpart of Operation Paperclip secured for them untold talent and assisted the initial strides in missile weaponry. The Cold War had come into the open between two of the mightiest allies on Earth.

## Operations Analysis

A contemporary mathematics of looming variety which endeavors to systematize the explosions of growth and event by which society is proceeding toward its future. In operations analysis, the various mathematics of probability are applied to complex situations in the hope that mercurial chance will be hounded into the open and caged. The economic and the military are two social categories where risk is especially deplored, and operations analysis has found substantial niches within the modern corporation and government. In a world of increasing and capricious consumption and complex traffic, OA guides the firm through a jungle of decisions. How much inventory should a particular retail outlet keep on hand? How many ships must wait in line for how long before it is financially correct to expand harbor facilities? Which should be increased, when and to what extent—human maintenance crews or the equipment they service? In military planning, OA is enlisted to sustain the effectuality of real assets in a world of hostile phantasmagoria. (*See* Strategic Studies; Monte Carlo; War-Gaming; Competitive Games.) An operations analyst is called an operator. Since World War II, the increase of operators within the modern corporation and the military can be described as an explosion. When a procedure which has been employed to establish order within an explosion explodes itself, some interesting results are bound to follow. Alarmed spokesmen for OA decry a drift toward charlatanry; the applied mathematician is overselling his product and hoodwinking his mathematically naïve and awed client. More liberal spokesmen take a longer view of the situation and speak of growing pains; money and power are new and bewildering to the mathematician; he needs time to grow into his new role in industry and government.

## Oppenheimer, Julius Robert

Variously, "oppie," bob, "father of the a-bomb." physicist: quantum theory, cosmic rays, nuclear physics, particles, relativity. b. new york city, april 22, 1904. s. julius oppenheimer (bus.) and ella nee freedman (art.). m. katherine harrison nee puening, '40, one s. one d. b.a. harvard, '25; ph.d. göttingen, '27. natl rsrch fellow, harvard, '28; fellow, intl educ bd, leiden univ, '29. assist/assoc prof physics, cal inst of tech and univ of cal, '31-'36; prof, '36-'47; dir, inst of adv'd studies, '47- . "I began to feel the need to participate more fully in the life of the community." / "It is desired that clearance be issued for the employment of Julius Robert Oppenheimer without delay, irrespective of the information which you have concerning Mr. Oppenheimer. He is absolutely essential to the project." (L. R. Groves, Brigadier General, to the District Engineer, Manhattan District, July 20, 1943.) dir, los alamos scientific lab, '43-'45. chrm, gen advisory committee, atomic energy comm, '46-'52. member, bd of overseers, harvard coll, '49-'55. fellow: amer acad of arts and sciences, amer philo soc, amer phys soc; member: royal danish acad of sciences and letters, brazilian acad of science; hon mem: jap acad of science; hon fel: christs coll, cambr. hon d.sc. penn, '46, harv, '47; ll.d. cal, '48; hon d. c. l. oxf, '53; wedgewood awrd, georgia hardwood lumber co; nominee, hall of fame, pop mech mag; *officier de la légion d'honneur;* medal of merit, u.s.a.; *persona non grata,* aec, '54, *priznyat' opyat',* '63.

## Orbit

A path more or less indefinitely extended or of a repetitive character, like the orbit of the moon around Earth. Earth satellites describe an *elliptical* orbit, going around the planet continuously; the elliptical orbit, which closes upon itself, is described by a satellite which is launched with a speed of 18,000 miles per hour. A launching speed of 25,000 mph allows a satellite to escape Earth altogether in a *parabolic* orbit—a curve that never closes. Above 25,000 mph awaits the *hyperbolic* orbit. This orbit extends to infinity; it is wide open; it characterizes the beginning of interplanetary flight. (*See* Trajectory.)

## Orbital Garbage

Orbital devices which have outlasted their useful life in space. Such satellites are a nuisance to trackers of orbital objects from the ground. Depending on the nature of the garbage, it could be towed to a central depot and parts reclaimed, kicked out of orbit to burn up in the atmosphere or refitted with new parts by astronauts operating from a maneuverable spaceship.

## Orbital Spies

Satellites investigating and reporting on ICBM launchings and general military operations in selected areas of Earth. Midas, or Missile Defense Alarm Satellite, operates 1,500 miles above sea level; six Midases will be required to insure adequate and continuous coverage of U.S.S.R. launching sites, and the detection gear will be actuated only when making passes over Soviet territory in order to conserve power. Midas swells the warning time about enemy ballistic missiles to 24–30 minutes, a good 13 minutes better than ground-based radar.

## Orbiting H-Bomb

In the absence of an antisatellite weapon, the orbital bomber provides an almost invulnerable base. All land and sea bases for ballistic missiles have a degree of vulnerability to surprise attack. An orbiting H-bomb has a maximum of mobility and thus a minimum of vulnerability. In addition it claims two significant advantages: salvo capability and recallability. Weapons in orbit are already launched; no time need be wasted in putting them into operation; they are assured of salvo strength. Also, an orbiting weapon can be recalled. Once an ICBM is launched, it is committed to its mission.

A bombing satellite could be launched long in advance of a war, with any desired degree of leisure in a peaceful environment, taking advantage of weather and convenience to production and supply sources.

## Outer Space

Henri Michaux, the Belgian poet, has offered in *The Future,* an excerpt from which follows, a poetic context within which the connotations of space sound their overtones:

Nothingness
Withdrawing everywhere like panic, O
Misery, misery
O last memory, little life of everyman, little life in each
    animal, little
Punctiform lives;
Never again.
O emptiness,
O Space, unstratified Space . . .
Space
Space

This position, somewhat tendentious and extreme even if allowance is made for poetic license, receives a needed and sober counterbalance in the definition of Dr. Hubertus Strughold, an authority on space, and the first man to simulate weightlessness by anesthetizing his buttocks before going up in a small airplane. Dr. Strughold is Professor of Space Medicine, Adviser for Research, School of Aviation Medicine, U.S. Air Force, Randolph Air Force Base, San Antonio, Texas.

Space, in common usage called outer space, begins at the end of the aerodynamically effective atmosphere around 200 kilometers (120 miles) (extra-atmospheric space). With regard to certain physiological factors, however, space reaches down as low as 20 kilometers (about 12 miles) (intra-atmospheric space-equivalent region). From 200 kilometers (120 miles) on, the potential satellite space of the Earth's gravisphere begins, and its satellite-holding power reaches as far as 1½ million kilometers or about 1 million miles. Beyond this region, which may be called "deep space," the Sun's gravitation becomes predominant. In the direction of the line Earth-Moon, the gravitational divide between these two celestial bodies lies at a distance of 332,000 kilometers (193,000 miles) from the Earth, or 58,000 kilometers (35,-000 miles) from the surface of the Moon. These average figures indicate "where a rocket leaves the gravitational field" of the Earth and enters that of the Sun or the Moon, which in both cases requires escape velocity.

## Overkill

Of current origin, a military term referring to the annihilation of a target by a destructive force in excess of what the target actually calls for. The term is used usually with a qualifying "factor." Thus, if one bullet of a certain size in the right spot, say, the lungs, is enough to kill a person, but he is killed having drawn three bullets in that spot, he is said to have been overkilled by a factor of 3. However, the term is more commonly applied to nuclear targets. Thus, if a particular urban target can be destroyed by one 15-megaton nuclear device, but instead draws three such devices, it is said to have been overkilled by a factor of 3. Such estimates are exceedingly pertinent to all phases of offensive and defensive military strategy, for strategies planned on the basis of one particular factor are completely inappropriate to situations based on a different factor. For example, defenses against overkilling by a factor of 5 are useless against an attack conveying a factor of 8. Likewise, an attack with a factor of 5 would be ineffectual against a target defended for a factor of 8.

Since 1945 the practical limits on the size of overkill factors have widened year by year. It has been difficult for military strategy to keep pace.

# P

**Packing Fraction**   (*See also* Nucleus, Atom; Particle.)

The total mass of the various particles comprising an atomic nucleus varies depending upon whether the particles are weighed separately outside the nucleus or whether they are weighed packed together in the nucleus. The net mass of the nucleus is always smaller than the combined separate masses of the particles of which it is composed. This lost mass, or *mass defect*, is equivalent to the energy one would have to provide in order to separate the nucleus into its component particles. The mass defect divided by the number of particles in the nucleus gives the packing fraction for that nucleus. (*See* Fission; Fusion.)

**Paddle-Wheel Satellite**

On August 7, 1959, the United States sent Explorer VI, the first paddle-wheel satellite, into orbit at an altitude of 156 miles; in its course Explorer VI reached an apogee of 26,357 miles. Four paddle-shaped vanes jut out from the satellite, banks of 8,000 solar cells supplying electrical power to storage batteries, the supply center enabling Explorer VI to relay its information back to Earth tracking stations. The payload (*q.v.*) was a variety of instruments for measuring aspects of Earth-space.

The somewhat ungainly shape of this orbiting spheroid has earned it the occasional nickname The Tick, an unfortunate cognomen, since the wingless tick can't get off the ground and besides has six, rather than four, limbs. (*See, however,* Probe.)

**Panic**

Literally, of the goat-footed god Pan, who exploded into fury when his divine nap was disturbed by mortals, thus imparting "panic" to the human race. (Pan is also credited with inspiring sexual excitement and the thrills and elation frequently accompanying danger and fear.)

Though usually associated with anxiety and fear (*qq.v.*), panic is actually somewhat different: anxiety and fear are feelings; panic is a reaction to a feeling. Moreover, anxiety and fear bring groups together; panic degrades groups: orders given by superiors are no longer heeded; each individual behaves on his own behalf without any consideration for the rest; mutual ties come apart; a senseless apprehension is set free.

That the panic reaction is not well studied by psychologists is understandable. Panic cannot accurately be reproduced in laboratory animals; nor can human volunteers be employed for study, since experimental panic would be too painful, if not harmful. Thus, panic is usually studied in the "field," e.g., earthquakes, battles, air raids, social disasters. It is known to be contagious and is thought to be produced in its comparatively milder forms by a frustrated expectation of any sort, and in its more severe forms by extreme fright (*unanticipated* fear). Impulsivity, flight, frozen stupor are common accompaniments of panic. Soldiers in World War I in the front lines, expecting the enemy, fired thousands of rounds of ammunition before the enemy was even sighted, in so-called "shooting panics." In Quito, Ecuador, in 1949, a Spanish version of Orson Welles's invasion-from-Mars broadcast brought people, half clad, into the streets in wild confusion, mobbing and destroying part of a famous newspaper building. During the Second World War, numerous residents of London were reported not to have been able to get to air-raid shelters, being simply frozen on the spot by panic (an exceedingly primitive reaction thought to be a reversion to the protection by motionless camouflage of chameleons, or the death-like stillness of possums).

An example of extreme panic, so-called "silent panic," occurred in a London air-raid shelter in the spring of 1943: the shelter was rather crowded, and there was a bomb explosion nearby; the electricity failed, it became pitch-dark, somebody was heard to stumble on the stairs. No yelling or crying broke the silence. When help arrived, 200 of the 600 people were dead. Autopsies revealed no significant anatomical damage in the victims.

## Paranoia

As psychiatric conditions go, a fairly common one, characterized by delusional systems (*see* Delusion) of grandiosity and often of persecution, e.g., "I am stocking this supply of wheat germ and vitamin pills because I am being instructed by God through secret messages over television to save the populace from eating food that has been poisoned by Communist agents." "I am being followed by the FBI, my telephone is secretly monitored, I know my friends are testifying against me behind my back, I am really innocent, but I must protect myself." Radio was a popular feature of delusions during the 1930s. So were airplanes, capitalists, and Germans. Television, atomic radiation and electronic computers are in current vogue among paranoiacs. Religion is, of course, a perennial.

The delusional system always exploits some kernel of truth and reality, which makes the paranoiac patient unfortunately intractable in his convictions. If the delusional system is not arrested at a point where the patient is merely a "crank," and if it invades and motivates enough of his behavior without his being able to socialize it into a fanatic and popular crusade, hospitalization is required.

## Paranoid

Of or like, though less virulent than, paranoia (*q.v.*). Free of tangible delusion (*q.v.*), the paranoid individual is nevertheless highly suspicious and cautious, and is frequently legalistic, circumstantial, argumentative. These traits are responses to the unwavering point of view that the world is dog-eat-dog and that a person needs constant vigilance in order to survive. Since the kernel of truth here is not a small one, paranoid individuals not only appear sane; they often achieve startling competence in numerous walks of life, e.g., the law, psychiatry, statesmanship, by virtue of their sensitivity to conflict and their ability to anticipate hostile motives and intentions in their adversaries. That they often blend nicely with their surroundings would seem to make for difficulty in distinguishing paranoid individuals. However, numerous diagnostic criteria do exist. One simple measure is the question: What else does a person do besides dispute? If nothing else, more likely than not he is paranoid, and both he and his altercations soon grow tiresome. But such a question must be asked in a context where responses other than embattled self-defense are feasible and appropriate. In the context of real crisis, paranoid traits elude observation like black trees in a black night.

## Parity Conservation
A symmetry principle. The long-standing assumption, self-evident and unshakable, that nature does not distinguish between right- and left-handedness uniquely, that nature is ambidextrous. That is, if the mirror image of a phenomenon materialized, it would differ in no respect from that which it reflected except in being a reversal.

## Parity Nonconservation   (*See also* Parity Conservation.)
In 1957, Tsung-Dao Lee and Chen Ning Yang, two physicists, solved a puzzle as to why two particular subatomic particles—the tau and theta mesons—identical in all respects, decay into different quantities of similar products. Lee and Yang demonstrated, at a Nobel Prize level, that in some instances nature does not conserve parity. That is, if the mirror image of certain phenomena materialized, it would differ in certain respects from that which it reflected in addition to being a reversal. In some instances, nature violates neutrality: it makes a difference how you look at a thing.

## Parsons, Capt. William S.
Navy Ordnance expert, later Admiral. Captain Parsons completed the assembly of the bomb used in the

Hiroshima explosion. Because he feared the destruction of Tinian Island (*q.v.*), the B-29 American bomber base in the Marianas, if the plane cracked up on takeoff, Captain Parsons finished the bomb on board. Because he also foresaw possible capture, Captain Parsons had borrowed an automatic pistol from an officer just before entering the *Enola Gay* (*q.v.*). He was the only man on board who understood the bomb's mechanism and did not want to be captured alive.

## Particle

Any one of the currently profuse ultimate entities of matter and/or energy. While it is difficult to keep an exact count of the different particles being submitted as the basic stuff of the universe, the amount at mid-twentieth century varies between 25 and 35. Most of these particles figure in the structure of the atom and are revealed in the course of probing the atom. (*See* Atom-Smasher.)

A milestone in the quest for particles was reached in the early nineteen-thirties when five particles were finally demonstrated and considered sufficient to explain all forms of matter and energy. Three of these particles were the electron, a negatively charged particle located in the orbits of atoms; the proton, a positively charged and heavier particle located in the nuclei of atoms; and the neutron, a neutral particle also found in the nuclei. In addition, the photon, a particle of electromagnetic energy, accounted for light and certain ray phenomena. The graviton, a particle basic to gravitational activity, completed this comparatively simple and satisfying picture.

In 1935, a particle called a meson was predicted in order to account for certain minute discrepancies in the distribution of forces within the nucleus. Two years later mesons—however, not the predicted variety —were found in the atomic debris produced by cosmic rays. (One reason for the previous elusiveness of mesons is that they leap in and out of existence within 250-millionths of a second.) Subsequently, when the predicted variety was finally observed, mesons were sorted into categories: pi mesons and mu mesons of both negative and positive varieties and also of neutral varieties. Later, mesons were found to decay into neutrinos and positrons. Soon, there was a tau meson. There was also a kappa meson. And an exaltation of antiparticles like antineutrons and antiprotons came into the picture. And several kinds of V particles emerged and Xi particles and muons and pions.

These individuals are finally rounded up into families: leptons, mesons and baryons. They obey one of two kinds of mathematics: Bose-Einstein or Fermi-Dirac. Moreover, all particles possess at least mass (even zero mass), existence (some briefly—10-billionths of a second) and something like spin, and all particles behave in terms of integers of the Arabic number system.

To this state of affairs the possibility must be added that wherever particles do not exist, their potential counterparts do exist (*see* Antimatter), so that the ancient and persistent query which generates the quest for particles—"What is matter?"—is at last outdone by the query "What isn't matter?" For the time being.

## Patriotism

Love of or zealous devotion to one's country—*O.E.D.* From the Greek *patris*, fatherland. Modern psychology recognizes four fundamental needs operating in human beings: needs for recognition, response, adventure and security. Patriotism meets all these needs in such a satisfactory manner that it has been one of the constants observable in history. In the first case, man recognizes himself in his role as citizen of his own country; this process makes possible a merging of national purpose and individual identity; thus the individual conflicts and anxieties which so often harass modern man no longer alter the fundamental order of his life. The conscience of the nation is his conscience. Secondly, the patriot obtains all the advantages of built-in response operating within the society involving himself and other patriots (*see* Minutemen). In this connection, popular response to such symbols as flags, historical traditions and enemies improve the psychic integration of citizens. It is of the greatest importance to remember that man is a symbol-making animal. Man finds adventure, the third need, within a context of familiar and accepted national goals; thus his capacity for bravery and selfless action receives continuous approval, and his ordinary human anguish is funneled into an area of constructive excitement, war. The need for security, far from constituting a base human requirement, as some modern commentators would have it, is inescapably a part of the human condition. Man, at odds with environment, pressed by all the exigencies of contemporary life, and psychologically at odds with himself, must operate within a context larger than himself. Such is patriotism, and its incidental accompaniments—persecution of others, desire for territorial expansion, jingoism, assumptions of superiority, and murder—probably constitute necessary imperfections in a system of order.

## Patroiophobia

The fear of heredity either in oneself or in one's offspring. The fear is pinned to the presence of an alleged inherited condition running in one's immediate family. The patroiophobic goes from physician to physician for reassurance. However, just as hereditary disaster symbolizes, in these cases, punishment for some personal, unconscious crime, so medical reassurance symbolizes forgiveness.

Patroiophobia in respect to one's offspring is more common. In fact, in pregnant women this phobia is almost universal. At one point or another during pregnancy every expectant mother is gripped by the dread that she will deliver a deformed child. "Thus the world will at last see the ugliness of my past sins." Severe patroiophobia may interfere with the motivation to have children and may even lead to psychogenic sterility.

In view of the widely known relationship between radioactive debris and fetal malformation, it is understandable that this phobia has increased in intensity in contemporary Japan. In the United States as well, while very far from calamitous, the phobia has become more noticeable. However, the statistical incidence of deformed neonates is still low enough to suggest that the gestating patroiophobic is responding to a non-real danger. Her fear, though deeply felt, is still in the category of the irrational.

## Payload

Compd. of *pay* + *load,* orig. Middle Eng.; *pay,* retaliation or punishment inflicted, penalty or retribution suffered, as: *When they receive their proper pay, in what places must they burn?* (Babylonian *Book of the Dead); load,* a burden (of affliction, sin, responsibility, etc.), as: *Everyman cannot avoid his Load (The Rood of Everyman).*

Whence payload, (1) a burden of punishment, of penalty, of retaliation, as: *The Minuteman will bear its payload 4,000 miles;* (2) *Mil.:* in military guided missiles, the warhead, fuse and container; (3) the sum of the burden of each individual stage of a multistage rocket; for instance, in a three-stage rocket comprising the Daphne (200,000-pound booster), the Clytemnestra (100,000-pound second stage) and the Helen (60,000 pounds), Daphne's payload amounts to 160,000 pounds, whereas Helen is her own payload; (4) generally a rocket's or a satellite's useful weight of crew, passengers, some hardware and cargo; (5) appears also in the idiom *essential payload,* as in the following extract from the testimony of Brig. Gen. H. A. Boushey, Director of Advanced Technology, U.S. Air Force, to the Select Committee on Astronautics and Space Exploration of the House of Representatives, 1959: "I believe *man* himself will prove 'the essential payload' to the full utilization of space."

## Pentagon

A very large five-sided enclave in Washington, D.C., concerned with Defense, Contracts and Pressure; the Military.

The Pentagon, a crypto-state within a State, owns about 35,000,000 acres of land, 32,000,000 in the United States. The total value of its property exceeds $160,-000,000,000. Unhappy agent of the arms race, the Pentagon has nevertheless developed an industry which operates as a powerful thrust to the civilian economy, while the Pentagon strives to help Create, Meet, Equal and Balk antagonists to the State.

Until World War II, the United States had no armaments industry; in war it had made do in a tradition of necessary conversions. In 1776, Jameson writes, "Gunsmiths were numerous. But in this, as in other trades, there was little organization. Each gunsmith worked for himself, or perhaps had two or three men to help him, so that the committees of Congress had to make their contracts for small quantities, and place them here and there with individuals. . . ." Since the end of the Second World War, a vast realignment has taken place. The prime defense contracts for fiscal 1963 amount to significantly more than $50,000,000,000 for Defense and at least $7,000,000 for Civil Defense.

The five top contractors are earning from $1,000,-000,000 to $2,000,000,000 per year each, a largesse unencumbered with an overdose of competitive bidding.

The Pentagon does not sell armaments; it buys them and gives them away. What it sells—through radio, television, military speechmakers, public-relations experts, advisory seminars for businessmen—is anxiety. What it does is hunt. Its voices are those of Admiral Radford (total victory—not stalemate), General Twining (the war should be settled in one afternoon by pulverizing Russia), General Anderson ("Give me an order to [bomb Russia]. . . . When I went up to Christ I think I could explain to Him that I had saved civilization"), Navy Secretary Matthews ("We would become the first aggressors for peace").

The Pentagon is purer than those it supports and to whom it occasionally gives life: airplane manufacturers with contracts; missile-makers with contracts; subcontractors with subcontracts; ancillary small-business concerns with small business concerns, like makers of lighter vacuum cleaners with improved motor-winding insulation derived from defense research, ultrasonic watch repairers, cordless-electric-drill manufacturers, portable picnic-cooler sellers, renters of computers for processing petroleum.

The makers, repairers, manufacturers, sellers, renters

believe they want peace as they enjoy the sidelong shuffles of war technology; the missile-makers believe they serve policies of deterrence; and the Pentagon knows what it wants.

Generals and admirals, without a good clutch of corporals and petty officers, tend to function with decreased authority in lower rank, with reduced prestige, without easy recourse to the mesh of mass propaganda, and with less hope of high executive positions whence they can, after retirement from the Service, advise their old Employer about useful goods. General Dynamics, which traditionally receives the biggest contracts, employs more than 185 retired officers. The United States Congress has others, like Maj. Gen. Senator Strom Thurmond, Rear Adm. Representative James Van Zandt, and Brig. Gen. Senator Barry Goldwater, whose simultaneous allegiances to both their local electorate and their Reserve Units complicate the process of legislative decision, and subject their motives to the most agonized self-examination.

A man is what he does. The snake in a lake, the piranha on land, and the professional soldier in peacetime face similar problems. Human operations have the greatest animal adaptability, but a renunciation of decades of tendentious expertise conflicts with habits, which, like the under skin, are subject to continuous regeneration. What the soldier has he will not regain by what he might get. Neither the equalizations of death nor the prospect of national suicide can counterbalance the insidious terror implicit in merely being. What Desdemona's husband could not escape is the professional soldier's foreboding terror: *Othello's occupation's gone!*

### Permissible

A radiological term formerly indicating that dose of ionizing radiation (*q.v.*), over and beyond natural ionizing radiation, which is not expected to cause appreciable bodily injury to a person at any time during his lifetime. This definition was based on the assumption that there is a human threshold for radiation in respect to which there are doses of ionizing radiation small enough to be devoid of biological hazard. In the late nineteen-fifties, with additional evidence, this assumption turned out to be untenable. The current definition of *permissible* was not then based on the idea of a safe dose but was based on a philosophy of risk, morality and good judgment. A permissible dose of ionizing radiation represented an estimate of how much we could afford to risk biologically for the benefits of this radiation. Subsequently, experts (*q.v.*) perceived that *permissible* still held unhappy connotations. The term *Radiation Protection Guide* (RPG) was adopted. This term was defined as the radiation dose which should not be exceeded without careful consideration of the reasons for doing so.

## Permissiveness

A recent doctrine of child-rearing informed by a special interpretation of psychoanalytic scripture and the myth of the Noble Savage. The interpretation is that man is perfectible; the myth has it that human nature is basically good. Adherents of permissiveness locate the wellsprings of evil in the corruption of the nursery, which corruption can be avoided by paring away opposition to the child's instinctual inclinations and by gratifying the child's instinctual needs on demand, so that frustration and its resentments are prevented before they occur. The permissive mother is one who isolates her authority from her strength, renouncing the former and placing the latter at the disposal of the child. The assumption here is that the child is closer to the natural truths of his existence and is, in a sense, wiser than the parent and will therefore use the strength more fittingly than the parent could apply it. In the process the child will evolve internally a sense of authority more wholesome than that which would otherwise be imposed on him externally.

This doctrine has been open to question. Its critics assert that it is a godsend to those who cannot distinguish between authority and cruelty, leadership and tyranny. The rebuttal damns such critics as agents representing the sick society. This controversy is one of the staples of history.

**Physical Half-Life**  *See* Effective Half-Life.

**Pickaback Satellite**
On June 29, 1961, a Thor-Able-Star rocket carried up into space Transit IV-A, a navigation satellite (*q.v.*); Greb, a little satellite developed by the Naval Research Laboratory; and Injun, a 40-pound satellite constructed for the study of the Van Allen radiation belts. Transit, Greb and Injun combined to produce the first tripartite celestial delivery.

**Pile**
Also, atomic pile. Obsolescent for Nuclear Reactor (*q.v.*).

**Pioneer I**
Intended as a space probe to the moon, Pioneer I exploded two minutes after it had left the ground, in August, 1958. This rocket is now nameless, having transferred its title to the second rocket in the series, Pioneer I (*q.v.*).

**Pioneer I**
The second rocket in a series of United States moon probes, launched on October 11, 1958. It did not travel fast enough to pull away from Earth and fell after rising to an altitude of 71,300 miles.

**Pioneer III**
Launched on November 8, 1958, this third attempt to reach the moon met with failure in the third-stage firing. The title was transferred to the fourth rocket in the series, Pioneer III (*q.v.*).

**Pioneer III**
This rocket, intended as a moon probe, rose 63,580 miles on December 6, 1958, and fell.

**Pioneer IV**
American space probe (*q.v.*) rocket (*q.v.*). Pioneer IV's payload (*q.v.*) was a gold-plated cone weighing 13.4 pounds, containing two Geiger counters, a photoelec-

tric cell and a radio transmitter. Four stages bore it ultimately to its present position as an artificial planet circling the sun, the first to accomplish this after the Soviet Lunik (*q.v.*). No radio waves have ever traveled as far as those received from Pioneer IV at a distance from Earth of 407,000 miles, at which point the radio stopped working. This American radio was able to transmit signals from a distance 33,875 miles farther out toward the sun than the radio in Russia's Lunik.

## Planck's Constant

In a universe of incessant fluctuation, where size, weight, intensity and even time vary with speed and location, this is one of few absolute, unvarying quantities, hence called a constant: $6.6 \times 10^{-27}$ (0.000,000,-000,000,000,000,000,000,006,6 or 66 ten-thousandths of a trillionth of a trillionth).

This tiny number, whose existence was established by the Nobel Prize-winning physicist Max Planck at the turn of the twentieth century, is used to calculate the magnitude of those infinitesimal particles of energy basic to all emissions of radiation and electricity. Designated by the letter $h$, Planck's constant provides some notion of the lower ranges of the behavior of matter and energy, just as the constant $c$ in Einstein's formula $E = mc^2$ (*q.v.*) provides some notion of the upper ranges. (*See* Quantum.)

## Pleasure

An experiential concomitant of the reduction of excitation; failure to reduce excitation leads eventually to pain. The capacity for excitation, which is the indispensable antecedent of pleasure, is a criterion distinguishing the living from the nonliving.

In lower organisms, the behavior leading to the reduction of various states of excitation is specific and adaptive; here the pursuit of pleasure insures survival. In man, however, behavior leading to pleasure has grown increasingly nonspecific and maladaptive; while still urgent, the pursuit of pleasure may come into conflict with survival. As a regulator of human behavior, pleasure alone does not do. Reality (*q.v.*), another regulator, needs to be enlisted. Between the two, pleasure very clearly rules, but like a slow-witted tyrant over an indispensable subject.

## Plimsoll's Mark

To prevent dangerous overloading, a line on the outside hull of British merchant ships indicating the legal limit of submergence. Hence, any burden of stress beyond which a situation begins to capitulate, alter, damage or deteriorate.

## Pluto

The rocking outrider of the solar system, 3,675,000,000 miles from the sun. Pluto is very cold and completes an orbit in 248 Earth years. Its volume is very nearly the same as Earth's. It is very far away. Almost nothing else is known about Pluto.

## Plutonium

An Nth Country's (*q.v.*) back door to the nuclear club, *plutonium* is one of the transuranium elements. (*See* Elements, Man-Made.)

If uranium 235 (*see* Uranium) were the only highly fissionable material, the vision of economically realistic nuclear power would be dim; this variant of uranium is rare and expensive, suitable only for initiating nuclear technology and for providing a fission-trigger for a finite stockpile of thermonuclear weapons. (*See* Fission-Fusion Bomb.) The hopes for widespread nuclear power reside in the feasibility of manufacturing other highly fissionable material out of less fissionable, but relatively abundant, material. Nature stocks a fair amount of fissionably sluggish uranium 238. When this metal is exposed to neutrons (*q.v.*), as it is in a nuclear reactor, it is transformed through a series of radioactivity into the long-lasting metal plutonium. Plutonium is highly fissionable and can be used approximately like uranium 235 to enrich reactors and to create bombs. It made its debuts as the bomb stuff for the Alamogordo test and the Nagasaki raid. That a plutonium-breeding program costs merely millions puts nuclear energy within the reach of numerous small powers. France entered the nuclear club through plutonium technology, periodically dismantling her reactors and removing the nascent plutonium.

There was a time in the post-Hiroshima era when it was believed that plutonium could not be used as the fission-trigger for a thermonuclear device. However, this technological problem was surmountable.

## Politics of Despair

A term used to denote the voting behavior of the Communist voter in Italy and France who, unlike the Communist party member, has found no substitute for the symbols he opposes. By extension, a form of behavior symptomatic of illness in the body of the world.

## Positive Control   *See* Fail-Safe.

## Postattack Blackmail

A war tactic designed by an attacker to minimize damage to his own country while inflicting severe first-strike blows on the enemy. The attacker, avoiding the enemy's cities, strikes at air defense and offensive forces. If a sufficient proportion of the air defense is crippled, the cities will remain unprotected and subject to annihilation by even relatively small subsequent attacks. At this point, the attacker, having severely injured the retaliatory forces of the enemy, notifies him that his cities have been spared only with the understanding that he is to stay away from all the attacker's cities. Otherwise the enemy's population centers will be treated as hostages and each destroyed city in the attacker's country would be immediately followed by the destruction of x cities in the enemy's territory. The attacker could say, for instance, "If you destroy Omsk, I will pulverize Sioux City, Secaucus, Great Falls, Tonawanda and New York."

The most effective way to reduce the chances of Postattack Blackmail involves the placement of all missile bases in the hearts of cities with no preparations to evacuate civilians. In addition, such a posture would constitute an unquestionable demonstration of peaceful intentions.

## Posture

Sense of the position and carriage of the body—posture
—is not perfectly understood. It seems to operate
through the Vater-Pacini corpuscles in the subcuta-
neous tissues of the hands and feet, and near the joints
and tendons as well. Changes in muscle form, which
take place in movement, stimulate these corpuscles
and provide information on the stance of the various
limbs in relation to each other. This information is
not dependent on any external phenomena.

The meaning of the term involves solely a reflexive
awareness of self, unconnected with the perceptions
of such complex realities as anxiety, panic, hope, fear,
terror, irrationality, empathy. Philosophically, then,
the term connotes an *Anschauung* very near solipsism,
the view that self is the only reality, the only really
existing thing.

The degree to which the term is defined by the
individual for his self, and its irrelevance in the context of multileveled human behavior, is admirably
illustrated by the attitude expressed in the ironic
works on posture by recent experts (*q.v.*). In considering one of many possible postures, they emphasize the
need for such capability as would, in the face of critical provocation by an enemy, enable the posturing
state to loose a first strike in order to bewilder that
enemy, insecure then as to whether the path of safety,
in relation to its own potential survival, lay rather in
direct attack than in a provocation.

## Postwar Postage, Free

Free franking privileges instituted for the use of survivors of thermonuclear attacks. In the event of some
disruption of communications due to blast, fallout,
fireball, radiation, firestorm (*qq.v.*), unexpectedly large
bombardment, food poisoning, poor water distribution (*q.v.*), the government of Canada, for instance,
has stockpiled postage-free postcards to be used for
change-of-address notifications.

## Preattack Mobilization Base

The most farsighted military planning cannot guarantee a foolproof posture (*q.v.*). The effective use of a

Preattack Mobilization Base—or Insurance Against a Change in Policy—entails a willingness to concede the fallibility of careful and complex hypotheses and preparations. Circumstances might force a government to spend either less or more than its current estimates provide for; a relatively small amount of money spent on advance planning and physical preparations may very well be disproportionally rewarding: research is not cheap, but the omission of research promises great unreadiness. Whatever might be useful must be researched. All the researched programs need not be developed; but the damage possible without adequate development is so great that a great deal must be developed. All items developed do not have to be procured; if, however, they are not, some may be procured in part. Even if they are not currently necessary, they may eventually be. Requirements can change; no nation wants to be caught on the near side of preparedness. Perhaps air defense is obsolete; nevertheless, some future war situation may require such defense.

The Preattack Mobilization Base might be extraordinarily important. This base consists of a capability to improve rapidly the ability to fight, or threaten to fight, limited, controlled, central and general wars. It also includes a *long lead time* list of items for defense or offense; by the quick spending of money such *lead time* items could be rapidly developed.

Insurance Against a Change in Policy, or Preattack Mobilization Base, disposes of some lacunae left in the concept of Counterforce as Insurance (*q.v.*), or Insurance Against Unreliability, which, in turn, met some demands imposed by weaknesses offered in the posture of Finite Deterrence (*q.v.*), or Insurance for Reliability, although the latter certainly had a better posture than mere Minimum Deterrence (*q.v.*). A remaining consideration, and not one of the least, concerns itself with responsibilities incurred by treaty arrangements, responsibilities which, in the case of the United States understanding with NATO, for instance, must be considered as significant in home defense as the protection of the national soil proper. A strike against Berlin is a strike against Sioux City.

To the degree that Preattack Mobilization Base, or

Insurance Against a Change in Policy, does not include this consideration, it too manifests an essential weakness of posture. (*See, however,* Credible First-Strike Capability; *see also* Heart of Darkness.)

## Preemptive Attack

An attack provoked by an imminent and certain enemy strike. Such an attack requires that warning be unequivocal, although early warning is almost certain to be equivocal. The principle then involves an alternative series of conditional possibilities in which the attacked state will strike first only if the enemy strikes first.

## Prevail

From Latin *praevalere,* to be very able. A term often used currently in official statements relative to military problems. In general, an attenuated form of the verb "to win" (obs.).

## Probe

From Latin *probare,* to prove. (1) A surgical instrument, commonly of silver, with a blunt end, for exploring the direction and depth of wounds; (2) the proboscis of certain members of the class Insecta.

Modern aerospace technology, reworking and transforming existing terms (*see* Hardware; Aquarium), has adopted the word *probe* in general accordance with definition (2).

Nevertheless, the first definition remains interesting because of its connection with the geology and cosmology of the sixteenth and seventeenth centuries, the incubation period of modern technology. Thomas Burnet, a prominent churchman under Charles II, conceived of Earth as a "dirty little planet." It was fissured and irregularly surfaced through the maleficent advent of the Deluge, which occurred through God's omniscience at the same time as man's Fall from Grace. The Earth had originally been a smooth solid sphere, corrupted later, and fallen. For Richard Hooker, a sixteenth-century divine, the heavenly bodies, controlled by Providence, moved in their orderly ways, and with their movements assured man of his stability in a regulated universe. If chaos were to beset the regularity of the spheres, wholesale dissolution threatened Earth.

If the moon should wander from her beaten way, the times and seasons of the year blend themselves by disordered and confused mixture, the winds breathe out their last gasp, the clouds yield no rain, the earth be defeated of heavenly influence, the fruits of earth pine away as children at the withered breasts of their mother no longer able to yield them relief: what would become of man himself, whom these things now do all serve?

Hooker and Burnet, unable in the adolescence of scientific method to investigate either geology or the ionosphere objectively, probed the depths of the wounds in Earth and the confusions of the sky: indices of man's Fall into corruption.

Such metaphysical fancies weigh little now. Science and technology, in their progress since the Elizabethan era, have permitted man to use plants, animals and minerals to an unprecedented degree; by overcoming disease and lack of sanitation, science and technology have permitted more men to remain alive longer on Earth than ever before. Such considerations have made Probe (2) a crucially significant metaphor for the modern Probe, whose makers see ahead to an increasing overpopulation which may reduce Earth—in the absence of some immense and beneficial decimation of the population—to a giant putrescent asylum for 50,000,000,000 people in the twenty-first century.

Disturbed by this prognosis, technologists looked for a noun to convey adequately the full meaning of space exploration by test spheres, earth satellites or any instrument-bearing unmanned vehicles in space, used to report back information by radio or other means on the conditions in which they move, areas for potential future settlers or sources for usable material.

After a long search within the crowd of airborne animals, space technicians found the emblem they had sought, the Asilidae, or robber flies. The robber fly is a large insect. It has a long, hairy body and elongate, bristly, prehensile legs (see Paddle-Wheel Satellite). The robber fly preys upon other insects, extracting their body fluids by means of its probe, a long extension of the underlip, functioning as a piercing mouth. The robber fly larvae live in rotting wood.

Often accused of dullness, of hobbling the imaginative and life-enhancing swell of the moral sense in favor of the mechanic round, the technologists, in their poetic grasp of their process and of the function of their instruments, imply the reverse. They are the New Humanists, determined through a reconnaissance satellite to suck out knowledge from a specific galactic area or member, one body reaching out to another, and, with great difficulty, to draw it back through the Probe to Earth in the service of man at the center, man the measure, the great artificer.

Now as defined by this context, the New Humanists see in the Asilidae larvae the present state of man, beleaguered, striving to rise and to escape from a corruptible home, soon to be outworn.

They seek, not unlike Hooker and Burnet, a Resurrection and a New Place. And the instrument, relatively weak and undependable as it may appear, called upon to conduct the virgin unmanned investigations of lunar and planetary environments, to prove the astounding range of human adaptability, is very much the Probe (2).

## Projection

A common mental device for disposing of personally unacceptable ideas originating within oneself by assigning them to other people, often in a distorted form. Thus, "I hate him" (unacceptable—dangerous?) becomes "He hates me" (acceptable). This can lead to fear of him. It can also lead to hatred of him but with justification: "I now hate him because he hates me." At the core, however, is an even greater unacceptable feeling, to wit, love. Thus, actually, "I want him to love me" (unacceptable—humiliating?) becomes "I hate him" (unacceptable—dangerous?) becomes "He hates me," which is the only idea in the series likely to be conscious. The prototype for this mental device is the infant's practice of spitting out or vomiting up unwanted food, thus making external what was internal but painful.

This psychological mechanism was discovered by Sigmund Freud early in the twentieth century in his analysis of a European statesman. (*See* Paranoia.)

## Propulsion

Oh, yes, we shall get to the moon—but of course I daren't tell Hitler yet.
> —Wernher von Braun, Technical Director of the German V-2 project, in the early 1940s (*see* Rocket)

Missiles and space vehicles are powered by motors embodying the principles of Newton's third law of motion: *to every action there is an equal and opposite reaction.* Hot gases are expelled under extreme pressure from the combustion chamber and pushed forward out of the nozzle. This is *thrust,* measured in pounds. The ratio of thrust over weight determines the acceleration of the rocket. The duration of acceleration determines speed.

Two main types of propellant are in general use, solid and liquid chemical fuels. Ordinary jet aircraft, flying within Earth's atmosphere, use oxygen from the air; they are *air-breathing* vehicles. Missiles and space vehicles, which leave Earth's atmosphere, must carry their own source of oxygen for travel in airless space.

The simplest form of rocket engine is the solid-propellant motor. In a solid rocket a blended granular mixture of fuel and oxidizer is cast into the combustion chamber. The propellant encloses a central cavity parallel to the length of the rocket. The shape of this cavity determines the speed of burning. The motor is ignited by an electric spark, and the hot gases, pushing against the closed end of the rocket chamber, stream out of the narrow nozzle. The solid propellant is much favored for military missiles: solid-fuel rockets are ready for launch almost immediately upon demand. Such weapons as Minuteman and Polaris can be off with very little preparation.

The liquid-propellant rocket requires long countdowns and a much more complex fueling process than the solid-fuel rocket. In addition, the risk of failure in liquid systems is greater: the oxidizer must be kept at very low temperatures, and frozen valves and lines from the oxidizer to the combustion chamber are an operational hazard. The fuel and oxidizer in this type of motor must be housed in separate tanks, then pumped or forced by compressed air into the combustion chamber. In the chamber, the mixture of chemical liquid fuel and oxygen forms the propellant and leaves through the nozzle like the thrust gases in the solid-propellant engine.

The exhaust velocity for solid fuels is lower than that furnished by liquid motors. Liquid hydrogen, for instance, yields more than 14,000 feet per second, which is near the limit for chemical propulsion. Since escape velocity requires much more speed than this, rockets are constructed in stages and build up to "escape" by the total of all their thrusts. Liquid-propellant systems are clustered to provide greater thrust for delivery of larger payloads (*q.v.*) as in the Saturn booster, or first-stage rocket, under development. Saturn would yield 1,500,000 pounds of thrust. The most powerful chemical propellant system is used in the Nova, or F-1, engine, which is designed to burn fuel and liquid oxygen to produce a thrust equal to the total of the Saturn cluster. Nova itself will be clustered and used as one of six such engines, providing 9,000,-000 pounds of thrust, designed to send manned missions to the moon and the planets without the need for orbital refueling. (*See* Manned Space Station.) Such a system could send a payload of about 35–40 tons to the moon.

Nuclear rockets are still basically in the planning stage. The easiest way to use nuclear power for space flight involves replacing the liquid-system combustion chamber with a reactor. The reactor, containing a fissionable fuel, directs its heat to the liquid propellant going through it, and the liquid, vaporized, leaves the nozzle to provide thrust. Exhaust velocities of 25,000 to 30,000 feet per second can be achieved with nuclear reactors, twice as fast as those available from chemical liquid systems. Some protection against radiation from the reactor may be necessary in space flight, but manned flight may need shielding against space radiation in any case. Since the exhaust velocity of nuclear systems is high, the same trip, with the same payload, will require a smaller number of stages. On the other hand, much greater payloads will be carried to space targets by nuclear engines.

Reactors with a gaseous core, capable of operating at up to 18,032° F., though presenting a difficult engineering problem, may be built to furnish exhaust velocities of 50,000 feet per second. Space vehicles could then carry millions of pounds of payload through the solar system.

The fourth major category in propulsion systems is the electrical, the thrust-producing capabilities of a stream of charged particles—ions—accelerated by electrical or magnetic forces. Thrust is very low and electrical propulsion is not envisaged as useful for taking off from Earth. However, such a system could accelerate a space vehicle from orbital to escape velocity and could also be useful as a constantly dependable thrust source in outer space, where the amount of thrust needed for acceleration becomes small, because of the lack of major gravitational forces acting directly upon the space vehicle.

In addition, a system for using the sun's radiation pressure, for "solar sailing," may develop a future source of thrust without the consumption of fuel.

The first liquid-propellant rocket flight was made on a farm near Auburn, Massachusetts. A rocket designed by Dr. Robert Hutchings Goddard climbed 41 feet into the air on March 16, 1926.

**Protium**  *See* Hydrogen.

**Pseudologia Phantastica**  *See* Lie.

**Psychochemicals**
Incapacitating agents able to produce in their victims temporary mental confusion, anesthesia, narcosis, paralysis or blindness. Pharmaceutical houses supply the

Army Chemical Center with about 400 compounds each month for possible exploitation of their medically undesirable side effects. Leaving aside possible variability in tolerance, individual hypersensitivity, allergic reactions, excitement, laryngospasm and stupor, these weapons, the Defense Department has suggested, "would make it possible to paralyze temporarily entire population centers without damage to homes or other structures. . . . Many forms of chemical and allied warfare are more 'humane' than existing weapons." Although it is impossible to ascertain the possible effects of temporary insanity in an urban, industrial or military population, there is little doubt that for the first time in history, war "will not necessarily mean death," as the former chief chemical officer of the U.S. Army, Gen. William Creasy, testified.

## Psychopath

Incorrectly, any person possessed of a sick mind. Thus, often used abusively.

Correctly, a person whose way of life is based on a grand show of good intentions that covers up a basic insincerity and fraudulence. Psychopaths are clever, charming, irresponsible, emotionally shallow, flattering, double-crossing, evasive, impulsive, arrogant, opportunistic, and fanatic. They are excellently suited to be swindlers, con men, zealous patriots, and political leaders of the sort that rises to sudden, brilliant—though short-lived—prominence.

# Q

**Quantum** (Pl., quanta)

The fundamental package of energy. Discrete quanta, acting in concert, give rise to spectacles of continuity. Thus the appearance of continuity in a beam of light, in the pull of gravity, in rate of motion, in intensity of heat, is reducible to the gush of discontinuous quanta. The observation of quanta, rather than of their various spectacles, may be likened to our looking through a snowfall to the flakes composing it.

However, the failure of this analogy in two important respects should be noted: snowflakes are divisible and vary in size. But quanta are indivisible, and all quanta of the *same* phenomenon are precisely the same. This monadistic character of quanta leads to a simple law which reigns over most systems in the universe: while lower or higher magnitudes of phenomena involve lower or higher magnitudes of quanta, these magnitudes differ as multiples of integers, never fractions. Much of the universe is restless in fits of whole numbers. (For the multiplicand of integral magnitudes, *see* Planck's Constant.)

# R

**Rad** *See* Relative Biological Effectiveness.

## Radiation
The transport of energy in the absence of a material carrier; also the energy so transported.

Unlike, say, an electric current, which requires a material conductor, radiant energy travels only by means of its own velocity, and the energy it gives up to an object upon collision is its sole carrier. Radiation is divided into categories according to its energy, which, in turn, is a function of wavelength and frequency. (For some of the categories of radiation *see* X Ray.)

Sunlight was formerly the most popular example of radiant energy. Actually a mixture of different radiations, sunlight reaches Earth through a journey of 92 million miles of virtually empty space. Its impact upon Earth's atmosphere and Earth itself dissipates sunlight into numerous effects, though mainly into heat.

Most types of radiant energy can now be generated on Earth itself. For example, visible white-light radiation is practically omnipresent since Edison's invention of the electric light bulb. As for radio-wave radiation, it is estimated that in the United States alone 4 billion man hours a year are spent watching television receivers of this type of radiation—this is twice the man hours spent on productive labor. Ultraviolet radiation is common in indoor swimming pools, resorts and other places. X-ray radiation is widely employed in medicine, dentistry, metallurgy, and, until recently, in the fitting of children's shoes. Since mid-twentieth century, the radiation from nuclear reactions, while not as entertaining or as abundantly produced, has begun to rival radio waves in public interest and attention.

## Radiation Effects

Scientists disagree on the relative incidence of harmful radiation effects upon an attacked population. In general the effects may be divided into short-term and long-term hazards.

Injury due to nuclear radiation may not be apparent until hours, days, weeks, months or years after exposure. The cardinal symptoms of radiation disease are nonspecific; they may occur by themselves or in combination with other more usual disease symptoms. Injuries due to burn or atmospheric overpressures from thermal and blast effects of nuclear detonations will complicate diagnoses in postattack conditions.

The short-term effects of exposure to radiation include disease caused by action upon the blood-forming organs, upon the gastrointestinal system, and upon the central nervous system. These categories correlate with progressively higher exposures to gamma rays and neutrons; in addition, they are useful for the sorting and handling of casualties after a thermonuclear attack.

The range from 0 to 1,000 rad is a continuum from slight effects (0 to 200 rad) to death, usually by disease related to insult upon the blood-forming organs (200 to 1,000 rad). Symptoms in response to a radiation dose within the continuum 200 to 1,000 rad show very little correlation with dosage. Prompt nausea and vomiting usually characterize any injury within the continuum. In general, early symptoms are transient; victims of dosages below 300 rad or so often display small hemorrhages under the skin or increased bleeding tendency at 4 to 6 weeks after exposure. There is no exhibition of convulsions, or irrational behavior. Loss of hair tends to occur throughout most of the range 200 to 1,000 rad. Below 200 rad little or no hair is lost; above 1,000 rad, the individual dies before depilation.

The most prominent injuries occur in the blood. The total white blood count—defense against infections—goes down; this symptom fluctuates for a few days after exposure even near the upper limits of the continuum 175 to 1,000 rad, but eventually the blood-forming system gives out; the bone marrow is no longer capable of producing cells and the individual dies, a victim of marrow death (*q.v.*).

The dose region from 1,000 rad to 5,000 rad inflicts disease on the gastrointestinal tract. (*See* Intestinal Death.) For at least 6 days after the insult to the gastrointestinal system there is no way to separate victims of such dosages from individuals exposed to much less radiation. Medical workers will recognize serious damage to the gastrointestinal system primarily by the death of the affected individuals.

The dose region above 5,000 rad to the whole body involves the central nervous system. Victims of dosages in this range die quickly. (*See* Central Nervous System Death.) Most of them will not be gotten into medical channels because of the rapid onset of symptoms and the general destruction in the areas characterized by such massive doses of radiation.

Aside from external gamma radiation—the prime agent in the foregoing pathologies—ingested fission products would also prove serious. Crops in heavily contaminated areas would threaten the lives of all survivors.

Some important long-term effects of radiation include damage from inhalation, mutations, leukemia, and life shortening.

Radioactive particles which become fixed in the body near radiosensitive tissue continue their activity *in situ* for a long time. Thus a relatively small dose becomes significant over the period of internal radioactivity. Inhaled materials in the upper portion of the respiratory tract can travel to the gastrointestinal tract within a period of hours, or at the most several days. Other radioactive inhaled material is removed into the bloodstream within minutes or hours and thence proceeds to one of the organs of the body, or several. Radioactive materials may also proceed from the lung to the lymph nodes. Radiation from internal sources can produce lung cancer, cancer of the bone, cancer of the liver, cancer of the gastrointestinal tract. No estimated dosages are available, due to the paucity of victims of radioactive particle inhalation.

The effects of mutations will be spread over more than 30 generations in the wake of an atomic onslaught. The number of mutations resulting in fetal or postnatal deaths may range, for instance, in the 30 generations following exposure, anywhere from 4,800,-000 to 385,000,000 United States citizens.

Leukemia (*q.v.*) is definitely induced by large sublethal doses of radiation. This disease begins to show up a year or two after exposure, and appears most frequently 5 to 8 years after exposure. In other words, some of the individuals killed by radiation had their deaths postponed by a number of years. Data on survivors of the atomic attack on the city of Hiroshima (*see* Enola Gay) demonstrate an incidence of leukemia in the population exposed at from 0 to 1,499 meters from the explosion 20 times greater than in the population farther out, 1,500 meters and beyond.

Radiation produces a life-shortening effect sometimes computed as equaling the loss of 10 to 15 days of life for every rad for individuals receiving more than 100 roentgen of radiation. (*See* Relative Biological Effectiveness.) In general, the end of a substantial number of postattack lives may take place anywhere between 4 and 11 years before their expected "normal" occurrence.

Almost all of these effects are irreversible.

## Radioactivity

A natural procedure by which matter divests itself of an exotic nuclear structure. The outcome is stability.

In atoms, stability is contingent upon ratios between certain particles in the nuclei. When these ratios are disrupted beyond certain limits, radioactivity occurs and restores the nuclei to the more banal arrangements. Nuclear ratios become unstable through additions or subtractions of nuclear particles, as in the bombardment of matter by high-velocity rays. (*See* Atom Smasher.) Fission (*q.v.*) can give birth to atoms with unstable nuclei. But at this point in the history of Earth, nature has been responsible for far and away the greatest production of unstable nuclei. Small but significant amounts of matter—like uranium, thorium, certain variants of hydrogen and carbon—all with radioactive nuclei, originated with Earth itself and have been decaying ever since, relentlessly toward stability.

Radioactivity is the emission of particles from unstable atomic nuclei. Either of two types of particles is emitted: alpha or beta (*qq.v.*). A gamma (*q.v.*) ray is also released whenever the emission of a particle does not carry away quite the energy it has represented in the nucleus. The decay of a uranium atom begins with the emission of an alpha particle. It proceeds roughly as follows. A thorium atom results. Thorium, being also unstable, releases a beta particle, and is converted to protactinium, another unstable atom, which throws off a beta particle and reverts to another variant of uranium. Again, an alpha particle is discharged; a variant of thorium occurs, which discharges, this time, an alpha particle. Radium appears in the series and gives up an alpha particle, producing the unstable element radon. The decay continues through variants of polonium, lead and bismuth and comes to rest finally in the stable end-product, non-radioactive lead. Gamma radiation has accompanied the disintegration throughout. This, of course, is only one of a variety of radioactive series, but with available mathematics and data, any series can be predicted and plotted.

But prediction and plotting are about all that can be done. Though attempts have been made, radioactivity cannot, as yet, be impeded or hastened, let alone controlled. A radioactive substance like uranium can be melted, frozen, pounded, compounded, electrified, soaked, amalgamated, but its decay proceeds with indifference at its own steady rate.

### Radioisotope
An isotope is a variant of a chemical element. It has the same chemical properties, as well as the same (*iso*) place (*tope*) on the periodic chart of elements as the element it is a variant of. Isotopes of the same element

differ from one another only physically, which is the result of differences in the number of neutrons in the atoms; the number of protons and electrons, however, is the same, which accounts for the chemical similarities. Most elements have one or more isotopes. By adding neutrons to an otherwise stable, nonradioactive isotope, radioactivity (*q.v.*) is imparted to the isotope, and the isotope is then referred to as a radioisotope.

Since radioisotopes enter chemical reactions precisely as their nonradioactive variants do, they can be introduced in plant and animal food for the study of biological processes; their course through the organism can be traced with a radiation detector. Radioisotopes, since they are always emitting biologically hazardous radiation, can be fed in lethal quantities to undesirable insects and vermin as pesticides; how to remove these radioisotopes from crops, to prevent human contact, once they've done their job, and how to remove the dead pests, are problems. Their solutions will be a boon to agriculture and may even end the insect and vermin plague in the surplus-grain elevators that now dot American farmlands. Mixing radioisotopes of known rates of decay with industrial products like rubber airplane tires obviates the necessity of stamping a date on the tires; the age can be determined by computing the amount of radioactivity left in the tire. A radioisotope introduced in golf balls insures their recovery by means of a sportsman's radiation counter. Currency can be invisibly marked with radioisotopes to make counterfeiting difficult. Uses for radioisotopes are being proposed increasingly.

Of the 1,000 or so identified isotopes, about 750 are radioisotopes. A few of these 750 occur naturally, usually in minute but detectable quantities. The rest are man-made. Radioisotopes can be produced in accelerators (*see* Atom-Smasher) but this method is very costly. A better source is the nuclear reactor (*q.v.*). (*See* Columbia River; Nuclear Thimbles.) But the most economical means of producing abundant amounts of radioisotopes is still a nuclear-bomb burst. If underground, the radioisotopic debris from the burst can be captured. Above ground, the debris, of course, cannot

248

be captured and is literally cast to the winds. (*See* Fallout.)

# RAND

There can be no tampering with the national security. [It] must be absolute and without concessions for reasons of admiration, gratitude, reward, sympathy or charity.
—Gray Committee in the AEC Oppenheimer case

With our audience, in spite of our strong efforts to be objective, we cannot avoid being influenced by what we know it likes to hear. Feelings of loyalty and friendship are involved, as well as a normal liking for applause.
—Bernard Brodie of RAND

A corporation, not to be confused with Remington-Rand of typewriter fame. Upper-case RAND (Research and Development) is the most prestigious (Latin *prestigium* = juggler's trick) of a genre of corporations, now booming, whose products are labeled sanity. RAND sells strategic and tactical advice. Sired by the Douglas Aircraft Company in 1946 and then abandoned, RAND was a seminar of destitute experts. However, in the postwar world, the corporation's product proved to be a bonanza. RAND currently commands an annual budget of $13.5 million and keeps busy some 900 experts, 600 of whom are said to rank high enough to merit blackboards in their offices. Located in Santa Monica, California, the corporation's second base of operations is Washington, D.C. In the nation's capital RAND personnel enjoy clearance, sit on seventy government committees, testify incessantly at Congressional and military hearings and distribute fresh publications almost daily. These publications are addressed to security problems and range from studies of Russia's gross national product to presentations of technical systems of mathematical analysis. Most of RAND's publications exceed both the intellectual attainment and the practical concern of the clients whose funds get them written and published, but the general feeling is that they are probably urgent and should continue. The following findings exemplify RAND's contribution to an informed leadership:

1. The atomic air raid on Hiroshima produced neg-

ligible panic among the city's population. Shelter and evacuation were orderly. The psychological effects of air raids have been entirely exaggerated.

2. America contains possibly 700,000,000 square feet of underground mine space suitable for housing industrial operations.

3. Most strategic problems will yield to a combination of Experience, Rule of Thumb, Educated Guess, Prayer, and Multistage Decision Process Mathematics.

4. Total thermonuclear war, even with an enemy's surprise assault, need not result in the political extinction of the nation.

5. A shelter program should begin *outside* of cities.

6. Stockpiling sufficient equipment for 10 per cent of America's prenuclear-war oil-refining capacity would cost $100,000,000.

7. Radiation meters are currently the most significant equipment that could be purchased in the interest of the American public. This need could be satisfied entirely for $100,000,000.

RAND's chief client is the U.S. Air Force.

## RAT

The RAT will go a long way toward neutralizing the Soviet submarine threat; the U.S. Navy has described it as the greatest advancement in antisubmarine warfare since World War II. The RAT—Rocket-Assisted Torpedo—leaves its destroyer on a rocket; as it reaches its maximum altitude, the airframe separates like a clamshell, releasing the torpedo and opening the first six-foot parachute. This chute is subsequently shed as a second parachute opens to slow the torpedo's descent into the sea. On entering the water the second parachute and the nose cap, which has protected the RAT's delicate instruments, are dropped and the torpedo begins a circular search pattern. When its acoustic system picks up the enemy's sound, the torpedo homes on its target, intercepts him, and the RAT explodes.

## Reaction Formation

A manner of self-deception where "the thought is furthest from the wish."

Reaction formation is the assertion of behavior opposite to that behavior which would be expressive of an unacceptable wish. Such assertion denies the existence of the wish. Thus, shame might be a reaction formation against the wish to show off, disgust against the wish to smell and touch filth, meticulousness against the wish for disorder.

Aggression is a frequent victim of reaction formation, and pacificism is a common variety of this defense. Pacificism as a reaction formation, rather than as a course of political action, can be identified in its habit of provoking otherwise avoidable violence through a caricature of civil disobedience. The violence is subsequently exaggerated and celebrated with a quality of outraged martyrdom.

On the other hand, aggression may be used as a reaction formation against an unacceptable longing for passivity toward a powerful authority. Here there is a preoccupation with aggression as the exclusive solution to all interpersonal problems, the amount of aggression often being excessive with respect to the problem. There is the extreme case of the legionnaire who donned his uniform, complete with rifle, to exchange a pair of socks that was the wrong size. He recalled that the haberdasher was a strapping, muscular fellow.

### Reality
Nonexistent at birth, reality arises faintly during the first year of life. The encounter of a maturing perception with the forces of nature and the values of culture, reality is the last regulator of human activity to come fully into operation. It is also the most feeble. Reality evolves in the service of pleasure (q.v.), an earlier and more vigorous regulator. Reality modifies pleasure: *Not now, but later. Some, but not all. Presently. Softly. Afterward. Not here, but there. Tomorrow. Perhaps.* But reality never wholly dominates pleasure. The extrication of reality from the subjective must always be a matter of degree.

### Realpolitik
The *techniques,* as opposed to the morals and ethics,

of politics, usually in foreign affairs. Realpolitik refers to those opportunistic activities based on power and justified by the necessity of reconciling national security and destiny with the realities, rather than the ideals, of human conduct.

Therefore, a prudent ruler ought not to keep faith when by doing so it would be against his interest, and when the reasons which made him bind himself no longer exist. If men were all good, this precept would not be a good one; but as they are bad, and would not observe their faith with you, so you are not bound to keep faith with them. Nor have legitimate grounds ever failed a prince who wished to show colourable excuse for the non-fulfillment of his promise.

—Niccolò Machiavelli, 1532

Since realpolitik is political grammar rather than message, in the sense that democracy, royalism, fascism, communism are messages, it is as absurd to speak of its immorality and abolition as it is to inveigh against and ban the microscope because it reveals unpleasantness. Realpolitik leads directly to what is—with the possibility that what should be can then come to pass.

## Recovery

Unless the survivors of a thermonuclear war could escape death from starvation, exposure and disease and then go on to rebuild the nation, their "survival" would have little meaning.

Some of the important variables in recovery include casualties, destruction of wealth, organizational breakdown, postwar defense burdens and postwar assistance or interference by other nations. Mr. Sidney Winter of RAND (q.v.) believes that the effectiveness of postwar assistance depends on "our success in limiting damage to the United States." The most significant point is the extent of organizational breakdown. The Secretary of the Treasury, Mr. Dillon, has recently urged steps to assure the continued functioning of the banking system after an attack. (See Banking, Thermonuclear.) In both Hiroshima and Nagasaki there was an immediate mass exodus of the survivors, with almost no impulse to furnish care or help for the casualties. The marked apathy (*q.v.*) and resistance to the restoration of sanitary facilities and a safe water supply in both cities present an immensely fertile field for significant research. But no amount of research is likely to alter the fact that decisions will finally have to be based on a large measure of faith in, or skepticism about, the basic strength and resilience of the people and institutions of our nation. Much faith will be required. Not only are there likely to be millions of nonfatal casualties from the blast, thermal and radiation effects (*qq.v.*) of nuclear weapons, who will die if medical care is not provided, but additional millions will be threatened with death from exposure, disease, thirst and starvation. The resources and organization to meet these threats to the population will necessarily be drawn almost entirely from areas that have escaped damage, or have been damaged only slightly. The existence of such areas is highly desirable. (*See* Country B.) A reasonably rapid recovery, Herman Kahn (*q.v.*) suggests, can be obtained if we succeed in holding damage down to the equivalent of something like 53 metropolitan areas destroyed (*see* Country A), and if seven optimistic assumptions materialize: "(1) Favorable political environment; (2) immediate survival and patch-up; (3) maintenance of economic momentum; (4) specific bottlenecks alleviated; (5) 'bourgeois' virtues survive; (6) workable postwar standards adopted; (7) neglected effects unimportant." The failure of these assumptions to materialize will necessarily add to the burdens of recovery. Mr. S. Winter, testifying, like Mr. Kahn, before a committee of the House of Representatives, sees as justified an attitude of cautious optimism with respect to the ability of the nation to cope with the problems of economic reorganization and recuperation over a broad range of possible wars. But "there is a great need for further research in order to reduce or eliminate the uncertainties that now exist." Studies of this kind will fall within the Office of Emergency Planning functions. "The idea of distributing food around the country, so as to locate it more in proportion to population, is an excellent idea," Mr. Winter suggested in his testimony during a discussion of recovery. If, due to certain problems of chaos incidental to nuclear war, no capacity for processing exists in the area after blast, burn, and radiation, that "would certainly constitute an objection to the program . . . but after all unprocessed wheat can be eaten. There is no serious problem here . . . even grain exposed to direct fallout could be salvaged after disposal of portions that had actually come in contact with the fallout. That is just my impression."

## Regression
The recovery of behavior that was adaptational in the past in order to cope with situations in the present. Playfulness, rage, hallucinatory experiences, silliness, intoxication, obesity, daydreaming, weeping are states involving regression. Very deep regression, but brief and controlled as to time and place, is a feature of sleep. Regression also turns up in connection with creativity and problem-solving. The ubiquity of this process in human behavior reveals the liveliness of the child in the man—a liveliness for wisdom and absurdity. Thus, it can never be wholly deplored or wholly trusted.

## Relative Biological Effectiveness   (RBE)
A scale used to rate the various types of ionizing radiation (q.v.) for their biological efficiency. It has been difficult to standardize this scale because the efficiency of a given radiation may vary with the effects under consideration. However, it is assumed that, under most conditions, the RBE for X, beta and gamma radiations (qq.v.) will be unity.

The RBE scale is also functional in translating measurements of radiation dosage, such as the *rad* and the *roentgen,* into their biologically effective dose, or, as it is called, *rem* (roentgen-equivalent-man). The roentgen, a unit of air doses, is the standard measure of X-ray exposure. The rad, a unit of tissue doses, is, for most practical purposes, very much like the roentgen and is the unit recommended for use by the International Commission on Radiological Units. To determine the rem—the amount of ionizing radiation which produces in man the equivalent effects of one roentgen of X rays or gamma radiation—one multiplies the dose in rads by the appropriate RBE. It works like this: .25 rad of an alpha ray with an RBE of 4 for a particular effect would equal 1 rem and produce an effect of the same magnitude as 1 roentgen of X rays or gamma radiation. This all checks out best on the Standard Man (*q.v.*).

**Rem** *See* Relative Biological Effectiveness.

## Repetition
Observations of certain behavior, like recurrent nightmares and other recurrent acts leading to pain and suffering, suggest an impulse in humans to redramatize earlier experiences irrespective of any advantage that doing so might bring from the point of view of pleasure or reality (*qq.v.*). It seems that there is an imperative to master old defeats regardless of current problems. Why this should be so is not clear. The compulsion to repeat remains as obscure to comprehension as it is haunting to behavior.

## Repression
It is not the unpleasant which we forget; rather, we fail to remember that which, *if* remembered, would be unpleasant.

Of the several mental processes which unconsciously keep the unconscious (*q.v.*) unconscious, repression is probably the most celebrated in view of its entrance into common usage. In common usage, however, its specificity tends to get lost. While other mental processes work over unpleasant stimuli into disguises which can remain conscious, repression banishes from consciousness all affects, ideas and impulses associated with threatening stimuli. Repression, therefore, has to bury a great deal. The mind is impoverished and its range of attentiveness to feelings, ideas and external objects is considerably narrowed. Alleviation of distress is the aim. The price is self-knowledge.

Repression is needed to some extent by everybody, but it is especially characteristic in those people who go through life leaving things very much as they find them.

## Resurrection Machine

I candidly admit that in my practice I have not found any reliable example of the knight of faith, though I would not therefore deny that every second man may be such an example. I have been trying, however, for several years to get on the track of this, and all in vain. People commonly travel around the world to see rivers and mountains, new stars, birds of rare plumage, queerly deformed fishes, ridiculous breeds of men—they abandon themselves to the bestial stupor which gapes at existence, and they think they have seen something. This does not interest me. But if I knew where there was such a knight of faith, I would make a pilgrimage to him on foot, for this prodigy interests me absolutely . . . the only thing that can save him is the absurd, and this he grasps by faith. So he recognizes the impossibility, and that very instant he believes the absurd; for if, without recognizing the impossibility with all the passion of his soul and with all his heart, he should wish to imagine that he has faith, he deceives himself, and his testimony has no bearing, since he has not even reached the infinite resignation.

—Søren Kierkegaard, *Fear and Trembling*

The Resurrection Machine is a hypothetical construct contrasting with the Doomsday Machine (*q.v.*). The Resurrection Machine involves the mutual assent of the Soviet Union and the United States to a deliberate hobbling of their power to carry out a first strike upon each other's territory.

Minuteman and Polaris, good examples of the difficulty in discriminating between first-strike and second-strike (retaliatory) weapons, lend themselves to the Resurrection Machine hypothesis. If the Polaris submarines were by mutual agreement kept out of firing range of potential targets, and if the Minuteman missiles were mechanically hobbled against any but second-strike activity, such national attitudes, implemented analogously in the Soviet Union, would lead to an international situation more promising than the current fear-laden stalemate of reciprocal paranoid states of mind.

Each power, still in control of a crippling arsenal

of second-strike hardware, could rest more easily in the acceptance of a status quo less invidious than a series of first-strike brinks and threats—given the necessary reliability to insure faith in standby inspection procedures, faith in the methods of hobbling, faith in abstention from initial violence, faith in the possibility of communication between states, faith that, acting in self-interest, states should choose to survive.

## Rocket
A contemporary instrument, its roots in thirteenth-century China. The Chinese inventors of explosive powder packed tubes with it and the rocket shot into the air as a stream of hot gas escaped rapidly, in conformity with the three laws of motion formulated four centuries later by Isaac Newton: (1) A rocket will move until gravity arrests it; (2) the weight of a rocket equals the product of its mass and gravity forces: thus rocket motors must be sufficiently powerful to overcome the drag of gravity; (3) the action of the exhaust going in one direction engenders an equal reaction moving the rocket in the opposite direction.

Medieval rockets flourished only a short time; targets could be more accurately destroyed by the gun. The modern intercontinental ballistic missile (ICBM), a big rocket armed with nuclear bombs, can travel 5,500 nautical miles with a reasonably expectable error of no more than one mile. Since the explosive, blast and radiating capacity of the warhead can easily compensate for the distance from target, a near-miss is a hit.

The government of *Reichsführer* Hitler initiated the return of the rocket. The V-2 was an instrument very impressive in its potential. Political necessity curtailed further experimentation on German soil, but a significant number of rocketry specialists found adequate situations in such states as the U.S.A. and the U.S.S.R., where they continue their work.

As an indirect result of their quests for national security and peace through deterrence, these two states opened the door to the Space Age. Scientists of the U.S.S.R. had developed a very powerful rocket engine

to deliver a very heavy A-bomb warhead. Once success was attained in their project with a lighter and
more effective H-bomb, the rocketry specialists found
themselves with an oversize ICBM and excess thrust
capacity. They adapted what they had to send Sputnik
I (*q.v.*) into space on October 4, 1957. The U.S.A.,
also interested in space, used Jupiter-C, an Army missile, and Sergeant, an adapted Army missile, with a
Redstone engine developed by the V-2 specialists. On
the last day of January, 1958, Explorer I, 166 pounds
lighter than Sputnik I, arced into orbit (*q.v.*).

In their search for more effective rocketry, the specialists are developing rockets such as the Atlas and
the Saturn, with 360,000 and 1,500,000 pounds of
thrust respectively. But since the flight velocities required for astronautics far exceed those obtainable
with a single rocket unit using conventional propulsion (*q.v.*) techniques, the multistage rocket provides
adequate velocities. One rocket or more is carried to
high speed by another rocket, to be launched independently when the first rocket is exhausted. Stages
may be interchanged. Thus the Centaur upper stage
becomes the upper stage of the Saturn C-1 and C-2,
and the second stage of the Saturn C-1 becomes the
third stage of the Saturn C-2, a less powerful version
of the C-3.

**Roentgen**   *See* Relative Biological Effectiveness.

**Rongelap**

In the meantime, the Rongelap people provide an interesting group of subjects exposed to a level of radiation appreciably above the world average. Present indications are that
the body burdens of radionuclides will not reach levels
which, from known data, will result in morbid processes.
—*Medical Survey of Rongelap People, March 1958,
Four Years After Exposure to Fallout,* prepared for
the U. S. Atomic Energy Commission

On March 1, 1954, an unexpected change in wind
direction, following hard upon the American detonation of the first fission-fusion-fission bomb at Bikini

Atoll, resulted in the severe irradiation of 64 Marshallese individuals. They lived on the island of Rongelap, 105 nautical miles from the detonation site. Two days after exposure, they were evacuated from the affected island, to which they returned when Rongelap was judged by American authorities to be safe for human habitation, three and one-half years later.

The yearly inspections by American medical teams to which the Rongelapians submitted dealt primarily with the effects of beta particles, directly involved with damage to the skin, and gamma radiation, with internal injuries. (*See* Beta; Gamma.)

The gamma radiations do not appear to have had lethal effects. The only symptoms ascribed to these penetrating radiations included nausea, vomiting and diarrhea within the first two days; but medical findings five years after the detonation could isolate no illnesses or diseases directly associated with acute radiation effects. The incidence of miscarriages and stillbirths appeared to be somewhat higher than in the unexposed Marshallese, but a deficiency of vital statistics precludes definite conclusions as to whether or not this was a radiation effect. Suggestive evidence of slight lag in growth and development of exposed children was being evaluated on the basis of better age data obtained by the medical team.

The Rongelapians were returned to their atoll in July, 1957, after having been transported to Majuro Atoll; the village at Rongelap was completely rebuilt by the United States of America. "An interesting sidelight is that some of the people, particularly the older ones, prefer to live beneath their houses, probably because it is cooler . . . ," states the 1958 medical survey. This return to the slightly contaminated island caused some increase in body burdens of cesium 137, zinc 65, and strontium 90. However, the levels are far below the accepted maximum permissible dose (*see* Permissible), and the inspecting team assumed no untoward effect would result.

If the Rongelapians had only been a little more careful, they would have sustained much less damage from the beta particles.

Had they not been in the habit of using heavy hair

oils, the fallout would not have collected on their heads.

If they had only worn hats, it would have helped.

If they had worn shoes, their feet would have been spared.

If they had worn scarves, shawls, or high-necked shirts, their necks would have been spared.

If they had worn shirts, their beltlines and armpits would have been spared.

If the boys had worn long pants, their thighs would have been spared.

They were, however, careful enough to receive the radiation in relatively benign doses; had they been a few miles farther north, the stronger gamma radiation there would have affected their white blood count and other immunizing mechanisms more quickly. In that event, infecting organisms, entering through the open lesions caused by the beta-particle burns, could not have been repelled, and a good number of the afflicted would have died.

Within the first two days a number of natives experienced a little bit of itching and burning of the skin; some complained of lacrimation.

Only two weeks after exposure did skin lesions and loss of hair appear in almost every Rongelapian. The more profound beta lesions became infected and required treatment with antibiotics, to which they responded nicely. The medical report stated: "Mild pain was associated with the deeper lesions and some difficulty with walking resulted with the deeper lesions located on the feet . . . by no standard could these people be considered incapacitated." The only permanent damage consisted of residual scars, atrophies, and depigmentation.

Without the knowledge owed to the Bikini wind shift, the Atomic Energy Commission said, "We would have been in ignorance of the extent of radioactive fallout and therefore . . . much more vulnerable to the dangers from fallout in the event an enemy should resort to radiological warfare against us."

## Russian Thistle

An annual tumbleweed, a species of saltwort, Salsola

Kali tenuifolia, native to Eurasia, introduced into the United States from there; a weed with prickly stems and globular purple flowers, a sometime emblem of knighthood.

Though few native plants reestablish themselves within one-third of a mile of ground zero (*q.v.*), this specimen has proved to be a vigorous invader of the nuclear-weapons test site maintained by the AEC in Nevada. It flourished on the scorched land even during the first growing season after an explosion.

# S

## Saturn

aaaaaaa ccccc d eeeee g h iiiiiii llll mm nnnnnnnnn oooo
pp q rr s ttttt uuuuu                                    —Huygens

Galileo in 1610, and subsequent observers, had seen
something extraordinary in the shape of Saturn; the
"appendages" seemed to disappear after the initial
sightings. Not until 1655 did Huygens explain the
peculiarity. He said: "A thin flat ring, touching at no
part and inclined to the ecliptic, surrounds it." But
since he was not certain of his observations, he continued his inquiries privately and established priority
by publishing the series of letters above. When properly arranged, they form the Latin sentence *Annulo
cingitur, tenui, plano, nusquam cohaerente, ad eclip-
ticam inclinato.* The 28-degree inclination of the three
thin rings makes them almost invisible from Earth in
two portions of Saturn's orbit around the sun.

The rings do not consist of continuous solid or
liquid matter. They are composed of individual particles probably produced by the breakup of a single
Saturnian satellite which came within the "danger
zone" of its attracting planet, as Earth's moon un-
doubtedly will in time. At that point Earth will most
likely be surrounded by a similar ring or series of rings
and there will be more moonlight, as well as an intermittent rain of broken fragments when the tiny moons
collide with each other and fall to Earth like huge
meteors. Such bodies are probably falling on Saturn
now.

Besides the billions of small elements making up
the rings, Saturn has nine satellites, more than any
other planet: Mimas, Enceladus, Tethys, Dione, Rhea,
Titan, Hyperion, Iapetus, and Phoebe. Little Phoebe

has a diameter of about 150 miles; big Titan, one of 3,000 miles, larger than the moon's—2,160 miles. Tethys has a revolution double that of Mimas; Dione's revolutionary period is about double that of Enceladus. Rhea is the last of the five inner satellites. Mimas, Enceladus, Tethys, Dione and Rhea all take less than 5 days to circle the mother planet; Phoebe takes the longest, 550 days; in between come Titan, Hyperion and Iapetus, taking 16, 21 and 79 days respectively. The first three outer satellites, Titan, Hyperion and Iapetus, each have a feature of interest: Titan is the brightest, Hyperion the smallest, and Iapetus always seems brighter, when seen from Earth, to the west than to the east; Phoebe orbits Saturn from a distance three and one-half times greater than Iapetus and shares with four of Jupiter's satellites the distinction of retrograde motion (*see* Jupiter). It took about 250 years to discover all nine Saturnian satellites: Titan was discovered in 1655; Phoebe was the last, in 1898. Herschel discovered Mimas and Enceladus; Cassini discovered Tethys, Dione, Rhea, and Iapetus; Huygens discovered Titan; Bond discovered Hyperion and Pickering Phoebe. Huygens discovered the rings in the same year that he discovered Titan. Pickering also discovered a tenth satellite, Themis, in 1905. But nobody has been able to find it since and so, unlike Mimas, Enceladus, Tethys, Dione, Rhea, Titan, Hyperion, Iapetus, and Phoebe, it doesn't count.

Saturn, almost twice as far away from the sun as Jupiter, is second in size to it; its atmosphere and construction are very much like Jupiter's as well—a small core of rock, a surrounding layer of ice and proportionally a much larger atmosphere. Saturn is at least 180° F. colder and has a great deal of marsh gas— methane—in its atmosphere, with no ammonia to speak of.

In Babylonian astrology, Saturn was identified with the god Ninurta. For the Greeks, Saturn is associated with the color gray and the element lead. In later periods, *Saturn's day* was associated with the Jewish Sabbath.

Saturn is, at its nearest approach, 744,000,000 miles from Earth.

## Science

A life unexamined is not worth living.          —Socrates

To err is human.                              —Latin proverb

A broad inquiry, by means of numerous subsidiary disciplines, into the true nature of the universe. Its chief exponents liken it to humanity in general, whose perpetuation requires the intermittent observation of its own errors.

## Scientism

The promotion of goods, services, values or decisions in the name of scientific method. Hence science as practiced. One who practices science is called a scientist. The practice allows for a large variety of human inclinations. Scientists are variously idealistic, ambitious, ordinary, academic, practical, foolish, careless, trustworthy, decent, and indecent; some are comic, some tragic, some vulgar, and some are in the grand tradition.

## Second-Order Threat

That order of potentially antagonistic military activity, possibly occurring in 10 to 15 years from the date of preventive concern, against which a few billion dollars a year spent early and wisely may, like a stitch in time, save nine. Too many historical precedents demonstrate the tragedy resulting from insufficient long-range planning and preparation; in an earlier age had the luckless Czar of Russia, for instance, considered in 1902 what might happen to his country in 1917, he could have gone to Switzerland.

## Sensory Deprivation

An experimental technique which reduces the intensity of stimuli reaching a subject. One method is to suspend the subject in a tank of water at body temperature with a blacked-out headpiece for breathing, thus eliminating visual, auditory, gravitational and interpersonal experiences. The mental alterations that soon overcome the deprived subject are similar to those suffered by sensory-deprived individuals in nonexperimental situations, e.g., shipwreck, solitary confinement, separation from one's military unit in strange terrain. The alterations include: increased suggestibility (*see* Brainwash), disorganized thinking, depression, and, in extreme deprivation, hallucinations and delusions (*q.v.*).

## Shelf Life

The amount of time a particular food retains its nutritive capacity in a fallout shelter. For instance, "The short *shelf life* of bread precludes its effective use in nuclear-bomb shelters." (*See* Grandma's Pantry; Survival Biscuit.)

## Shelter—Best Educated Guess

There are at least a couple of shelters in the United States equipped to deal successfully with chemical and bacteriological attacks. Most shelters are somewhat equipped to deal partially with a certain amount of radiation in some localities at particular distances from blast and thermal effects of some nuclear explosions. (*See* Shelter, Emergency; Form 1356.)

A shelter built by the American Chemical Society with a capacity of 700 people utilizes a complete chemical-bacteriological-radiological air-filter system and will be sealed against CBR particles in the air. This system is essential to any shelter outside the area near ground zero (*q.v.*). The filter involves three prefilters separated by right-angle bends, then a filter for radiological and bacteriological particles; next a chemical-particle filter, and a final right-angle bend. The filter transmits 4 cubic feet of good air per minute per person; two 35-kilowatt diesel generators will provide electrical power for the air blowers and other electrical equipment. Water will be furnished by two large storage tanks, sealable at a moment's notice.

The CBR shelter of the American Chemical Society is the result of its Best Educated Guess.

Enough ACS-type shelters to protect all American citizens against radiation, biological infection and disease, and chemically induced paralysis could be constructed for a little under $12,000,000,000. Unfortunately, a highly efficient shelter system may lead to the use of greater fractions of stockpile energy (*q.v.*) with undesirable results.

## Shelter, Emergency

The rural resident, being closer to the earth than the inhabitant of a large city, could rely on caves, some culverts, root cellars and similar places to provide emergency protection against radiation from fallout; the city dweller outside the A-ring (*q.v.*) may take advantage of some built-in shelter possibilities: subways equipped with soft-drink vending machines, peanut machines, chewing-gum machines, toilets, and concessionaire stands selling high-energy candies. Deep basements and the center cores of high-rise buildings also offer some protection against radiation.

## Shelters, Soviet

Structures found on blueprint paper or on the ground in the Union of Soviet Socialist Republics. Their location is a matter of some dispute in the United States of America. Mr. Leon Gouré, of RAND (*q.v.*), an expert in Soviet civil defense, at a hearing of a subcommittee of the Committee on Government Operations of the House of Representatives in the Eighty-seventh Congress, first session, held August 1, 2, 3, 4, 7 and 8, 1961, said, "The Soviet Union has built over the years a considerable number of shelters sufficient for a substantial part but by no means all of the city residents." He added, "It is not a mere paper program." He continued, "At the same time it appears to be far from complete although," he suggested, "it has made considerable progress." Mr. Gouré submitted as exhibits photographs taken by travelers in the Union of Soviet Socialist Republics. Although no photographs of shelters were presented, Mr. Gouré identified sealing or blast doors concealed at the entrances to the station platforms of the subway systems in Moscow, Leningrad, and Kiev. These contentions have been challenged by Harrison E. Salisbury of *The New York Times,* who, after four weeks and 12,000 miles in the U.S.S.R., considers Mr. Gouré *avant-garde.* In December, 1961, he wrote, "Diplomats, foreign military attachés and correspondents who have traveled widely in the Soviet Union report that there is no visible evidence of a widespread shelter program. . . . This correspondent . . . failed to turn up evidence of a single Soviet bomb shelter." Either Mr. Gouré or Mr. Salisbury is right.

## Sheol
A place, found in the Jewish Prophetic Books. An underground abode, location of a semiconscious, nerveless existence after death, beyond the bounds of communion with nation or God; place without moral distinction where all the dead go, where all the dead remain forever.

## Skin
Skin in the human being covers and protects the entire body; it is continuous with the mucous membranes lining cavities which lead to the excretory organs, functions as a tactile and sensory organ containing nerve endings.

The skin is an elastic, semitransparent organ which, with its modifications and accompanying structures (hair, nails), serves to protect the body. The outer layers of the surface of the skin contain only dead cells which form a useful barrier against bacteria.

The skin is composed of the outer epidermis and the inner dermis. The protective epidermis is constantly scraped off; it is replaced by the multiplying cells from below. The dermis includes a complex of connective tissue, lymph vessels, blood, sweat- and oil-producing glands, and hair roots. Sensory nerve endings appear in both zones of the skin.

The sweat glands of the skin excrete water and salts; the evaporating sweat and the water escaping from the skin capillaries help the body to lose heat. Temperature receptors in the skin pass impulses to the central nervous system (q.v.). From the temperature-regulating centers in the brain, impulses are then sent out to the sweat glands, the smooth muscles and the arterioles of the skin.

The skin sensations are heat, cold, pressure, touch, and pain. (*See* Beta; Rongelap.)

## Sloth

> yet otherwise,
> His life he led in lawlesse riotise;
> By which he grew to a grieuous malady;
> For in his lustlesse limbs through euill guise
> A shaking feuer raignd continually:
> —Edmund Spenser

A sluggish, indolent, unalert disinclination to exert oneself, Sloth is one of the deadly sins (*q.v.*). The antithesis of precision and fastidiousness, Sloth is deeply involved with these qualities, as a rebel with authority. The fundamental perfectionism of the slothful person sits on the cruel throne of conscience. The sin in Sloth is its defiance of conscience—the inner surrogate of external authority—for in Sloth the individual strikes back: "You cannot judge me. I disqualify you by giving you nothing to judge."

## Soft Landing

A gentle landing upon the moon or other celestial body. For such landings, the oncoming vehicle requires rocket thrust to offset its downward speed; it also needs mechanisms and sensors for guiding the instrument package to a mild and appropriate descent away from craters and mountains. Near the moon no braking by air is possible since the moon has no atmosphere. Radar altimeters and radio guidance inform the computer aboard the vehicle, and the computer in turn instructs the rocket engine so that the needed amount of thrust is generated. If the retrothrust is applied too soon, the vehicle will stop too high above the lunar surface and then impact at great speed. Grasshopper-leg structures also cushion the possible shock.

Technologists have devised a lunar rover which leaves the vehicle upon landing, assembles itself by inflation, and in obedience to orders from Earth trundles over the moon's surface to telemeter back information about its excursion.

## Sophie Tucker

An American cow, the property of the U. S. Department of Agriculture. With "Madame Curie," another cow, "Sophie Tucker" was fed small quantities of radioactive strontium 90 in scientific experiments aimed at developing a reliable system for the decontamination of radiated milk. The strontium was removed from the milk by filtering the liquid produced by the cows. Costs for removing the strontium would consist of about 10 cents per quart above normal processing expenses. The Department foresaw no emergency that would require use of the technique. Dr. Sam Hoover said, "Dairies should not go jumping into this thing right now." (*See* Hot-Spotters.)

## South

A transcendent reality. Like the Indian—who voyaged across the Bering Strait—and other immigrants to America, Southern man, in his varied origins, can point to a specific ancestral home and language different from his modern environment. The processes of democracy, however, have enabled Southern man to exercise his will and his wit in bypassing the petty provinciality of separate national and linguistic derivations. *E Pluribus Meridies.*

The tragic obstinacy of Northern man, new mechanic and contriver, emphasizes the unremitting pressure against which the power of the Southern Idea struggles. The conditions of modern debasement were forcefully expressed by William Wordsworth in 1800:

For a multitude of causes, unknown to former times, are now acting with a combined force to blunt the discriminating powers of the mind, and, unfitting it for all voluntary exertion, to reduce it to a state of almost savage torpor. The most effective of these causes are the great national events which are daily taking place, and the increasing accumulation of men in cities, where the uniformity of their occupations produces a craving for extraordinary incident, which the rapid communication of intelligence hourly gratifies. . . . Reflecting upon the magnitude of the general evil, I should be oppressed with no dishonorable melancholy had I not a deep impression of certain inherent and indestruct-

ible qualities of the human mind, and likewise of certain
powers in the great and permanent objects that act upon it,
which are equally inherent and indestructible; and were
there not added to this impression a belief that the time is
approaching when the evil will be systematically opposed,
by men of greater powers, and with far more distinguished
success.

The chill epiphanies of Northern man—*equal access
to equal opportunity*—cannot indefinitely mask the
arbitrary and loveless nature of affection by fiat. The
grubby pluralistic farrows of Northern man are replete
with a viscous toleration which dampens the heart's
spontaneous movements. Law enjoins embraces in
widely circulated factory posters; civil-rights merce-
naries commit advertising displays portraying a series
of varicolored faces marked by the same plastic smiles.
"What the imagination seizes as Beauty must be truth,"
Keats said in one of his letters. Equally, what the law
imposes as just must, in wronging the passions, cripple
the straitened heart.

A true bill will not ignore the imperfections in any
world view. But in the interest of fairness, it is clear
that ontological assertions of democracy present themselves in forms peculiar to the particular subculture.
The Southern emphasis on individual rights is also
known as States' Rights. It is hardly possible to over-
look in this phrase the subtle philosophical association
to the microcosm—the little State of Man entitled to
its own sovereignty within the family of the sociopolitical community.

"What thou lovest well remains." The encouraging
tendency of American Negroes to band together under
the aegis of the Moslem dispensation indicates a capacity to learn from Southern man the direction of their
own best interests. The disciples of Elijah Muhammad
—in claiming the title Black Man, in withdrawing
from efforts at integration of races, in their desire to
construct a self-sufficient society outside a hostile environment—demonstrate an understanding of the springs
of action which assures their ultimate success.

And Southern man, enjoined by tradition, and in
a spirit of protective reverence for what his imagi-

nation seizes as beauty, incorporates the only attitude ultimately bound up with the best hope of that unhappy race blindly wandering into the wrong places.

## Spasm War

*Spasm* (spæ·z'm). . . . Sudden and violent muscular contraction of a convulsive or painful character.    —*O.E.D.*

That war conceived of as an uncontrolled operation, irrespective of the relationship between any specific destruction and the desired goal. The Spasm War, very much a concept of Automatic Mutual Annihilation, cuts through the categories of plan, order, and mutual assumptions characteristic of most historical wars, and goes counter to socioanthropological conceptions of the ritual nature of mankind. (*See* Competitive Games.)

## Sputnik I

In the fall of 1957, the Soviet Union successfully launched the first artificial Earth satellite. Vice-President Nixon soberly observed in October of that year, "We could make no greater mistake than to brush off this event as a scientific stunt." The moment was auspicious for renunciations. President Eisenhower asked in 1957 for "even the sacrifice of some seeming self-interest." His successor advised the same. New committees were established, a prominent scientist was appointed as Presidential assistant, Congressional investigations into lags were instituted, the Advanced Research Projects Agency came into being (*see* X), Western strategy and tactics were reexamined, and experts discovered enormous lacunae in American education.

After the initial confusions, new philosophical underpinnings were constructed. After millennia of penetrations, Man the Digger, *homo fodens*, could venture further into himself and his environment only at the risk of utter fragmentation. A new element, space, imposed itself—the airless place waiting for *homo emergens*, Rising Man, to be born. Sputnik announced the fourth major revolution in modern consciousness, following upon the Copernican, the Darwinian and the Freudian.

Subsequent to the long assaults upon the integrity of self, often marked as beginning clearly with the Augustinian confessions, the great cycle turned civilization again, in a new phase, to the examination of surfaces. Acute critics of society had for some time discerned portents of the future in the work of artists, commonly the forerunners of change: the new space in painting stemmed from the destruction of conventional Renaissance perspective as early as the nineteenth century; the mid-twentieth-century school of French novelists emphasized the forgotten significance of surface.

For *homo emergens,* the direct assaults upon the body's obstinate imposition of limits on new perceptions and sensations, assaults so rife in the romantic period, will mark only a historical antecedent. Few regressions to the nature of *homo fodens* will be needed for the extension of man's physical capacity for wonder. Inconceivable planetary surfaces, gravities and temperatures will institute the slow functional adjustments in the New Man. His progressive withdrawal from the Old Place will inevitably produce, as Adlai Stevenson has said, "the new men, who, having seen our little planet in a wholly new perspective, will be ready to accept as a profound spiritual insight the unity of mankind." (*See* Probe.)

## Sputnik II
The first Earth biosatellite, launched on November 3, 1957, carrying X-ray measuring instruments and radio transmitters. Also aboard was the dog Laika, being measured as she flew. When the oxygen gave out, Laika transmitted no further information.

## Standard Man    (*See also* Hypothetical Boy.)
In an effort to explore and discuss questions of radiation permissibility (*see* Permissible) calculations need to be based on some common organic denominator. One common denominator is called the Standard Man.

Excluding the contents of his gastrointestinal tract, Standard Man weighs 70 kilograms, of which 65 per cent is oxygen, 18 per cent is carbon, 10 per cent is hydrogen, 3 per cent is nitrogen, 1.5 per cent is calcium, 1 per cent is phosphorus, with diminishing traces of sulphur, potassium, sodium, chlorine, magnesium, iron, copper, manganese, and finally 0.00004 per cent iodine. Forty-three per cent of his total body is muscle, 14 per cent is fat, 8.7 per cent is skin, 14.2 per cent skeleton, 7.7 per cent blood, the rest distributed over teeth, lungs, glands, nerves, etc. His brain weighs 1.5 kilograms, his heart .3 kg., his testes (two) .04 kg. Standard Man consumes 2,500 cc. of water per day, 700 in food, 1,500 as liquids, and 300 as a product of breathing. He excretes 2,500 cc. of water per day, 500 as sweat, 400 in breath, 100 by feces, 1,500 by urine. The raw materials composing Standard Man are worth about $1.07.

## Stockpile Energy

The amount of fission energy available within the next ten years for use in a major war. (*See* Beach Energy; Kahn Energy.) The magnitude of one Stockpile for the United States of America amounts to approximately $4 \times 10^6$ megatons, 40,000,000,000,000 tons or 1³⁄₁₀ Beach. This figure has a certain scientific interest: in the context of an effective shelter program for the two major nuclear adventurers, there is a high likelihood that the struggle would be protracted and the force of blows rendered proportionally more intense. If the United States and the Soviet Union each applied a significant fraction of one Stockpile to each other, the result, in Beach, would suffice to dispose of all populations on Earth. Thus a highly effective shelter program in both the United States and the Soviet Union might dispose of the enemy, and of the rest of the world.

A catastrophe in this order of magnitude could almost certainly be averted if both states renounced shelter programs and placed their important military installations in the midst of heavily populated cities (*see* Postattack Blackmail). In that event, the application of one Kahn by each state might limit deaths to nearly the total populations of the United States and the Soviet Union.

## Strategic Studies

A major category of contemporary missile and space research. It includes Missions and Methods, concerned with International Conflict Models, Limited War Weapons, Systems Engineering, and Operations Analysis (*q.v.*). Both Missions and Methods lead to Interdisciplinary Systems Research, involving Preliminary Systems Design, Computer Simulation of Large-Scale Systems, Systems Operations Analysis and Evaluation, Strategic and Tactical Operations Planning, and Political and Economic Evaluation. All these direct themselves, by predictable necrophilic synthesis, to a Strategic Studies Group of Cislunar and Global Scope and a Depth on the Military Subsystems Level. The Study Magnitudes in terms of man-months differ, especially in summer.

## Strategic Warning Time

Amount of time available for preparations against forthcoming attack, measured in days, weeks or months. (*See also* Tactical Warning Time.)

## Strontium 90    (*See also* Strontium Unit.)

A radioisotope (*q.v.*) of element 38 whose common isotope, strontium 87, is used to supply the red color in fireworks and signal flares. Strontium 90, which yields up 99 per cent of its radiation over a period of 200 years and is not produced by nature to any appreciable extent, had practically vanished from Earth until it was restored in the fission reactions of the mid-twentieth century. Since 1945 mankind has strewn approximately a barrel of strontium 90 about Earth's atmosphere. Following a fission reaction, strontium 90 remains aloft because its precursor is radioactive krypton, a gas which subsequently decays into strontium 90 microdust. Rainfall carries this microdust downward where it lights here and there on soil and plants.

Strontium 90 is notorious as a bone seeker. The skeleton consists to a large extent of tiny crystals of calcium salt. These crystals are bathed in fluids from which fresh salts are enlisted to maintain the skeleton. Though the skeleton prefers calcium salts, strontium salts will also do. Ingested with food, strontium 90, along with calcium, finds its way to the skeleton where it stands a good chance of being incorporated in a forming crystal. Since these crystals are forming most rapidly in growing children, strontium stands its best chance in children. Once incorporated, it stays a long time. (*See* Effective Half-Life.)

Strontium 90 emits beta rays which, in the bone structure, causes anemia, leukemia, and other ills. Though methods exist for removing strontium 90 from certain foods like milk, it is impossible to remove it from bone; chelating agents—chemicals which capture and carry off radioisotopes—have a stronger affinity for calcium and would destroy the skeleton before getting to the strontium 90. A chelating agent for strontium 90 in bone is considered remote.

### Strontium Unit   (*See also* Sunshine Unit.)

MR. KAHN: I suggest we would be willing to accept something like 50 to 100 sunshine units in our children, in the postwar world, not because we are happy about the idea but because it is a little difficult to achieve much less than that unless we make some preparations.

REPRESENTATIVE HOLIFIELD: We have been using the term "strontium unit" rather than "sunshine." Some of us are allergic to this term "sunshine." We prefer the term "strontium."

MR. KAHN: I could not agree with you more. Strontium 90 is manufactured by men. Sunshine is not. Let us keep it to a manufactured object.

SENATOR ANDERSON: I think that term sunshine came because the first time they said if the fallout came down very, very slowly, that was good for you. And then later they said if it came down very fast, that was good for you. We decided to take the sunshine, in view of everything.

MR. KAHN: I prefer not getting into that debate. I deal in a number of controversial subjects, but I try to keep the number down. To continue, one might be willing to accept 50 or maybe a hundred, even, strontium units in our children . . .

—Hearings, Joint Committee on Atomic Energy,
Eighty-sixth Congress, 1959

A strontium unit is the measure of the concentration of strontium 90 (*q.v.*) in food and in the body. The concentration is taken as the ratio of strontium 90 to calcium. One strontium unit is one micromicrocurie (*see* Curie) per gram of calcium. It is 1/50 that concentration which gives the skeleton a radiation dose equal to the RPG for individuals, and is one-thousandth the maximum permissible body level of strontium 90. (But *see* Permissible.)

## Stuff
An essential part of the nuke (*q.v.*). The fissionable and/or fusionable material of any "atomic bomb."

## Successor-State Theory
Term applied to the possible recognition that Communist China is the legitimate heir to the rights and obligations of mainland Nationalist China, a recognition complicated by the presence of a tiny surrogate of Communist China's dead parent state, victim of a curious metempsychosis, lying offshore.

## Sun
A main sequence star of spectral type G-zero with a surface temperature of about 11,000° F. Originally the sun and its planetary family constituted a darkness in the galaxy, a vast veil of diffuse, rather cold gas. The sun is an immensity in its nine-planet system, of which Earth occupies the third-farthest orbital position, 93,-000,000 miles away, after Mercury and Venus. Mars, Jupiter, Saturn, Uranus, Neptune and Pluto follow in order. The sun is 332,000 times heavier than Earth and 743 times heavier than the mass of all its planets, and operates as an enormous heat engine for the release of elemental energy. The sun's atmosphere consists of atoms beginning to break up, and farther toward its center, matter is transformed in increasingly violent motion. While the pressure at the center of Earth, for instance, must be one of millions of atmospheres, that at the center of the more massive sun must be about 50,000,000,000 atmospheres. The pressure plays its part in keeping the sun from collapsing, a result indicative of what Earth would experience if

it became an active mass in one uninterrupted series of thermonuclear explosions, or nuclear burning. Hydrogen becomes helium. The sun can have no life.

The sun consumes 600,000,000 tons of hydrogen every second; it loses 300,000,000,000 tons of mass every day, but this, compared to its total mass, is not important. The sun is no immensity in the galaxy, belonging to a similar company of some 5 billion middle-class stars, most of which probably possess planetary systems like our own. Certain planetary orbits move within the life zone, a band of hospitable limits for life of some kind. The star nearest to Earth, Alpha Centauri, moves some 250,000,000,000 miles away. The sun has used up only half of its being and will produce medium heat over a period of 5 billion years or so before it cools off. It lies midway between the extremes of weakly luminous, cool stars and brilliant, hot stars, neither a sun prodigal of its hydrogen supply, like the hot star blazing its way through its body in 100 million years, nor a conservator retaining its hydrogen inheritance for 100 billion years. The sun became hot when gravitational forces caused much of the diffuse, cool gas to condense toward a central core, the globs of matter accelerated their motion and the great mass began to glow with its self-induced heat. The early random collision of hydrogen atoms produced fusion (q.v.) and the core temperature rose. As it rose, the sun swelled under the pressure of greater central heat, and assumed a new size and a capacity to radiate heat from its surface. It effectively became a self-regulating thermostat.

The sun probably occupies space at the tip of one spiral arm of the Milky Way, one of the 100,000,000 galactic systems, each of which rotates in giant circles around its nucleus, a giant company of stars, many of which have life histories similar to that of the sun. Our star in its 10 billion years then transmits energy stored or converted by Earth, a planet in a life zone. With one exception, all usable forms of energy are directly or indirectly due to the star. Man has used elemental Earth matter for the production of atomic and thermonuclear energy.

## Sunshine Unit

Now obsolete, the former name of the current strontium unit (q.v.). Derived from Project Sunshine, a program of the Atomic Energy Commission to determine
the worldwide distribution of strontium (q.v.) from
atomic-weapons testing and its consequent effects on
life. Perhaps the grim association to vitamin D, known
as the sunshine vitamin, influenced the name change
of this unit. Like strontium 90, vitamin D is also found
in milk and other foods. (Though the vitamin can and
does facilitate the absorption of strontium 90 into the
bone structure, its more salubrious function is to facilitate the absorption of calcium and other minerals.)
And, again, like the vitamin, for which an intake unit
has been established—the minimum daily requirement (MDR)—an intake unit was established for the
sunshine unit—the maximum permissible concentration (MPC). However, the parallel ends abruptly with
the comparative confidence in the accuracy of the two
intake units: the lack of controlled experimental opportunity on human beings makes the MPC an exceedingly speculative figure. It is arrived at catch-as-catch-
can, from radiation accidents here and there.

## Superego

In ordinary usage a frequent, though sometimes stilted,
synonym for *conscience*. However, there is a difference:
*superego* connotes not only the critical faculty of mind
but also the origin, dynamics and imperishability of
this faculty. Conscience is an experience; superego is
the theory that explains it.

The superego is heir to the precise manner in which
an individual has been made to gain independence
from external authorities. While it alters throughout
the life of an individual, its most vigorous outlines
are laid down in those early years when the child faces
the daily task of fathoming the life-style of the parents. The superego feeds indifferently on conflict,
inconsistency, reason, growing larger as authority
grows smaller. Its development sets free that inner
voice which says, "I am my own judge." That the judge
is largely unconscious, irrational, corrupt and unim-

peachable is offset by two ingenious defendants, for which *see* Ego *and* Group.

## Surface Burst
A nuclear explosion detonated at an altitude low enough to permit its fireball (*q.v.*) to intersect the ground. Compared to an air burst (*q.v.*) a surface burst produces damage to a smaller area with less widespread thermal effects, blast effects and fire storms (*qq.v.*). However, it does have the advantage of producing cratering (*q.v.*), the sucked-up earth of which soon descends again, pelting the local area with massive fallout (*q.v.*). A surface burst over water is a water burst, and sucks up water.

## Survival Biscuit
Parched and crushed wheat. 150,000,000 pounds will be made into wafers, known also as bulgur wafers. They taste like graham crackers, somewhat. The Pentagon plans to put enough bulgur biscuits in community fallout shelters housing 30,000,000 people to provide a 2,000-calorie-a-day diet for 5 days per person. The biscuits will have a shelf life (*q.v.*) of 5 years. The feeling of security resulting from this program is expected to ameliorate popular sensations of potential panic or fate (*qq.v.*). Bulgur is issued in the "Food for Peace" program and has been served on occasion at the White House for demonstration purposes. The bulgur wafer will be the only food stocked in the shelter in addition to one half-quart of 5-year water per person per day.

# T

## Tactical Warning Time

Amount of time available for preparations against forthcoming attack, measured in hours. (*See also* Strategic Warning Time.)

## Talion Law   (from Latin *talis* = such)

A principle of social regulation based on retaliation. Talion law requires that the punishment fit the crime, as the Biblical "an eye for an eye, a tooth for a tooth." Though the irresistible plausibility of this law is somewhat inconsistent with the law's actual social effectiveness—the law repeatedly fails to deter—the plausibility is perhaps a matter of the profound origins of the law in individual history: dread of the talion is a characteristic of the thoughts of all small children. "If you use your eyes for evil indulgences, you will spoil them; your teeth, you will lose them. And it will serve you right." Talion law begins personally. It evolves into perverse variations; thus Kafka: "It is enough that the arrows fit precisely the wounds that they have made." And it goes on to acquire a validation by consensus that elevates it to a rank of logical principle.

## Teller, Edward

Atomic scientist extraordinary. (*See* Fission-Fusion Bomb.) Born, Budapest, Hungary, January 15, 1908, the son of a prominent attorney. An intellectually gifted Jew, hence a refugee from Budapest of the nineteen-twenties to the more tolerant German universities of Karlsruhe, Munich, Leipzig. Ph.D., physical chemistry, University of Leipzig, 1930. Associate, Leipzig and Göttingen, 1929 to Hitler's ascendancy. Thence to Copenhagen, London, Washington, Denver, Chicago,

Berkeley. Teller has studied with Niels Bohr and Werner Heisenberg. He holds eight doctorates, possibly
nine, possibly ten. He wrote poetry near Karlsburg.
He lost a foot one Sunday afternoon in Bavaria. He
wept beside Fermi's deathbed. He played the piano
at Los Alamos.

## Thanatos

Also, death instinct. One of two primal instincts (*q.v.*)
attributed to man, the other being Eros (*q.v.*). The
function of Thanatos is to restore higher organic organization to a simpler, pre-vital state. In this, Thanatos is expressing a tendency evident elsewhere in
nature for organization to run down into greater simplicity. (*See* Entropy.) Thus this instinct tends to re-
instate earlier levels of development by impelling the
individual toward passivity, and to bring about the
cessation of vital integrity in the organism through
injury and destruction. Human life proceeds as a compromise between the two primal instincts. The compromise is sometimes poorly made, with the result that
human life and products are squandered and destroyed.
When the compromise is well made, nations can flour-
ish in power and beauty. The laws that regulate the
compromise are obscure.

## Thermal Effects

Thirty-five per cent of the total energy in a nuclear
blast is contained in thermal radiation. As the altitude
of the burst increases, the proportion of thermal energy
increases at the expense of blast energy.

Flash burns of the retinal tissues of the eyes, caused
by sighting the exploding fireball, have affected the
retinas of test rabbits at distances of 345 miles; the protective blink reflex time for the rabbit is about $\frac{1}{4}$ of a
second; for man it is about $\frac{1}{4}$ of a second. Retinal
burns may or may not cause blindness, depending
upon the portion of the eye injured and the severity of
the injury.

On a clear day, a 20-megaton airburst (*q.v.*) would
produce second-degree burns to exposed skin 31 miles
from ground zero (*q.v.*), third-degree burns 27 miles

away. Second- and third-degree burns almost always become infected, and exposure to ionizing radiation (*q.v.*) makes treatment more difficult: the body's defenses against infection and bleeding have suffered. Burn victims might be classed into three groups for postattack treatment: individuals suffering from burns on less than 25 per cent of their bodies, 25–50 per cent, and more than 50 per cent. The last group could not be helped; the first two present extremely difficult treatment cases, requiring long and careful medication and rest. The absence of competent medical assistance would almost necessarily doom the victims of most second-degree burns.

A 10-megaton bomb will cause burning of newspapers, cartons, trash piles within a radius of 25 miles. The fires will then spread to buildings in an area covering almost 2,000 square miles, with grave danger of a subsequent firestorm (*q.v.*). Firestorms will almost inevitably result from megaton bombings of large cities. Survival measures are not readily apparent. Such storms have the capacity to inflict immense damage: a large proportion of the population would die before succumbing to the effects of radiation.

**Thin Man**    *See* Fat Man.

**Thyroid**
A deep-red glandular mass; its two lobes lie on opposite sides of the upper trachea. An isthmus of tissue connects both halves across the ventral surface of the trachea. The thyroid is supplied with blood by the superior and inferior thyroid arteries; its many lymphatic vessels are quite large. The thyroid is smaller in men than in women and children.

The thyroid is an endocrine gland. Although the thyroid glands possess some ducts, they yield directly to the blood materials of great importance for growth and differentiation of distant parts, or for the regulation of their physiological functioning. The thyroid produces hormones, chemical substances specific to the gland that secretes them. The hormones are distributed through the blood to exert a specific effect on some part or activity of the body. The thyroid hormone influences the rate of oxidation in all body cells. Measuring the heat production of the body under certain standard conditions of inactivity, basal metabolism, determines the health of the thyroid gland. Oxidation reactions are the means by which the body procures energy; thus the thyroid indirectly modifies a great variety of organic activities, including bone growth, sexual maturation, hair growth, heart rate, muscle tone, intelligence. (*See* Iodine 131.)

**Time**   (from Old Teutonic root *ti,* to stretch)
One of three basic factors (distance, shielding) believed to make the hazardous effects of fallout preventable. Traditionally a concept characterized by a significant variety of denotations in both Eastern and Western cultural traditions, e.g., *What time is it?; time is the mercy of eternity*—William Blake; *The time of flowers*—*Bhagavad-Gita.*

## Tinian Island

`Tinian is a miracle . . .
   —From the testimony of Dr. Philip Morrison before a
                                     Senate committee

Tinian, an island in the Marianas, became in the spring of 1945 the largest airport in the world. Six 10-lane runways, each almost 2 miles long, were constructed by leveling a great coral ridge. Tinian was chosen as the site for the atomic-bomb base because of its proximity to Japan and also due to its appropriateness for the maintenance of high security conditions.

The streets on the island were laid out along the lines of Manhattan Island, with long avenues and numbered cross streets going east and west. The atomic-bomb scientists, living in a small townlet of 21 tents, dwelt near Times Square, and the field from which the *Enola Gay* and the *Great Artiste* (*qq.v.*) took off was located in upper Manhattan. The two main streets were Broadway and Eighth Avenue, both very busy arteries.

The island held several hundred B-29s and tens of thousands of trained specialists. An isolated section of Tinian, closely guarded, held several laboratories in Quonset huts as well as one air-conditioned building in which the group of scientists prepared the atom bomb for its delivery.

The members of the 509th Composite Group of the 313th Wing of the 21st Bombing Command of the 20th Air Force did not participate in the daily strikes upon the territory of Japan with the other bombers on the island. They went on missions, three planes at a time, dropped one bomb, and came back. This training for the atomic raid on Japan also inured the Japanese high command to the possible danger potential in a formation of this size.

The last few shipments of material arrived at Tinian on August 2, 1945, from Alamogordo (*q.v.*). Three days later, the B-29 *Enola Gay* was ready to take off.

# TNT

Also trinitrotoluene, trotyl, triton, tolite, *et al.* A pale-yellow crystalline powder formed by the successive treatment of toluene with gradually stronger mixtures of nitric and sulphuric acids. TNT is classified as a high explosive by virtue of its high energy yield and low sensitivity to percussion; it requires a husky detonator to explode it, otherwise it burns with a slow flame. Discovered by J. Wilbrand in 1863, the Golden Period for explosives, TNT was first produced and used in large quantities during World War I. Its use was curtailed considerably, however, by the rapid depletion of supplies of toluene, a colorless, oily liquid obtained from coal tar and petroleum. Between World War I and World War II toluene production, especially from petroleum, grew more ingenious. TNT became the standard explosive of World War II. The combined warring nations produced several thousand tons of it daily.

TNT melts at about 176° F. Hence it can be loaded into ammunition gracefully by being melted in iron kettles over steam and then poured. Fifty per cent of the weight of the large one- and two-ton aerial demolition bombs—"blockbusters"—used widely in World War II consisted of TNT. One such bomb can demolish several city buildings, if the bomb is luckily placed and the buildings are not too far apart.

## Touareg
A nomadic group inhabiting the Sahara Desert regions, in an area characterized by relatively few oases. Touareg warfare includes such acts as child violation, the ravishment of women, the sale of women into slavery. The disputants, however, have reached a stabilizing entente in regard to the continued viability of the society; wells may not be poisoned. The exercise of choice and abstention, here demonstrated in a less complex social context, furnishes an example, relevant to the high cultures, of Limited War (*q.v.*).

## Trajectory
Trajectory, as opposed to orbit (*q.v.*), usually is associated with paths of limited extent, paths having clearly identified initial and end points.

## Tranquilizer
The common name for a numerous family of drugs which reduce anxiety (*q.v.*) without bringing on unconsciousness, as sedatives tend to do. A boon to psychiatry in reaching formerly intractable patients, tranquilizers are also being consumed in increasing amounts by the general population for eliminating the hitherto routine anxieties of everyday life.

But since it is routine anxiety which motivates a person to consider his behavior in respect to other people, the widespread use of tranquilizers among the general population raises some concern about the danger of a general impoverishment of interpersonal sensitivity. However, energizing drugs, which can be taken in combination with tranquilizers, are being rapidly developed to meet this danger by restoring the depleted sensitivity, or something very much like it.

## Translation
Also, displacement. An effect produced in populated

areas by the blast wind of a nuclear detonation, where people are lifted and thrown about violently, causing injury to other people. A person so affected is said to have been *translated*. This danger from "human missiles" is estimated to exist over an area of 800 square miles for a blast of 20 megatons (*q.v.*). The term *translation* is chosen for its apt etymology; Latin *trans,* across, and *latus,* borne. (*See also* Blast Effects.)

**Tritium** *See* Hydrogen.

**Two-China Policy**
The discovery by the United States of America, the United Nations and other power structures of 3,691,-502 square miles of territory off the coast of Formosa: the diplomatic recognition of mainland China. This discovery, when it occurs, may equal in historical importance the travels of Christopher Columbus, an Italian seaman who found a short route to India. China at present is completely surrounded by water.

# U

## Ultra-Nutrient
A boon to space travel, this synthetic is being sought by the U. S. Army Department of Research and Development. When injected into the bloodstream, the ultra-nutrient eliminates the need for eating, drinking and breathing.

## Uncertainty, Principle of
Also known as Heisenberg's principle of indeterminacy, after the physicist Werner Heisenberg, who, in 1925, demonstrated with respect to the atom that the more accurately we attempt to specify the *position* of a particle in space at a given time, the less accurately can its *velocity* be determined, and vice versa. We simply cannot know in one and the same moment both the location and the speed of a given particle. The common idea of simultaneous certainty about both has no correspondence in nature. This principle sets an inescapable limit on accuracy.

## Unconscious
An attribute of human functioning originating in the condition that the survival of the individual depends upon the loss of innocence in a renunciation of atavistic wishes. The unconscious is the repository of our defeated, paradisiacal infantilism.

An inferred entity, the unconscious is constructed out of its observed effects upon behavior, frequently in retrospect: a process is assumed to be unconscious when it was active at a certain time, although at that time we knew nothing about it.

Abuses of the concept are widespread. For example, though it is true that the unconscious is stocked with unperceived wishes, it does not follow that unconscious wishes represent what the individual *really* wishes. Also, the unconscious of the statesman is as unconscious to the statesman as the unconscious of the artist is to the artist.

## Undoing

The transformation of the pleasure of a forbidden wish into the imperative of a personal superstition: undoing employs some definite action which actually or magically cancels out something threatening to the individual. The most frequent forms of undoing are personal acts of atonement and compulsive ceremonials. The need to touch, to count, to go through elaborate and irrelevant preparations prior to a simple act are common forms of undoing. That which is being undone is kept from awareness. Derivatives of undoing are seen in everyday actions like unlocking and relocking a locked door to check whether it was locked in the first place, or, similarly, setting and resetting an alarm clock. Undoing is directed against aggressive and sexual ambitions and is prominent in rigid, orderly characters who can be trusted to show great thoroughness with trivial matters.

## Upper Volta

Autonomous West Central African republic, formerly a French possession, completely independent since August 5, 1960. The chief urban centers are Ouagadougou, Bobo-Dioulasso, Ouahigouya, and Koudougou. The population includes the Mossi, the Bobo, the Gourounsi, the Lobi, the Samo, the Tougan-Marka, the Dioula, and the Boussancé. Among the important crops produced by the Upper Volta are niébé, millet, fonio, sorghum and shea nuts. The agricultural research stations at Seria, Banfora, Farako, Kamboinse, and Niangoloko play a role in intensifying production. Kiéré has manganese, Kaya has bauxite, Goundoudy has copper, and some cassiterite has been found near Tenkodogo and Ouagadougou. In the eleventh century the empire-building Mossi from East Africa established two kingdoms, spread into the Upper Volta and created feudal empires and kingdoms; created the empire of Moro Naba, whose capital was at Tenkodogo and afterward at Ouagadougou. Ouedraogo was the Mossi leader, and called "The Stallion"; his mother was Nyenneanga the Slender, daughter of the King of Gambaga. One of Ouedraogo's grandsons became ruler of four kingdoms: Tenkodogo, Zandoma, Oubritenga and Fada-N'Gourma. In the fourteenth century the empire of Yatenga arose in Zandoma. In Ouagadougou the original empire, consisting of Tenkodogo and Oubritenga, persisted down to modern times; the Moro Naba empire surpasses in cultural continuity Brazil, Argentina, Belgium, Italy, Germany and the United States of America.

## Uranium

A soft, heavy, silvery-white radioactive metal found chiefly in the mineral pitchblende. Discovered by M. H. Klaproth in 1789, uranium was named for the planet Uranus, which had been discovered eight years earlier. In 1842, the metal was further refined by the chemist E. M. Peligot, yet for the ensuing hundred years it possessed no important practical use except later as a laboratory aid in the study of radioactivity; but even in this regard it was soon rivaled by the metal radium, which is about a million times as radioactive as uranium.

During the nineteen-thirties Enrico Fermi was experimenting with the bombardment of uranium with neutrons (*q.v.*) in an effort to study the effects of the newly discovered neutron particle on atomic structure. For a brief time it was believed that he had succeeded in building up a more complicated atom than uranium —a trans-uranium atom. This was an erroneous conclusion soon corrected; Fermi was actually breaking down the uranium atom roughly in half (*see* Fission).

Shortly thereafter, it was learned that natural uranium is a blend of two variants. Uranium 238 is the relatively abundant variant; uranium 235 is much rarer. The difference in cost between the two variants —$35,000 per ton for U 238 as against $10,000 per pound for U 235—is largely the consequence of the stupendous capital outlay and technological advancement required for the separation of the rare variant from natural uranium. This rare variant is the only naturally occurring substance capable of being fissioned by neutrons of random velocities. As neutrons are released by ever-present, sporadic natural fission in a mass of unseparated uranium, these neutrons are slowed down in their passage throughout the remaining mass and cannot go on to fission the preponderant amount of U 238. But in a mass of pure U 235, it does not matter that the released neutrons acquire hodge-podge velocities; they are still capable of fissioning the receptive nuclei of U 235, with a release of fresh neutrons. Thus, the rare variant can sustain a chain-reaction. Practical uses for the more abundant variant have also been found. (*See* Fission-Fusion-Fission Bomb; Plutonium.)

An artificial variant of uranium—uranium 233—can now be produced by spicing nuclear reactors with the readily available radioactive metal thorium. The neutron activity in reactors converts thorium into U 233. This artificial variant of uranium sustains a chain-reaction elegantly and is excellent stuff for bombs. India, for example, is accumulating large reserves of thorium for subsequent conversion to U 233 in her blossoming reactor program.

## Uranus

The seventh planet from the sun, discovered in 1781, 1,600,000,000 miles from Earth at its minimum distance, 19 times as far from the sun as Earth.

Uranus is similar to Jupiter and Saturn in its construction: a rocky center surrounded by a layer of ice. On Uranus, the ice may be about 6,000 miles thick; the overlying atmosphere may have a depth of 3,000 miles. The atmosphere shows a great abundance of methane—marsh gas. Any ammonia in the atmosphere would probably have been frozen out by the extreme cold, less than —297.4° F.

Uranus has five moons. The disc of Uranus is of a pale sea-green color.

# V

## V-2

The first European rocket successfully used in modern warfare, by the German Reich: 1,120 launched against Great Britain and 2,500 against other European targets in World War II.

Hundreds of V-2 rockets were carried to the United States after the war, accompanied by some of their technicians (*see* Rocket). The Soviet Union, another European power, also found the V-2 invaluable, in the development of its T-1, S-8 and T-4 missiles. A similar German missile, the A-4/A-9, originally designed to bomb New York City in World War II, bred the Russian T-2.

Along with American assistance to the walled-in town of Berlin and Soviet protection of beleaguered East Germany, the V-2 symbolizes the mutual interests of the three major adventurers of the twentieth century. (*See also* Wall.)

## VAB

Commonly, Van Allen Belt. 600 miles above Earth's surface is a region of energetic atomic particles, which rings Earth like a doughnut. Hovering 100 miles above the ceiling of the material atmosphere, this region resides in empty space, so that it was not possible until recently to detect its existence: energy is discernible only if intercepted by matter of some kind. In 1958 the Explorer satellites, instrumented by James Van Allen, passed into this region with radiation counters, which were energized.

The Van Allen Belt of radiation is held in place by Earth's magnetism. Intensely energetic protons make up the inner ring of the region closest to Earth; low-energy electrons make up the outer ring. The thickness of the region is not known, but it seems to approach 40,000 miles. Its origin is also obscure. One theory has it that cosmic rays (*q.v.*), which have to pass through the region—and do so quite easily—set neutrons free upon colliding with Earth's atmosphere 100 miles below the region; many of these neutrons splash back toward outer space, decaying as they go; the decay—protons and electrons—gets caught in Earth's magnetosphere; thus VAB is supplied at its inner ring, while it leaks at the outer periphery.

The Belt's role, if any, in the complex equilibria that sustain life on Earth is yet to be ascertained. However, in the race for interplanetary space, man has already cast a somber eye on VAB. Though VAB's vast outer region is soft radiation against which protection of a spaceman is thought to be no problem, the inner region, it is feared, is quite hard; unless a traveler escapes Earth through its polar gateways where VAB tends to fade away, he will have to pass through what may turn out to be lethal levels of radiation. At 600 miles away, this would be the very outset of his trip. If shielding against VAB's inner ring proves to be impractical, and if this ring cannot be plowed through at high speeds with brief exposure to the traveler, who rolls up in a fetal position to duck the radiation, then VAB will have to be punctured or swept away altogether prior to interplanetary flights. Currently scientists are poking about the region with satellites and rocketed thermonuclear bombs. Some hold that this is all wrong; others insist there is nothing to worry about. When the question of bombing the Belt was put to Van Allen himself, he said, "Magnificent idea!"

## vab

The Little Van Allen Belt. Lower-case vab was put in space by a magnificent high-altitude thermonuclear burst in July, 1962. The burst, part of a United States testing exercise, illuminated the heavens above the Pacific Ocean for 3,000 miles and created interesting effects in the electromagnetic environment everywhere on Earth. One of the purposes of the spectacle was to study the possibility of an antimissile system. One of the by-products, anticipated by an assemblage of prominent and competent American scientists, was a radiation belt predicted to be a minor perturbation, perhaps not even detectable at all. As the initial phenomena of the burst cleared, data from Injun I, a satellite which had been orbiting 600 miles above Earth for a year prior to the burst, fulfilled the expectation that the radioactive effects of the burst would arrange themselves along Earth's magnetosphere with the composition and shape of a miniature VAB (*q.v.*). The data also supported the prior conviction that the new radiation belt would be a flash in the pan; 200 miles high, 400 miles deep, most of it, Van Allen said, would disappear "in a matter of weeks and months." This general conclusion was made more precise in a government announcement: within 20 to 30 weeks, vab's density would be down to one-tenth of 1 per cent. Prior apprehensions about a high-yield burst in the vicinity of VAB, mainly on the part of British scientists, were unfounded.

The artificial Little Van Allen Belt rings Earth at an altitude of 750 miles. Doughnut-shaped, it is 3,000 miles deep and resides within the larger, natural Van Allen Belt, adding to VAB's radiation density. vab has extinguished the transmitters of three orbiting satellites, one of them British, and has caused a thorough revision of the American space program. The lifetime of vab is estimated at the very least 5 years and possibly a century. (*See* Scientism.)

## Vanguard I

The discoverer of Earth's true shape. Vanguard I, a satellite launched on March 17, 1958, is the smallest— $3\frac{1}{2}$ pounds, 6.4 inches—and highest of the first nine Earth satellites; it will last the longest, 200 years. Vanguard I reaches a high point in orbit (apogee) of 2,453 miles above Earth. One of its two radio transmitters, powered by a chemical battery, went dead when the battery ran down. The other one, powered by a solar battery, continues beeping to tracking stations.

Calculations of Vanguard's orbit showed that while

the orbit changes its position, it also changes its shape slightly. Vanguard I is pulled with unequal strength by the Northern and Southern Hemispheres. From the unequal pulls of gravity the shapes of the two hemispheres reveal their asymmetry.

Earth is slightly pear-shaped.

## Vanity

The heapes of people thronging in the hall,
Do ride each other, upon her to gaze:
Her glorious glitter and light doeth all mens
    eyes amaze.
—Edmund Spenser

One of the deadly sins (*q.v.*). Vanity connotes a combination of inner emptiness and great outward show. In meaning and function it is close to the current term *glamour*. The sin here appears to reside in the enticing promise that fulfillment requires no further exertion than a happy, finger-snapping availability.

## Venus

In size, Venus is the sister of Earth; in almost every other respect Venus is unknown. It is only 200 miles smaller in diameter than Earth and has therefore a similar capacity to retain an atmosphere. But no one has ever seen through it to the Venusian surface. The planet lies perpetually shrouded by a white, cloudy and dense upper atmosphere which contains carbon dioxide and a possible minute proportion of oxygen and water vapor. One set of recent findings suggests both water and oxygen on the planet. Such an environment would drastically change the common scientific opinion about the planet's atmosphere: Venus would then maintain the climate of a steaming jungle rather than that of an arid desert. Whether Venus has seasons or not is a matter of conjecture; no fixed point on its surface has been observed and charted to establish the presence of possible seasonal rotation. The length of its day and the speed of rotation are unknown.

Like Mars, Venus may have used up its free oxygen

in combination with rocks and sediment. Had vegetation sprung up on Venus at any time in the past, the plants might have replaced the lost oxygen. Such conjectures are made possible by astronomical ignorance of the surface and lower atmosphere of the planet. In any case, the temperatures, ranging from more than 212° F. to —10° F., are not, and probably never were, conducive to any forms of life conceivable from an Earthly context.

Venus comes nearer to Earth than any other planet, 25,000,000 miles, but so little is known about it that Venus space probes are of the greatest importance in preparing for a manned expedition to circumnavigate the planet. (*See* Probe.)

## Vulcan

The tenth planet, discovered in 1860 and discarded soon after. In 1860 Dr. Lescarboult saw the planet Vulcan passing across the face of the sun. Leverrier, the discoverer of Neptune, computed that Vulcan's orbit lay about 13,000,000 miles from the sun, that the planet moved in orbit in a period of 19.75 days, and had a diameter of approximately 1,000 miles. Leverrier had predicted the appearance of this planet, orbiting between Mercury and the sun, to account for discrepancies in Mercury's orbital path—as he had predicted the existence of Neptune to account for some aberrations in the motion of the planet Uranus.

The theory that effectively spotted a previously unknown planet was inappropriate for the problems of Mercury's orbit. The Einsteinian general theory of relativity states that Newton's law of universal gravitation was almost correct. It did not show the fact that the elliptical path of a planet around the sun was not absolutely fixed, but moved in rotation around its own focus. The slight changes in Mercury's orbit are understood without the need to posit the existence of another planetary force acting upon it; Vulcan was no Neptune.

W

## Wall

By August, 1961, the number of refugees arriving in West Berlin from the German Democratic Republic exceeded 3,000 per day. The exiles passed through East Berlin, which, on August 13, 1961, joined the traditional company of walled cities, or, in this case, semiwalled cities. In one stroke West Berlin, a contiguous territory, also became a half-walled city. The Wall departs in one highly significant and some minor details from the tradition of walls. Both Permanent Fortifications and Field Fortifications have historically been planned to give shelter to the whole population of a country, as in Nineveh and Babylon; to augment security against the attacks of neighbors, as in feudal castles; or to protect the inhabitants and property of rich medieval towns, such as Carcassonne. The economy of the German Democratic Republic, however, already desperately short of manpower, required the construction of its concrete and barbed-wire obstacle to impede further emigration of its own citizens and to protect them from unhealthful excitations.

On October 16, 1940, a wall functionally similar to The Wall was erected around the city of Warsaw, in Poland, by the government of Germany to prevent the spread of contagious diseases. It encircled only about 75 blocks within the city, containing some 600,-000 people, 450,000 of whom had come there since the beginning of the Second World War. The Warsaw wall measured 8 feet in height and was crowned by broken glass. Certain dissimilarities between this wall and The Wall appear upon close examination. Perhaps the most singular involves the reduction of the population inside the enclosure from 600,000 to 40,000 in the fall of 1942 by massacre and deportation, as well as the extraordinary invasion of the enclave by the government which had erected it as a sanitation measure.

Obviously, categorical distinctions offer difficulties, but Penology, rather than Fortifications and Siegecraft, might constitute the proper historical category for The Wall, were it not for the potential armed conflict resulting from the near-war between East and West, another complicating variable. Thus the category most appropriate for an understanding of The Wall may be that of Penological Fortification, Premartial Siegecraft, or Fortified Anti-Exilic Penology. This confusion of genres not only reflects a pervasive romantic contemporary tendency; it also illustrates the difficulty of defining the relationship between the people and government of such crypto-autonomous nations as the German Democratic Republic.

Minor differences between The Wall and other walls also demonstrate its hybrid nature. Flat bastions, Demibastions, Tenaille bastions, Redans, Ravelins, Demilunes, Counterguards, Simple and Double Tenailles, examples of Hornwork, Crownwork and Crowned Hornwork, Traverses and Double bastions (or Cavaliers) are absent from The Wall. It maintains, however, several traditional features: Concrete blocks, Watchtowers, Armed Guards, Built-up Areas, and Points of Interest—and several modern analogues to Tenaille bastions and Cavaliers, such as Tank Barriers and Barbed-wire fences.

The Chinese "Great Wall," built by the Emperor Ch'in Shih Huang Ti after 228 B.C., eventually reached an extension of 2,500 miles, and Roman walls filled in hundreds of miles of territory not closed off by such natural boundaries as the Rhine and Rhone Rivers. As walls go, The Wall is a little wall.

Will walls catch on? Modern technology and nuclear adventurism put in some doubt the continued growth of walls in Western Europe. But man is an intermittently wall-making animal. After the fall of Rome, the twin sciences of Fortification and Siegecraft were kept alive only in the Eastern Empire; in Western Europe they almost disappeared. The unscientific Huns and Goths knew nothing about them, and the Frankish kings could not restore the art due to the contempt their warriors felt for handicrafts. Not until the eleventh century was Siegecraft revived in the West. Clearly the modulations of fashion make it almost impossible to predict whether the traditional Chinese aptitude for walls, for instance, will ever be revived. Many ancient cities in northern China, partly demolished by wars and famines and fire, where no house was left standing, or human beings, still retain their crenellated walls with bastions and towers.

## War

A state of armed and aggressive hostility characterizing the relations between two states or power units; an instrument of national policy until August 27, 1928, when the Kellogg-Briand Pact, affirmed by 14 signatories at Paris, outlawed it. *War is hell*, W. T. Sherman; *The fittest place where man can die/ Is where he dies for man*, M. J. Barry. (*See* Doomsday Machine.)

## War-Gaming

A procedure by which two or more players test different assumptions concerning war conditions. In the United States, for example, an equation of a foreign nation's capability and probable intentions with the United States' own capability and probable intentions would be *war-gamed* among various national security agencies—the National Security Council, Office of Defense Mobilization, Federal Civil Defense Administration, Atomic Energy Commission and Joint Chiefs of Staff. Extragovernmental institutions, however, are entrusted with Games.

The Game takes place in offices or similar rooms, sometimes with fairly large opposing teams and umpires. A Game may take a few hours or a few months. Though not comparable in purity with, say, the game of chess, the ascetic renunciation of human involvements in war-gaming provides as pure a concern with the statistical variables of a war situation as presently possible. The equipment often includes electronic computers to assist each side to establish technological and operational rules, *planning factors*, which involve careful estimates of the use of given missiles, warheads, cleanliness or dirt of various nuclear explosives and similar hardware in different conditions. The dogged repetition of the same Game occasionally provides new insights into the possible manipulations of a situation. (*See* Judas Hole.)

## War Neurosis

Also, shell shock, though now obsolescent. A descriptive term for a group of disorders occurring during active warfare. The same disorders occurring in civilian life bear the more technical label "traumatic neurosis." A traumatic neurosis results when the mental apparatus is assaulted by a sudden, unanticipated stimulus too large to be mastered and discharged by the usual defenses of the apparatus. Such stimuli are common in warfare in the form of explosions, loss of close buddies, unexpected guilt at being instrumental in the death of large numbers of people, terror at the failure of vital equipment, etc. In civilian life a traumatic neurosis may result from participation in a serious accident like a shipwreck or plane crash or even the observation of such accidents. Bodily injuries, deaths, economic disaster may also be traumatic. Symptoms of traumata are usually more or less transitory, at least in their severity, and vary widely. The more common ones include prostration, nocturnal fears, paralysis, diarrhea, vertigo, cardiac disturbances, amnesia, nightmares, blindness, phobias.

The term "war neurosis" established itself during World War I. By World War II the concept of mental traumatization was full-blown as a result of two decades of study. Treatment procedures for traumatic neurosis were rather well developed. Variations of psychoanalytic therapy were useful, though under war conditions these procedures are not the most expedient and were reserved for special complications. During World War II the most extensive procedure was narcotherapy, a general term which includes narcosuggestion, narcocatharsis, narcoanalysis, pentathol interview, amytal interview; the patient is injected intravenously with either sodium pentathol or sodium amytal, which induces a serene, passive narcosis, during which a psychotherapist guides the patient by suggestion and analysis out of painful memories and conflicts caused by recent traumata. War neurosis was most common during offensives under heavy fire and where personnel was directly involved in releasing heavy explosives on the enemy, as in air raids over civilian centers. Technical literature swelled with studies of the traumatic neurosis. Narcotherapy, with its dazed, anguished, perspiring patient and heroic therapist, was a common scene in the movies and fiction of the period.

Following World War II large numbers of civilians exposed to traumata became available for study in bomb-torn cities like London, Hiroshima, Hamburg. Additional symptoms related to trauma came to light, among them depressions, delusions, severe boredom. In children a condition called hospitalism (*q.v.*) was studied. Even fatalities were ascribed to trauma. (*See* Panic.)

But currently much of this is being re-examined in the more objective atmosphere of peace and historical distance. The concept of trauma, which a decade ago embraced so much, is now shrinking as a phenomenon of upheaval and disaster. The rate at which it is shrinking is rather fast as these things go. (*See* RAND; Scientism.)

# Water

Water, Thales of Miletus teaches, is the primal element.

Water is the origin of things; Earth floats upon a sea of the elemental fluid; all things are full of gods.

Others teach that Water corresponds to the Humour Phlegm, and incorporates Cold and Moisture. The property of Water is to go down. The Water which surrounds Earth is called the Oceanic Sea; from it all the other seas, rivers and fountains are born, to return there at the end. Earth is crisscrossed by veins and caverns where the Water which comes from the Sea circulates in the body of Earth as blood does in the body of man. Water changes its savor and color according to the nature of the region it flows through, the veins of sulphur, gold and other metals it meets. Water becomes harmful while crossing rotting caverns. The rapidity of these subterranean waters sometimes determines air currents which warm the sulphur and cause earthquakes. Cities then fall into the Abyss.

A hole dug anywhere, in mountans or plains, will produce water, fresh or salt. Water from the Sea becomes fresh while crossing gentle lands; it becomes bitter or salty when it goes through black and sour passes. Certain undersea places hold dirty venomous beasts; waters which pass through them are lethal.

In Samaria there is a fountain which changes color four times a year. Some rivers run only three days a week. The Sabat River stops on the holy day. In Persia there is a river which freezes every night. In Epirus men introduce red-hot sticks into one of the rivers, and retrieve them still glowing. In Ethiopia there is a river which delivers warm waters at night, very cold waters during the day. In the Orient, some fountains produce materials useful in the manufacture of Greek fire, which can only be put out by a combination of vinegar, urine and sand; the Saracens sell this water more dearly than good wine.

Animals are made up of a greater proportion of Water than of Air; Water tending downward, animals are liable to quick decay and a short life.

## Water Distribution

The problem of storing and distributing water in shelters suggests some of the enormous difficulties in setting up an adequate protection system. The following extract from a Congressional hearing indicates the complexity of the situation facing the planners. Rogers Cannell is consultant to the Office of Emergency Planning and the Department of Defense; Herbert Roback is Staff Administrator to the Committee on Government Operations of the House of Representatives.

MR. ROBACK: Let's ask a little homespun question here. You say you can provision the shelters with food, you provision them with water. How do people drink water when they are packed into a shelter?

MR. CANNELL: You mean how do you package the water so they can drink it?

MR. ROBACK: How is it packaged and how is it consumed? Do you have cups?

MR. CANNELL: There is a full range of options on how you do it. If you wanted to you could all take turns drinking out of a bucket, or paper cups.

MR. ROBACK: I want to know if they plan to have people drink out of cups or out of the bucket.

## Weather Satellite

Weather satellites, measuring and photographing meteorological conditions such as cloud cover, storm location, precipitation, temperature, wind direction, heat balance and water vapor in a worldwide tracking and telemetering network, should be of incalculable benefit in planning personal activities, protection of life and property from weather disasters, safeguarding transportation, crop planning, industrial planning of products dependent upon the weather, limited weather control, and in the receipt of good will from nations not wealthy or powerful enough to enjoy their own weather satellites.

Vanguard II, for instance, specially equipped as a weather satellite, has two photocells, or Weather Eyes, one of which is always facing Earth. The Earth-facing eye sees a narrow strip of Earth ground, and a mirror reflects infrared rays from the strip onto a detector which converts the light energy into an electrical signal: strong light, strong signal; weak light, weak signal. The signals enter a magnetic tape recorder, making a tape subsequently transferred to a ground station where Earth receivers play the record, after which the signals are fed to an oscillograph, which in turn produces a line of light which is photographed to produce a picture, strip by strip, of what the Eye saw.

This is studied.

## Weightlessness

Zero g. A prevalent, and erroneous, notion concerning weightlessness has it that such a state is the result of the absence of gravity forces upon a spacecraft. Although the pull of gravity does weaken as distance increases, it will never completely disappear. As a vehicle moves through space, it passes from the gravitational force of one celestial body into the force of another. In the Earth-moon line, for example, a vehicle will leave the gravitational pull of Earth and enter the moon's field at a distance of 193,000 miles from Earth, or 35,000 miles from the surface of the moon. (*See* Outer Space.) Moreover, the vehicle is also influenced by the gravity of the distant sun and other planets of the solar system. Gravity is omnipresent.

Weightlessness is a condition which occurs during any unobstructed fall, regardless of the mass of the falling body or the gravity pulling it. Weight is the result of opposition to the pull of gravity. Weight is measured by a device that intervenes between a body and its attraction by gravity. Thus a hand scale upon which a stone is suspended can weigh the stone because the scale obstructs the stone's falling to the ground. However, if both scale and stone, still attached, were dropped from a window, the scale would register zero ounces as both fell freely. The stone (and scale) would be weightless.

When a space vehicle manages to get far enough from a celestial body so that it is being acted upon by gravity but yet is not pulled back to the surface of the body, the vehicle and everything in it will be weightless if the rocket engine is turned off. The vehicle is then coasting unobstructed by air friction, acceleration, or deceleration. It is entirely without resistance to gravity and is falling freely through space on a curve shaped by the particular speed with which the vehicle was originally launched. When the engines are turned on, their force counters gravity, and weight returns to the vehicle and its occupants.

Before the advent of manned satellites, scientists were concerned about the effects of weightlessness on space travelers. There was concern, for example, that carbon dioxide caused by exhalation would remain suspended in front of the space traveler's nose, so that he would suffocate from his own breath. Or he would drown in a glass of water if some means like a squeezable container were not used. Experimentation has laid to rest many apprehensions. Major Titov, who was weightless for about 25 hours, described sensations of nausea but not much else.

Simple rotation of the vehicle by electric motor during space flight would generate centrifugal force and would return weight to the vehicle and its contents. Also, once the fuel problems are solved, mild and constant acceleration and deceleration during flight would restore weight. Of the multitude of problems in space flight, weightlessness is comparatively the least; it is also the most popular.

## White Room
A room kept surgically clean for the assembly of such delicate mechanisms as gyro systems for space travel.

## World War VIII
In a series of wars, some historical, some postulated, but all drawn upon for educational purposes, an expert on hypothetical wars and associated concerns (*see* Button) has drawn the reasonably expectable posture (*q.v.*) of military technology for World War VIII occurring in 1973. Each war, starting with World War I, is spaced approximately one technological revolution apart from the next. World War VIII, one technological revolution ahead of World War VII, and 26 technological revolutions behind World War XXXIV, will play itself out (*see* Monte Carlo) in a technological context composed of the following extrapolations and breakthroughs: advanced satellites; primitive space ships; controlled thermonuclear reactions; californium bullets (*q.v.*); cheap, fast transportation for Limited War; disguised warfare; Doomsday Machines (*q.v.*); cheap simple missiles; cheap simple bombs; and 50,000 buttons.

## Wrath
Full many mischiefs follow cruell Wrath;
Abhorred bloudshed, and tumultuous strife,
Vnmanly murder, and vnthrifty scath.
                                        —Edmund Spenser

One of the deadly sins (*q.v.*), wrath is anger mixed with bitter memory. It is aggressive vengeance on the present for humiliations of the past. It is fanatic and cowardly. Wrath retaliates against the weak for the transgressions of the strong and causes suffering without gain or purpose. It settles nothing.

# X

**X**
A weapons category in ARPA, the Advanced Research Projects Agency of the U. S. Department of Defense; potentially one of ARPA's most interesting and useful investigations.

Thermonuclear fireballs (*q.v.*) cannot be controlled; their lethal gamma rays, neutrons, and X rays (*qq.v.*) fan out indiscriminately. Such relatively gross operations permit flexibility only in the size of the warhead directed against a target, or in the level of the burst, surface or air. The H-bomb is not a precision weapon.

An effort to amplify the deterrence capacity of the United States resulted in the adoption by the military, in 1961, of the LASER, Light Amplification by Stimulated Emission of Radiation, in a highly promising instrument transforming electrical power into a single optical beam. The resulting ray machine, when fully developed, might melt an enemy missile; alternatively it could penetrate the enemy missile's circuits, turning its guidance devices into a chaos of random associations and dismissing the rocket pell-mell into limitless space; a third possibility involves the premature detonation of the nuclear warhead in its space trajectory.

The difficulty of isolating real missiles from among a host of dummies, a difficulty relevant to the problems of the Nike-Zeus, would be obviated by the silent sweep of a LASER-like instrument. Thus a school of ICBMs could be annihilated in a matter of seconds.

The brightness of the beam is irrelevant; the significant variable involves the amount of energy in that beam. Light particles, or photons, manifest pressure; this pressure in ordinary situations is so minute that its disintegrating effects do not obtrude themselves. When a sufficient number of watts course through the beam, the pressure becomes irresistible.

Such energy waves travel at the speed of light; thus death, or target kill, depending on the target, will be instantaneous.

X weapons also include promising research on the qualities of radar and high-freqency radio waves. These waves, unlike the LASER instrument, would merely touch off the aura of ions present around the bodies of all satellites and rockets as they travel through the ionosphere, between 50 and 250 miles from Earth. An appropriate high-frequency beam could explode this ionic envelope like a bomb.

Radar waves, in sufficiently high-energy force, could create ball lightning in the ionosphere directly in the path of the enemy. Like the invention of gunpowder and the airplane, the apocalyptic nature of X weapons may ultimately pacify the troubled currents of Earth's history.

## X Ducat

The ducat, a coin of varying value, usually of gold, was formerly used in many European countries. Roger II of Sicily first struck a ducat. Many ducats minted in the twelfth, thirteenth and following centuries still appear in collections. Coins are the most imperishable of antiquities, are often hoarded, and disclose a considerable amount of information about the past.

In 1957, 200,000 gold X ducats were minted by the European Economic Community (*see* Common Market) for use in Belgium, Luxembourg, the Netherlands, France, Italy and West Germany, future members of a united Europe. Almost 200,000 gold X ducats have entered into collections.

## Xenophobia

An hysterical symptom characterized by a morbid dread of strangers. In the actual, or even imminent, presence of unfamiliar individuals or groups, xenophobics display an anxious defensiveness: they become suspicious, withdrawn, isolated and frequently take to rude flight. These reactions discourage the xenophobic's making contacts with strangers, so that strangers become even stranger, and a vicious cycle ensues.

Forced contacts, however, do not succeed in mitigating the xenophobic's apprehensions of exploitation and assault by strangers; for the source of these apprehensions is not in the stranger but in the xenophobic, whose defensiveness is directed actually against his own latent malevolence. It is the xenophobic who wishes to annihilate strangers without rational provocation, and his phobia, in denying this, succeeds in sustaining his self-image of gentility and humaneness. Xenophobia usually inspires elaborate and ingenious doctrine about the motivations, intentions, character and habits of strangers.

## X Ray

X rays are produced in a high-vacuum glass tube in which a beam of particles, emitted from an electrically heated metal filament, is trained upon an electrified metal plate. The particles stopped suddenly by the target give rise to X rays.

X rays are waves of radiant energy (*see* Radiation). In a scale of various types of wave ranging from long waves to short waves, X rays are among the very short. The length of a wave is the distance between any two of its peaks, and such a scale begins with miles-long electromagnetic waves at one end, growing shorter through radio waves of hundreds of feet, past visible light waves of a tiny fraction of an inch, into invisible ultraviolet waves of even shorter length, to X rays and gamma rays, these last two being so short that special units of measurement need to be employed to describe them. Computed to be as short-waved as 38-billionths of an inch, X rays, prior to the ability of science to make such a measurement, were not thought to be waves at all, but rather a peakless stream of some sort.

Very short waves like X rays oscillate rapidly, are highly energetic and penetrate deeply. X rays will pass through a human body more readily than visible light passes through a sheet of paper. This penetrance of X rays is exploited in the photography not only of the inner bones and organs but also of the inside structure of metal products. However, X rays do not pass through matter without some amount of disruption of the matter, and this is especially true of its encounter with living tissue. (*See* Ionizing Radiation.)

X rays were discovered in 1895 by Professor Wilhelm Konrad Roentgen of Munich. He assigned to this hitherto unnoticed ray the conventional algebraic letter for the unknown. Shortly thereafter X rays were enlisted as one of the first probes into the secrets of the twentieth-century atom. Much that we have learned about the nature of heredity we owe to the discovery in 1927 by H. J. Muller that X-ray bombardment can induce a high mutation (*q.v.*) rate in the gene (*q.v.*). Today the X ray is still our standard for appreciating and measuring the effects of other ionizing radiation. (*See* Relative Biological Effectiveness.)

# Y

## Yield-to-Weight Ratio

Colloquially, bang-to-size ratio. With the megatonnage of atomic weapons no longer the competitive issue it once was among nations (*see* Fission-Fusion-Fission Bomb), technology has turned its attention from the yield to the weight of the weapon, for the ratio of yield to weight is an important factor in the delivery of bombs to their targets. The lighter and more compact the bomb, the simpler the missile which carries it.

# Z

## Zero

Like *cipher,* from the Arabic *şifr.* Though not a quantity, a nonetheless indispensable feature of the modern number system. And also the terminal interval of a famous number series beginning anywhere and proceeding backward through Four, Three, Two, One . . .

## Zero-Zero

A definitive plan for atomic disarmament, based on an absolute atomic-energy moratorium. The plan establishes control of weapon construction at its very source, the mining and traffic of fissionable raw materials, like uranium and thorium. These materials would be allotted to nations in such small amounts as to make the production of atomic weapons impossible. But these restrictions would also make impossible the development of nuclear power for peacetime purposes. Hence, Zero-Zero is opposed by the Soviet Union as a plot by capitalist monopolists to impede the industrial development of socialist states. As for the United States, the plan is an affront to that nation's industrial philosophy: a technology which exists must be used.

## Editor's Acknowledgment

*I am deeply indebted to my friends Professor Benjamin N. Nelson and Mr. William Herman, whose recommendations and enthusiasm meant so much to the morale of this undertaking.*

—*L. J. K.*

## Bibliography

"A. B." "Claude Eatherly—'War Hero,'" *Liberation* (January 1962).

*ABC Warfare Defense.* Navy Training Course, 1960, Navpers 10099.

Adler, Irving. *Seeing the Earth from Space.* New York: Signet, New American Library, 1962.

Ambassade de France, Service de Presse et d'Information. *The Republic of the Upper Volta.* New York, October 1960.

American Chemical Society Board Committee on Civil Defense. "Special Summary Report," *Chemical and Engineering News* (October 19, 1959).

Barden, John. "Germ-Gas Warfare," *The Nation* (April 30, 1960).

Beller, William, and Bergaust, Erik. *Satellite!* Garden City, N.Y.: Hanover House, 1956.

Bethe, Hans A. "Disarmament and Strategy," *Bulletin of the Atomic Scientists* (September 1962).

Blake, William. *Complete Poetry.* New York: Modern Library, Random House, 1946.

Bondy, François. "On Misunderstanding Eichmann," *Encounter* (November 1961).

Born, Max. *The Restless Universe.* New York: Dover Publications, 1951.

Bretall, Robert (ed.). *A Kierkegaard Anthology.* Princeton, N.J.: Princeton University Press, 1946.

Brodie, Bernard. *Strategy in the Missile Age.* Princeton, N.J.: Princeton University Press, 1959.

Burns, James MacGregor. "Kennedy's First Year," *The Nation,* Vol. 194, no. 1 (January 6, 1942), pp. 14-15.

Burton, Robert. *The Anatomy of Melancholy.* New York: Tudor Publishing Co., 1951.

Cantril, Hadley. *The Politics of Despair.* New York: Basic Books, 1958.

Carter, Lawrence J. (ed.). "Realities of Space Travel," *Selected Papers of the British Interplanetary Society.* New York: McGraw Hill Book Co., Inc., 1957.

Cater, Douglas. "The Lesson of Punta · del Este," *The Reporter* (March 1, 1962).

Christiansen, Gordon S. *Survival in Nuclear War a Vanishing Probability.* New York: War Resisters League.

Clarke, Arthur C. *The Exploration of Space.* New York: Harper and Brothers, 1951.

312

Cohen, Elie. *Human Behavior in the Concentration Camp.* New York: W. W. Norton, 1953.

Cook, Fred. "Juggernaut," *The Nation,* Vol. 194, no. 3 (October 28, 1961).

Cooper, Ralph S. "Rocket Propulsion," *Bulletin of the Atomic Scientists* (March 1962).

Cox, Donald, and Stoiko, Michael. *Spacepower.* Philadelphia and Toronto: The John C. Winston Co., 1958.

*Daedalus, Special Issue: Arms Control,* Journal of the American Academy of Arts and Sciences (Fall 1960). Wesleyan University Press.

Dampier, William. *A History of Science.* Cambridge, Eng.: The University Press, 1940.

Da Vinci, Leonardo. *The Notebooks.* New York: George Braziller, 1955.

Dietz, David. *Atomic Science, Bombs and Power.* New York: Dodd, Mead and Co., 1954.

Duggar, Benjamin M. *Biological Effects of Radiation,* Vols. 1 and 2. New York: McGraw Hill Book Co., Inc., 1936.

Ellison, Douglas G. "Operational Analysis," *Psychological Theory,* ed. Melvin Marx. New York: The Macmillan Co., 1951.

Elton, Charles S. *The Ecology of Invasions by Animals and Plants.* London: Methuen and Co., Ltd., 1958.

Faguet, Émile. *Dix-Septième Siècle.* Paris: Société Française d' Imprimerie et de Librairie, 1913.

Fenichel, Otto. *Psychoanalytic Theory of Neurosis.* New York: W. W. Norton, 1945.

Fowler, John M. (ed.). *Fallout.* New York: Basic Books, 1950.

Freud, Anna. *The Ego and the Mechanisms of Defense.* New York: International Universities Press, 1957.

Gamow, George. *One, Two, Three . . . Infinity.* New York: The Viking Press, 1947.

Gerard, R. W. *Unresting Cells.* New York: Harper and Brothers, 1959.

Glass, Bentley. *Genes and the Man.* New York: Teachers College, Columbia University, 1943.

Granville, Robert. "Death Ray Weapons," *Space World* (May 1962).

Greater St. Louis Citizens' Committee for Nuclear Information. *Nuclear Information,* Vols. 2-4, 1960-62.

Greene, Felix. *Awakened China.* Garden City, N.Y.: Doubleday and Co., 1961.

Greene, Jerry. "Congressmen in Uniform," *The Nation* (December 2, 1961).

Gruening, Ernest. "Exporting Trouble," *The Nation* (October 6, 1962).

Hanrahan, James, and Bushnell, David. *Space Biology.* New York: Basic Books, 1960.

Harland, W. B. *The Earth.* New York: Franklin Watts, Inc., 1960.

Hinsie, Leland E., and Campbell, Robert J. *Psychiatric Dictionary.* New York: Oxford University Press, 1960.

Hughes, Donald J. *On Nuclear Energy.* Cambridge, Mass.:

Harvard University Press, 1957.

Huizinga, Johan. *Homo ludens.* New York: Roy Publishers, Inc., 1950.

Ilg, Frances L., and Ames, Louise Bates. *Child Behavior.* New York: Dell Publishing Co., 1960, reprinted by arrangement with Harper and Brothers.

International Commission on Radiological Protection. "Recommendations," *British Journal of Radiology, Supplement No. 6.* London: British Institute of Radiology, 1955.

Jeans, Sir James. *Through Space and Time.* Cambridge, Eng.: The University Press, 1943.

———. *The Universe Around Us.* Cambridge, Eng.: The University Press, 1960.

Joyce, James. *A Portrait of the Artist as a Young Man.* New York: Modern Library, Random House, 1916.

Jungk, Robert. *Brighter than a Thousand Suns.* New York: Harcourt, Brace and Co., 1958.

Kahn, Herman. *On Thermonuclear War.* Princeton, N.J.: Princeton University Press, 1961.

Kelly, Robert. "The Poor Land of Tirol," *Armed Descent.* New York: Hawk's Well Press, 1961.

Lang, Daniel. *From Hiroshima to the Moon.* New York: Simon and Schuster, 1959.

———. "A Vapor Moving North-Northwest," *The New Yorker* (January 6, 1962.)

Langlois, Ch.-V. *La Connaissance de la Nature et du Monde au Moyen Age d'-Après Quelques Écrits Français à l'Usage de Laics.* Paris: Librairie Hachette, 1911.

Lapp, Ralph E. *Man and Space.* New York: Harper and Brothers, 1961.

———. "A Small Atomic Accident," *Harper's* Magazine (June 1961).

Laurence, William L. *Dawn Over Zero.* New York: Alfred A. Knopf, 1946.

Lawler, Justus George. "Catholics and the Arms Race," *Commonweal,* Vol. 76, no. 8, pp. 198-203.

Lewis, Oscar. *The Children of Sanchez.* New York: Random House, 1961.

Libby, Willard F. "Radioactive Fallout," *Bulletin of the Atomic Scientists* (September 1955).

Lieberman, E. James. "Psychochemicals as Weapons," *Bulletin of the Atomic Scientists* (January 1962).

Lowell, Percival. *Mars as the Abode of Life.* New York: The Macmillan Co., 1908.

Lyght, Charles E., *et al. The Merck Manual.* Rahway, N.J.: Merck and Co., 1956.

Mao Tse-tung. "The Snow," *The White Pony,* ed. Robert Payne. New York: The John Day Co., 1947.

Meerloo, Joost A. M. *Patterns of Panic.* New York: International Universities Press, Inc., 1950.

Michaux, Henri. "L'Avenir," *Henri Michaux, une Étude, un Choix de Poèmes, et une Bibliographie,* ed. René Bertelé. Paris: Edition Pierre

Seghers, series Poètes d'-Aujourd'hui.

Miller, William Lee. "Some Academic Questions about a New Yale Man," The Reporter (July 5, 1962).

"Minutes to Midnight," Bulletin of the Atomic Scientists (May 1950).

Montagu, Ashley. Human Heredity. Cleveland: World Publishing Co., 1959.

Neblett, William. Pentagon Politics. New York: Pageant Books, Inc., 1953.

New York State Civil Defense Commission. Grandma's Pantry Was Always Ready— Is Your Pantry Prepared . . . ?

The New York Times, Vol. 111-12. New York: The New York Times Co., 1961-62.

Nourse, Alan E. Nine Planets. New York: Harper and Brothers, 1960.

Odum, Eugene P. Fundamentals of Ecology (2nd ed.). Philadelphia and London: W. B. Saunders Co., 1959.

"The Oppenheimer Case," Bulletin of the Atomic Scientists (May 1954).

Partridge, Eric. Origins. New York: The Macmillan Co., 1958.

Plank, John N. "The Alliance for Progress, Problems and Prospects," Daedalus (Fall 1962).

Proceedings of First National Conference on the Peaceful Uses of Space, Tulsa, Okla., May 26-27, 1961. Washington, D.C.: U.S. Government Printing Office, 1961.

Ransom, Harry Howe. Central Intelligence and National Security. Cambridge, Mass.: Harvard University Press, 1958.

Reiss, L. Z. "Strontium 90 Absorption by Deciduous Teeth," Science (November 24, 1961).

Rivkin, Steven R. "The Hobbled Weapon," Bulletin of the Atomic Scientists (May 1962).

Roszak, Theodore. "Dilemma of the 'Just War,'" The Nation (April 14, 1962).

Rothenberg, Jerome. "A Poem for the President," White Sun Black Sun. New York: Hawk's Well Press, 1960.

Russell, Bertrand. The Analysis of Matter. London: Allen and Unwin, 1927.

Salsich, Peter W., Jr. "The Armed Superpatriots," The Nation, Vol. 193, no. 16 (November 11, 1961), pp. 372-75.

Sasieni, Maurice. Operations Research—Methods and Problems. New York: John Wiley and Sons, 1959.

Schneir, Walter. "The Campaign to Make Chemical Warfare Respectable," The Reporter (October 1, 1959).

Schubert, Jack, and Lapp, Ralph E. Radiation: What It Is and How It Affects You. New York: The Viking Press, 1957.

Scientific American, Editors of. The Scientific American Reader. New York: Simon and Schuster, 1953.

Scientists' Committee for Radiation Information. Effects of a 20-Megaton Thermonuclear Explosion on Columbus Circle. New York: New York Academy of Sciences, 1962.

"Shelters and Survival: A Report on the Civil Defense Muddle," *The New Republic* (January 15, 1962).

*The Shorter Oxford English Dictionary* (3rd ed.). Revised and edited by C. T. Onions. London: Oxford University Press, 1955.

Smyth, Henry DeWolf. *Atomic Energy for Military Purposes.* Princeton, N.J.: Princeton University Press, 1945.

Spenser, Edmund. *Poems.* London: Oxford University Press, 1959.

*State of New York Committee on Fallout Protection Survival in a Nuclear Attack, Plan for Protection from Radioactive Fallout.* Report to Gov. Nelson A. Rockefeller, State of New York, Albany, 1960.

Teller, Edward, and Latter, Albert L. *Our Nuclear Future.* New York: Criterion Books, 1958.

Thomas, Hugh. *The Spanish Civil War.* New York: Harper and Brothers, 1961.

Tillyard, E. M. W. *The Elizabethan World-Picture.* New York: Modern Library, Random House, 1944.

Tokay, Elbert. *Fundamentals of Physiology.* Philadelphia: Blakiston and Co., 1947.

Ulanoff, Stanley. *Illustrated Guide to U.S. Missiles and Rockets.* Garden City, N.Y.: Doubleday and Co., 1959.

United Nations, Food and Agriculture Organization of. *Man and Hunger.* Rome: United Nations, 1961.

United Nations, General Assembly, Thirteenth Session.

*Report of the United Nations Scientific Committee on the Effects of Atomic Radiation.* New York: United Nations, November 1958.

United Nations, Office of Public Information. *The Crime of Genocide.* New York: United Nations, 1959.

United States Atomic Energy Commission. *In the Matter of J. Robert Oppenheimer—Transcript of Hearing and Texts of Documents.* Washington, D.C.: U.S. Government Printing Office, 1954.

———. *Major Activities in the Atomic Energy Programs, January-December, 1961.* Washington, D.C.: U.S. Government Printing Office, 1962.

———. *Medical Survey of Rongelap People, March 1958, Four Years After Exposure to Fallout.* Washington, D.C.: U.S. Government Printing Office, 1958.

———. *Radiation Safety and Major Activities in the Atomic Energy Programs, July-December 1956.* Washington, D.C.: U.S. Government Printing Office, 1957.

———. *Radioisotopes in Science and Industry.* Washington, D.C.: U.S. Government Printing Office, January 1960.

———. *Some Effects of Ionizing Radiation on Human Beings—A Report on the Marshallese and Americans Accidentally Exposed to Radiation from Fallout, and a Discussion of Radiation Injury in the Human Being.* Washington, D.C.: U.S. Government Printing Office, July 1956.

United States Congress. *Civil*

316

*Defense, 1961.* Hearings before a subcommittee of the Committee on Government Operations, 87th Congress, 1st session. Washington, D.C.: U.S. Government Printing Office, 1961.

————. *Development, Growth, and State of the Atomic Energy Industry.* Hearings before the Joint Committee on Atomic Energy, 87th Congress, 2nd session. Washington, D.C.: U.S. Government Printing Office, 1962.

————. *Health and Safety Problems and Weather Effects Associated with Atomic Explosions.* Hearing before the Joint Committee on Atomic Energy, 84th Congress. Washington, D.C.: U.S. Government Printing Office, 1955.

————. *Hearings before the Special Subcommittee on Radiation of the Joint Committee on Atomic Energy, Congress of the United States, Eighty-Sixth Congress, First Session on Biological and Environmental Effects of Nuclear War.* Washington, D.C.: U.S. Government Printing Office, 1959.

United States Congress House Select Committee on Astronautics and Space Exploration. *The Next Ten Years in Space, 1959-1969.* Washington, D.C.: U.S. Government Printing Office, 1959.

————. *Space Handbook: Astronautics and Its Application.* Washington, D.C.: U.S. Government Printing Office, 1959.

United States Department of Commerce. *Maximum Permissible Body Burdens and Maximum Permissible Concentrations of Radionuclides in Air and in Water for Occupational Exposure.* Washington, D.C.: U.S. Government Printing Office, 1959.

Whitehead, Alfred North. *Science and the Modern World.* New York: The Macmillan Co., 1925.

Wiener, Norbert. *The Human Use of Human Beings.* Boston: Houghton Mifflin Co., 1954.

Emperor Yao. "Song of the Peasants," and "A Warning by the Emperor Yao," *The White Pony,* ed. Robert Payne. New York: The John Day Co., 1947.

Zoethout, William D., and Tuttle, W. W. *Textbook of Physiology.* St. Louis, Mo.: The C. V. Mosley Co., 1955.